DENTAL ANTHROPOLOGY

SOCIETY FOR THE STUDY OF HUMAN BIOLOGY

Although there are many scientific societies for the further-ance of the biological study of man as an individual, there has been no organization in Great Britain catering for those (such as physical anthropologists or human geneticists) concerned with the biology of human populations. The need for such an association was made clear at a Symposium at the Ciba Foundation in November 1957, on "The Scope of Physical Anthropology and Human Population Biology and their Place in Academic Studies". As a result the Society for the Study of Human Biology was founded on May 7th, 1958, at a meeting at the British Museum (Natural History).

The aims of the Society are to advance the study of the biology of human populations and of man as a species, in all its branches, particularly human variability, human genetics and evolution, human adaptability and ecology.

At present the Society holds two full-day meetings per year —a Symposium (usually in the autumn) on a particular theme with invited speakers, and a scientific meeting for proffered papers. The papers given at the Symposia are published and the monographs are available to members at reduced prices.

Persons are eligible for membership who work or who have worked in the field of human biology as defined in the aims of the Society. They must be proposed and seconded by members of the Society. The subscription is £2.10s. per annum (this includes the Society's journal *Human Biology*) and there is no entrance fee.

Applications for membership should be made to Dr. J. S. Weiner, Hon. General Secretary, Department of Human Anatomy, Oxford.

PUBLICATIONS OF THE SOCIETY

Symposia, Volume I, 1958: *The Scope of Physical Anthropology and Its Place in Academic Studies*, edited by D. F. ROBERTS and J. S. WEINER (out of print).

Volume II, 1959: *Natural Selection in Human Populations*, edited by D. F. ROBERTS and G. A. HARRISON. Pergamon Press (£1).

Volume III, 1960: *Human Growth*, edited by J. M. TANNER. Pergamon Press (members 10s. 6d.).

Volume IV, 1961: *Genetical Variation in Human Populations*, edited by G. A. HARRISON. Pergamon Press (members £1).

Volume V, 1963: *Dental Anthropology*, edited by D. R. BROTH-WELL. Pergamon Press (members 25s.).

SYMPOSIA OF THE
SOCIETY FOR THE STUDY OF HUMAN BIOLOGY

Volume V

DENTAL ANTHROPOLOGY

Edited by

D. R. BROTHWELL

A Pergamon Press Book
THE MACMILLAN COMPANY
NEW YORK
1968

THE MACMILLAN COMPANY
60 Fifth Avenue
New York 11, N.Y.

This book is distributed by
THE MACMILLAN COMPANY · NEW YORK
pursuant to a special arrangement with
PERGAMON PRESS LIMITED
Oxford, England

Library of Congress Card No. 62–22060

Printed in Great Britain by
THE DITCHLING PRESS LTD, DITCHLING, HASSOCKS, SUSSEX

CONTENTS

TOOTH MORPHOLOGY AND PRIMATE EVOLUTION

by **P. M. BUTLER**

Royal Holloway College, University of London

MOST of the identifiable remains of fossil mammals consist of teeth, and evidence obtained by a study of the teeth tends to dominate discussions of phylogenetic relationships. The reason for this is that the teeth are the most durable parts of the body, best able to withstand the destructive processes that intervene between the death of a mammal and the burial of its remains in a deposit where the palaeontologist can find them. In the Primates, these processes of destruction are particularly important; skeletons, even skulls, are rare, and in most cases all we have are teeth and jaws.

It is understandable, therefore, that the teeth of fossil primates have been described in much more detail than those of living forms. Dental characters predominate in the diagnosis of most fossil species and genera, and even some families. It is fortunate that the teeth, developing early in life inside the jaws, protected from external environmental influences, do reflect to a high degree the genetic constitution of the individual. In practice it has been found that, if adequately interpreted, teeth do provide a reliable basis for the discussion of evolutionary relationships.

However, the adequate interpretation of fossil teeth is by no means a simple matter. The number of specimens from any one locality is usually small, and it is difficult to make adequate allowance for variation. Indeed, there is reason to think that palaeontologists have tended to underestimate the variability of fossil species. For example, Granger and Gregory (1917) recognized eight species of *Notharctus* from the Middle Eocene

1

of North America, but P. Robinson (1957) has reduced these to three as a result of the statistical analysis of richer material. The study of the variability of the teeth in living species would be most valuable in the interpretation of fossil material, but except for man and the great apes (e.g. Remane, 1921; Korenhof, 1960) this is an almost unworked field.

When comparisons are made on a wider scale, between different genera or different families, other problems arise. When two forms resemble each other, can we assume that they are related, or is the resemblance due to parallel evolution? Here one has to guess at probabilities which cannot be estimated quantitatively: the more detailed the resemblance, the smaller will be the probability that the characters in question have evolved twice. But this rule breaks down when a simple and easily repeated genetic change gives a complicated result morphologically. To take an example: the minor crenulations of the molars are arranged in very much the same way in species of *Dryopithecus*, in the orang, and in some hominids such as *Sinanthropus* and subfossil Javanese. Korenhof (1960) argues that this condition is a primitive one which man inherited from pongid ancestors, and the paucity of crenulations in many human molars is due to secondary simplification. It is possible, however, that crenulation is due to a single gene, and that the resemblances are due to parallel mutation in related stocks.

At one time it was believed that the Lower Tertiary Apatemyidae were related to the modern aye-aye, which they closely resemble in the dentition, particularly in the enlarged incisors. But throughout its anatomy the aye-aye shows many detailed similarities to the other Madagascar lemurs, and it is more reasonable to suppose that its resemblance to Apatemyidae in the dentition is due to parallel evolution (Simpson, 1935). Enlarged incisors occur in a variety of mammals belonging to different families, and indeed different orders.

In other cases resemblances may indicate relationship. *Proconsul* and *Pliopithecus* are very close in dental characters, even where they differ from modern anthropoid apes. *Pliopithecus* is usually regarded as a primitive gibbon, while *Proconsul* is supposed to be nearer the great-ape group. Yet the degree of similarity is such as to suggest that it is artificial to divide the Miocene Pongidae between the two subfamilies, which probably diverged at a later date (cf. Butler and Mills, 1959).

Just as resemblances do not necessarily prove relationship, so differences do not prove the lack of relationship. It is a question of whether the observed differences could be bridged by a hypothetical evolutionary process which does not transcend the bounds of probability. There is obviously much room for difference of opinion here. Hürzeler (1958), for example, showed that *Oreopithecus* possessed a group of hominid characters, such as short face, small canines, lack of diastema, and unspecialized lower premolars. On this evidence he argued that *Oreopithecus* was related to hominids and not to pongids, and that therefore the Hominidae had already differentiated from the Pongidae well before the beginning of the Pliocene. Mills and I (1959) found numerous differences from both pongids and hominids, which seemed to indicate that *Oreopithecus* was evolving in a direction different from both these families. At the same time, hominids and pongids resembled each other in numerous ways in which they differed from *Oreopithecus*. It would in our view be easier to get human tooth patterns from those of *Proconsul* or *Pliopithecus* than to get them from *Oreopithecus*. This would imply that there was a common pongid–hominid stem, from which *Oreopithecus* had already branched off at an early date, and that its resemblances to hominids were due to parallel evolution.

It is often assumed that evolutionary change is irreversible: a large canine cannot give rise to a small canine, and therefore hominids cannot be derived from pongids. Such arguments must be treated with reserve: the Principle of Irreversibility does not appear as secure today as it was formerly believed to be. For instance, large and small canines occur in related genera of insectivores frequently enough to show that reduction of the canine is no very difficult process phylogenetically. Even the assumption that the number of teeth in the dentition is always reduced, never increased, may not always be correct. Variation in tooth number is widespread in Primates, and one can imagine circumstances in which an increased number could be of selective value.

Obviously we need to know more about what teeth can do in the way of evolutionary change. That means we must learn more about the ontogeny of the dentition, and in particular the ontogenetic basis of variation. We want to know more about how the ontogeny is modified genetically. We also need to study the functions of teeth more thoroughly so as to be in a position to assess the adaptive significance of observed variations and their possible selective value. I have only to mention these problems to show you how far we are from a really scientific dental morphology. We have indeed made a beginning, but so far we have only scratched the surface, and our knowledge of the teeth of non-human Primates is particularly superficial.

For example, a systematic study of the development of the dentition, through all its stages, has been made in non-human Primates only in *Tupaia* (Kindahl, 1957) and *Tarsius* (Greiner, 1929). Leche (1896) described the dentition of a few prosimian embryos, and Friant (1935) sectioned one embryo of *Indris*. Next to nothing is known about monkeys and apes, not even the rhesus monkey. There is no published work on the development of the cusps and other features of the crown that are of interest to palaeontologists; even in man only passing notice has been given to such details, though this will be shortly remedied by the publication of Dr. P. Turner's work on the deciduous molars. Genetical studies, confined to man, have been mainly concerned either with gross abnormalities such as anodontia which have little direct bearing on evolutionary problems, or with Carabelli's cusp, the ontogeny of which has not yet been investigated. Important pioneer work on the functional aspect of tooth-patterns has been done by Dr. J. R. E. Mills, but the bearing of the variation of tooth-patterns on occlusal relations has not as yet been studied.

My own contribution to the subject has been concerned mainly with what has come to be known as the Field Theory (Butler, 1937, 1939), and it is with this that I shall devote the rest of my communication. It is well established that the details of the crown of a mammalian tooth can be traced back in ontogeny to the folding of a sheet of epithelium (for a review of this subject see Butler, 1956). This forms the internal surface of an ectodermal enamel organ, which first appears as a bud on the dental lamina. It is commonly believed that tooth buds make their appearance in the embryo in serial order from mesial to distal, but though this is nearly true in man it is not the case in mammals generally. I have plotted the appearance of the successive tooth buds against embryo size, in the three primates

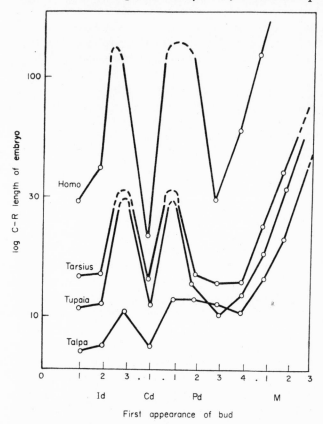

FIG. 1.   Serial order of appearance of tooth buds in the primary dentition of the upper jaw. Sources of data: *Talpa*, Sicher 1916; *Tupaia*, Kindahl 1957; *Tarsius*, Greiner 1929; *Homo*, Norberg 1929.

for which the data are available, and also for the mole, which probably retains the primitive condition, at least in its upper jaw (Fig. 1). The teeth are those of the primary dentition (deciduous teeth + permanent molars). You will see that in the mole Id^1, Cd and Pd^4 appear before their neighbours, and the teeth on either side of the canine are retarded. Pd^4 might be termed the initial cheek tooth. The more distal teeth, i.e. the permanent molars, do appear in serial order from front to back, but more slowly, as they can develop only as the jaw grows in length. If now we compare the three primates with the mole, we notice (1) a general retardation of tooth development due to a more rapid growth of the embryo, (2) the loss of the teeth on either side of the canine that were the last to develop in the mole, and (3) a retardation of Pd^4, slight in *Tupaia* but marked in man, where Pd^3 has become the initial tooth, perhaps due to a slower rate of growth of the jaw.

In this diagram we have a demonstration of the existence of what Dahlberg (1945) has called tooth districts. These must precede the appearance of the buds, for they determine their order of appearance. The diagram also shows that the differences between an incisor, a canine and a molar are not due to the times at which these teeth develop, but to their position in the jaw, for teeth developing at the same time have different patterns, and teeth developing at different times, such as Pd^4 and M^1, may closely resemble each other if they are in adjacent positions in the jaw. In general, from the initial cheek tooth forwards, the most precocious tooth germs develop into the largest teeth, while retarded tooth germs develop into smaller and simpler teeth, for example Id^2 as compared with Id^1 in man. This rule was first stated by Leche as long ago as 1895; he also recognized that there are certain exceptions, particularly in the replacing dentition. For example, in *Tarsius* Pd^2 is a minute tooth which develops very rapidly and erupts early, and its successor P^2 arises very early and comes up with the other deciduous molars (Leche, 1896; Dahlberg, 1948). I should perhaps mention that the order of appearance of the germs is not necessarily the same as the order of eruption, for teeth differ considerably in their rates of growth, and the order in which they erupt seems to depend more upon their rates of growth than on anything else.

If now we look at the complete primary series we find a spectrum of patterns, such that each tooth could be regarded

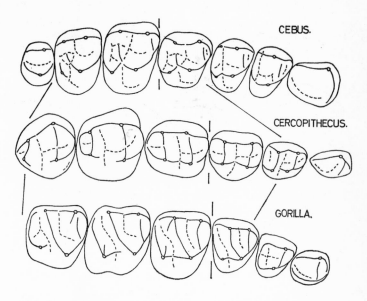

CEBUS.

CERCOPITHECUS.

GORILLA.

Fig. 2.   Primary upper dentition (Cd–M³) of representatives of the three superfamilies of the Anthropoidea, to show differences in extent of the region of molariform teeth.

as a modification of the tooth next to it (Fig. 2). Such a spectrum can be recognized in all eutherian and marsupial mammals, and even in early mammals of the Jurassic Period. The general nature of the spectrum, the changes that go on within it as one passes from one end to the other, are always essentially the same, though of course there are differences in detail. This spectrum could be explained if it were supposed that there exists in the embryo a continuous morphogenetic field or gradient, which controls the development of the tooth germs within it. Each tooth germ would develop according to its position in relation to the field as a whole, i.e. according to its local environment. It is likely that there is a stage in the development of the tooth germ when it is competent to react to the field; as a result it becomes determined, i.e. it will go on developing in a predetermined direction even if transplanted or explanted. We do not yet know when this process of determination takes place; it may be even before the tooth germ is histologically recognizable.

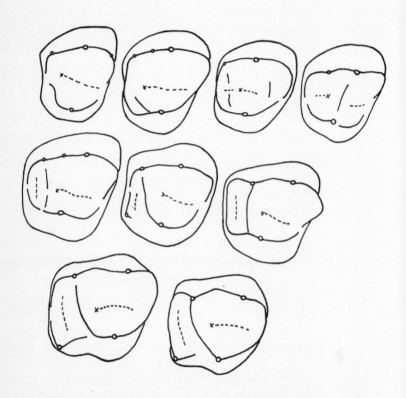

FIG. 3. Molarization of the upper milk-molars of *Homo sapiens*. Drawings of dentine caps, obtained from a single population (Bristol, England). Upper row, Pd³ at a low level of molarization; middle row, Pd³ at a higher level of molarization; lower row, Pd⁴. (*Specimens obtained by courtesy of Dr. M. V. Stack.*)

One could imagine a continuous field which has been, as it were, sampled at intervals represented by the positions of the tooth germs. If the sampling is done at a slightly different place, the resultant tooth pattern will be slightly different. This would be most obvious in regions where the field is changing rapidly, for example at the level where the molar pattern first appears: here, teeth will be more or less molariform according to their position. In man, the tooth in this situation is Pd^3, which shows a wide range of degrees of molarization (Fig. 3). The australopithecines and the cercopithecoid monkeys have on the average a more molarized Pd^3 than modern man, while in the Pongidae Pd^3 remains at a relatively low level of molarization (Fig. 2). Similar considerations apply to the degree of reduction of the distal molars. It is understandable from this that Pd^3 and M^3 should be more variable than Pd^4 and M^1 (Dahlberg, 1945).

This additional variation would be due to genes that influenced the shape and size of the field (in relation to individual tooth germs). It is reasonable to believe that such "field" genes exist, analogous to those that control the regional differentiation of the vertebral column.

There would also be another set of "pattern" genes, influencing the way in which the tooth germs react to any given level of the field. These would control the full molar pattern, for example. All the tooth germs of the series must have the same genetic constitution, because they are all parts of a single individual, and therefore they can be regarded as equipotential: all could, if situated in the appropriate part of the field, become molars or canines or incisors. What they do become, i.e. how their genetic constitution expresses itself phenotypically, depends on the position of teeth in the series. There is no tooth on which all the elements of the pattern are developed to a maximal extent, not even the first molar: each element reaches its maximal development at a characteristic position in the series. In some cases the character might be present only on one tooth, or on a few adjacent teeth. This is true for variant characters as well as for those that are normally present: a supernumerary cusp with maximal expression on M_3 would

B

have a different genetic basis from a topographically similar cusp with a maximal incidence on M_1.

When considering the evolution of molar patterns it is necessary to take the whole series into account, and not just one or two teeth that are regarded as typical. In primitive primates M^1 and M^2 were tritubercular, with only one lingual

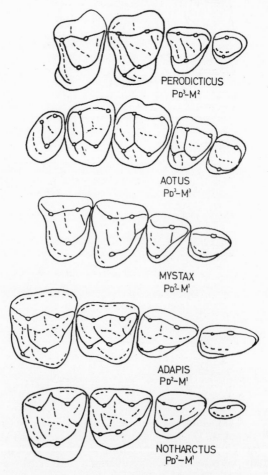

Fig. 4. To illustrate the relations of the hypocone to the protocone in some prosimians and ceboids.

cusp (the so-called protocone). Distally there was a cingulum ledge which, in a number of evolutionary lines, developed into a fourth cusp, the hypocone. However, in some groups the fourth cusp arose, not from the cingulum but from the distal ridge of the protocone; such a cusp has been distinguished as a pseudo-

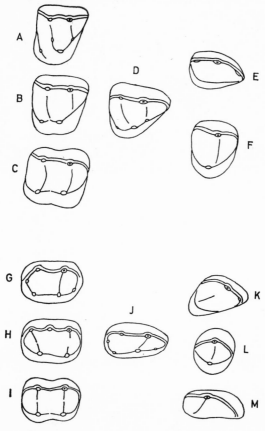

FIG. 5. Diagrammatic representation of types of primate tooth patterns. D and J are generalized semi-molariform milk molars, which may be compared with various types of molar patterns (A, G, "tritubercular"; B, H, hominoid; C, I, cercopithecoid), and with the simpler patterns of anterior teeth (E, K, incisors; F, L, "bicuspid" type of premolar; M, sectorial type of lower premolar).

hypocone. Now if we look along the series (Fig. 4) we find that in the most mesial cheek teeth the protocone stands on a lingual marginal ridge. Further back in the series this ridge becomes connected across the central valley to the metacone, by the development of the crista obliqua. When a fourth cusp arises it stands on the same lingual marginal ridge as the protocone, and thus it has the appearance of a pseudohypocone. It may retain this appearance throughout the series, or alternatively it may lose its connection with the protocone on the more distal teeth, and then it stands alone, as if it were part of a cingulum. The pseudohypocone and the true hypocone therefore intergrade, and there is no point in using the term pseudohypocone at all.

There are two rival interpretations of primate molar patterns. On the one hand there is the tritubercular interpretation, that the upper tooth crown is made up of a triangle of three cusps. On the other hand we have Bolk's Dimer theory and related interpretations, according to which the basic pattern consists of a longitudinal buccal ridge and a lingual cingulum-like structure which develops into lingual cusps in the molar region. These two interpretations are easily reconcilable because they are based on teeth from different parts of the series (Fig. 5).

I have spent much time on the field hypothesis because I believe it is a useful working tool, but it can be proved right or wrong only when new techniques have been developed for experimenting on mammalian embryos. Dental morphology is still struggling to get beyond the merely descriptive level. I hope I have shown the need for more co-operation between palaeontologists, geneticists and embryologists in this field.

REFERENCES

BUTLER, P. M. (1937) Studies of the mammalian dentition. I: The teeth of *Centetes ecaudatus* and its allies, *Proc. Zool. Soc. Lond.* **B 107**, 103.

BUTLER, P. M. (1939) Studies of the mammalian dentition. Differentiation of the post-canine dentition, *Proc. Zool. Soc. Lond.* **B 109**, 1.

Butler, P. M. (1956) The ontogeny of molar pattern, *Biol. Rev.* **31**, 30.

Butler, P. M. and Mills, J. R. E. (1959) A contribution to the odontology of *Oreopithecus*, *Bull. B.M. (Nat. Hist.), Geol.* **4**, 1.

Dahlberg, A. A. (1945) The changing dentition of man, *J. Amer. Dent. Ass.* **321**, 676.

Dahlberg, A. A. (1948) The milk and permanent dentitions of *Tarsius philippensis, Amer. J. Phys. Anthrop.* (N.S.) **6**, 239.

Friant, M. (1935) Description et interpretation d'un jeune *Indris, C.R. Ass. Anat. Montpellier* **1935**, 205.

Granger, W. and Gregory, W. K. (1917) Revision of Eocene primates of the genus *Notharctus, Bull. Amer. Mus. Nat. Hist.* **37**, 841.

Greiner, E. (1929) Zur Entwicklungsgeschichte des Gebisses von *Tarsius spectrum. Z. Ges. Anat.* 1. *Z. Anat. EntwGesch.* **89**, 102.

Hürzeler, J. (1958) *Oreopithecus bambolii* Gervais. A preliminary report. *Verh. Naturf. Ges. Basel.* **69**, 1.

Kindahl, M. (1957) On the development of the teeth in *Tupaia javanica, Arkiv. Zool.* (2) **10**, 463.

Korenhof, C. A. W. (1960) *Morphogenetical Aspects of the Human Upper Molar.* Utrecht. 368 pp.

Leche, W. (1895) Zur Entwicklungsgeschichte des Zahnsystems der Saügethiere, zugleich ein Beitrag zur Stammesgeschichte dieser Thiergruppe. 1. Ontogenie. *Zoologica, Stuttgart* **6**, Heft 17, 1.

Leche, W. (1896) Untersuchungen über des Zahnsystems lebender and fossiler Halbaffen, *Festschr. Gegenbaur, Leipzig* **3**, 125.

Norberg, O. (1929) *Untersuchungen über der dentogingivale Epithelleistensystem im intrauterinen Leben des Menschen.* Fahlcrantz, Stockholm.

Remane, A. (1921) Beiträge zur Morphologie des Anthropoidengebisses, *Archiv. F. Naturgesch.* **87** (Abt. A), 1.

Robinson, P. (1957) The species of *Notharctus* from the Middle Eocene, *Postilla* **28**, 1.

Sicher, H. (1916) Die Entwicklung des Gebisses von *Talpa europaea, Arb. Anat. Inst., Wiesbaden* **54**, 31.

Simpson, G. G. (1935) The Tiffany fauna, Upper Paleocene. III. Primates, Carnivora, Condylarthra and Amblypoda, *Amer. Mus. Novit.* **816**, 1.

DENTAL VARIABILITY IN A POPULATION
OF GIBBONS (*HYLOBATES LAR*)

by JOHN E. FRISCH

Biological Research Institute, Sophia University, Tokyo

IT is often said that progress in our understanding of primate and particularly hominoid evolution depends on the finding of many more fossil remains. While it is obvious that such new finds are highly desirable, it may be well to remember that, as Washburn (1954) pointed out some years ago, "no matter how many fossils are found, what we see in them will depend on our theories and on our experience".

One of the ways in which our experience can be enriched, and the subjectivity of our judgements correspondingly reduced, consists in observing the variability characteristic of living higher Primates (Schultz, 1956). This method appears to be particularly valuable in the study of the hominoid dentition. The considerable weight given by some workers to minute details of dental morphology and the relative neglect of the same features by other workers inevitably raises the question as to how we may objectively assess the taxonomic or phylogenetic significance of a given dental feature.

It seemed to the writer that some progress towards answering this crucial question could only be made by studying systematically the amount and nature of dental variability characteristic of living hominoids. Oddly enough, students of hominoid evolution seem to have devoted much more time and effort to a detailed study, and often to a repeated study, of every fossil tooth than to learning about the dentition of the living descendants of these same fossil forms. While a number of studies on dental variability in human populations have been published in about the last ten years (Pedersen, 1949; Selmer Olsen,

15

1949; Thomsen, 1955; Joergensen, 1956; Moorrees, 1957), similar studies on living non-human primates are almost non-existent. The article of Schuman and Brace (1955) on the dentition of the Liberian chimpanzee stands out as an exception. The valuable information it yields shows how rewarding this type of study can be.

The study of dental variability in a population of gibbons which provides the material for the present article, was undertaken as a further contribution to our knowledge of the hominoid dentition with a view to increase our insight into the paths followed by hominoid evolution. Thanks to the kindness of the Museum of Comparative Zoology (Harvard College) and to Dr. A. H. Schultz (Anthropologishes Institut, Zürich) who made his own unique Primate collection available, the writer had the opportunity to study the dentition of 155 gibbons (*Hylobates lar*) collected in 1938 in the district of Chiengmai (Thailand) by the Asiatic Primate Expedition. This sample of a natural population of gibbons comprises 69 adult males, 54 adult females and 32 juveniles with the permanent dentition only partially erupted. The age changes and variability of the skeleton have been studied by Schultz (1944). However, he did not deal with the dentition, except in its ontogenetic and pathological aspects.

The importance of this collection for an appraisal of dental variability is twofold. First, all specimens belong to one natural population forming presumably one single genetic pool and subject to identical environmental conditions. Second, the large number of immature specimens makes it possible to observe features which disappear after even a moderate amount of wear.

The present paper reports on three of the variable features observed in the population. For each feature the sample from Chiengmai is compared both with specimens of *Hylobates lar* of different origin and with other species of gibbons. This comparison aims at providing at least a provisory answer to the two questions: how characteristic is the variability here described for the entire species, and how does it compare with the variability of similar features in other gibbon species?

SUPERNUMERARY CUSPS IN THE MOLAR TEETH

A surprisingly high proportion of the molar teeth are found to be affected by supernumerary cusps. Since most of these supernumerary cusps apparently undergo faster wear than the usual cusps, identification of these cusps in the adult often presents considerable difficulty. An indication of their true frequency is therefore more likely to be gathered from the smaller sample of immature dentitions. It is then seen that out of 32 immature dentitions, 16 have teeth with one or several extra-cusps. Eight of these 16 show several types of extra-cusps on the same dentition. Table 1 shows the number of individuals affected by each kind of supernumerary cusp.

TABLE I

SUPERNUMERARY CUSPS IN THE MOLARS OF THE CHIENGMAI POPULATION

	N	Divided hypocone	Anterior marginal cusp	Carabelli-cusp	Others
M^1	32	4	4	3	2
M^2	21	3	0	0	1
	N	divided hypoconulid	anterior marginal cusp	*Tuberculum intermedium*	others
M_1	32	4	7	0	0
M_2	21	2	3	1	0

In the upper molars three main types of such cusps are observed. A distal marginal cusp, situated between the hypocone and the metacone and which appears to result from the division of the hypocone (Fig. 1). It is present in all erupted molars of 4 immature dentitions. In one adult dentition all molars are likewise affected and in 6 more adult dentitions the divided hypocone shows best on the last molar, while its presence on M1 and M2 is often dubious. This can easily be explained as the result of differential wear: the supernumerary cusp tends to occlude not in between the cusps of the opposing tooth, but rather against these cusps.

The Carabelli-cusp is found fully developed on one immature

dentition where both first upper molars, the only erupted, show the feature. The protocone is well separated from the cusp by the cingulum-furrow. The cusp is more pointed than is the case in man and, in this, follows the pattern of the other molar cusps. A Carabelli-cusp is also found, but much less marked, in 2 other immature dentitions where the half-erupted second molars show no such condition.

A minute but well-formed cuspule occurs immediately in front of the paracone, and always on M1 only, in 4 immature dentitions. The mode of formation of this cuspule appears clearly on other molars where the anterior marginal crest is considerably thickened in the corresponding region.

Supernumerary cusps are somewhat less frequent and especially less conspicuous in the lower molars. Among the 32 immature dentitions, the hypoconid is greatly enlarged and an accessory cusp has budded off from the main cusp lingually on 4 dentitions. The pattern, very clear on the newly erupted M2, is already largely obliterated on the M1. Comparison with the standard pattern in other dentitions shows that none of the distal cusps in these 4 specimens can be interpreted as the anthropologist's "*sixth cusp*".

Seven dentitions show a tiny cuspule on the anterior margin of the crown, between protoconid and metaconid, where it fills the space usually occupied by the *fovea anterior*. Comparison with other dentitions indicates that the cuspule originates as a thickening of the margin. The cuspule shows much better on the first than on the second molar.

A cuspule between the metaconid and the entoconid was observed on the second molar of one immature dentition. In its morphology it corresponds to the *tuberculum intermedium* of anthropologists.

Among 23 dentitions of *Hylobates lar* from localities other than Chiengmai that were examined by the writer and proved fresh enough to yield useful information, 7 were found to present some type of supernumerary cusp. The most frequent occurrence here again is the formation interpreted above as a divided hypocone (4 cases). The Carabelli-cusp and the *tuberculum intermedium* were observed on one dentition each. Only 2 dentitions showed some supernumerary cusps on the lower molars. These frequencies are not unlike those recorded for the Chiengmai sample. Noteworthy is the absence of marginal cuspules in either upper or lower molars, but this absence may be due to the rapid wear undergone by such cuspules and by the lack of immature specimens in the sample used. The absence of these marginal cuspules accounts for the very small number of dentitions affected by extra-cusps in the lower molars.

The similarity between the Chiengmai population and the more heterogeneous sample of *Hylobates lar* becomes still more evident when both are compared with the other species of gibbons (Table II).

TABLE II

NUMBER OF DENTITIONS AFFECTED BY SUPERNUMERARY CUSPS IN DIFFERENT SPECIES OF *Hylobates*

	N	Upper molars	Lower molars
H. lar (Chiengmai)	32	11	11
H. leuciscus	19	0	11
H. hoolock	69	1	10
H. agilis	39	0	6
H. concolor	36	0	1
H. moloch	57	1	2

Out of 220 dentitions belonging to all living species of *Hylobates* (Frisch, unpublished data), only 2 were found to possess a supernumerary cusp on the upper molars. On the other hand, supernumerary cusps are not unfrequent on the lower molar teeth. Here again, however, the interspecific differences in cusp frequencies appear to be quite significant. The *tuberculum intermedium* affects 10 out of 19 *Hylobates leuciscus* from Java and 6 out of 69 *Hylobates hoolock* from Burma, but it is not found in any of the other three species (*concolor, agilis, moloch*). Still, *Hylobates agilis* shows an extra-cusp on the talonid in 6 out of 39 lower dentitions, while the gibbons from Indonesia (*concolor*) and Borneo (*moloch*) total only 3 cases for 103 specimens.

Such clearly marked interspecific differences make it probable that the occurrence of supernumerary cusps is genetically controlled, especially in the case of cusps which tend to appear bilaterally (for example, Carabelli's cusp) or even on all molar teeth of the same dentition (for example, the divided hypocone).

There also appears to be a tendency for several kinds of extra-cusps to occur in the same dentition. It will be recalled that in the Chiengmai sample one half of the specimens affected by supernumerary cusps show more than one type of such cusps, sometimes even on the same tooth. It should therefore be considered whether one genetic factor may not be responsible, according to its penetrance, for the occurrence of one or several types of supernumerary cusps. Particularly interesting in this connection is the observation that out of 9 immature dentitions from Chiengmai that are affected by an anterior marginal cuspule in the upper or lower molars, as many as 7 also present some other type of extra-cusp. This strongly suggests that this type of supernumerary cusp is generally produced solely by a genetic factor of such penetrance that it simultaneously produces other extra-cusps as well. This interpretation would further explain why no single case of anterior marginal cusp was observed outside of the Chiengmai population. In the other populations the penetrance of the genetic factor responsible for the existing supernumerary cusps may never have been strong enough to cause anterior marginal cuspules to appear.

It is finally worthy of note that when molar teeth are differentially affected by a given type of supernumerary cusp, the first molar appears to be a more frequent target than the second or the third. This observation would seem to be at variance with expectations based on Buther's field concept which considers M1 to be the most stable tooth in the group.

POSITION OF THE HYPOCONULID

The position of the hypoconulid (or most distal cusp of the lower molars) in relation to the two neighbouring cusps (entoconid and hypoconid) appears to be quite variable in the sample of 91 specimens where small or moderate wear makes it possible to determine this position without difficulty.

Table 3 shows how variable the position of the hypoconulid is in the Chiengmai population. The location of the cusp is said to be lingual, central or buccal with reference to the mesio-distal length axis of the crown. If by far the largest portion of the cusp lies on either side of this axis, the position of the cusp is accordingly said to be lingual or buccal.

TABLE III

Position of the Hypoconulid in the Chiengmai Population of
Hylobates lar

	N	Lingual	Central	Buccal	Absent
M_1	91	18	70	2	1
M_2	81	7	61	8	5
M_3	62	2	21	25	14

Especially noteworthy, in view of further discussion, is the small proportion of molars with a clearly buccally situated hypoconulid. This characteristic is further reflected in the extremely rare occurrence of an entoconid–hypoconulid crest as well as of the *fovea posterior* which this crest usually defines. The proximity of the entoconid to the hypoconulid leaves in fact no place for such structures to develop. A trend is clearly seen for the hypoconulid to shift buccally from the first to the third molar.

These observations differ considerably from those reported by Remane (1921) in his comprehensive study of the hominoid dentition. A possible reason for the discrepancy became apparent to the writer when he noticed that Remane's sample included no specimens of *Hylobates lar*. This suggested that the position of the hypoconulid and its attending features might vary considerably between species. Further investigation on adequate samples of all living species of *Hylobates* proved this to be the case. Table IV summarizes the data obtained in this investigation, the full results of which will be published later.

TABLE IV

POSITION OF THE HYPOCONULID IN VARIOUS SPECIES OF *Hylobates lar*

	M_1				M_2				M_3			
	l	c	b	0	l	c	b	0	l	c	b	0
H. Lar (Chiengmai)	18	70	2	1	7	61	8	5	2	21	25	14
H. lar	–	17	9	–	–	17	6	2	–	10	8	4
H. lar pileatus	3	20	1	1	–	21	1	1	1	9	8	2
H. hoolock	–	26	22	–	–	27	17	–	–	18	6	10
H. concolor	–	11	14	–	–	10	13	1	–	7	11	1
H. agilis	–	7	22	1	–	8	25	–	–	10	7	11
H. leuciscus	–	14	12	–	–	12	12	–	–	7	9	1
H. moloch	–	8	51	1	–	20	32	1	–	7	22	18

It is seen that the populations of *Hylobates lar* from localities other than Chiengmai have somewhat different frequencies. The most obvious difference regards the total absence of lingually situated hypoconulids. The proportion of buccally situated cusps is also larger. However, when compared to other gibbon species, *Hylobates lar* still represents the species most closely similar to the Chiengmai population. Special mention must be made of the subspecies *Hylobates lar pileatus*. The frequencies for this well identifiable subspecies differ so much from those of other subspecies of *lar* that it is necessary to consider them separately. The position of the hypoconulid on the first two molars is more stable than in any other species or subspecies.

Comments on the respective frequencies of the various positions of the hypoconulid are reserved for later publication. Suffice it to stress here the considerable differences that separate closely related species and sometimes even subspecies. The frequent absence of the hypoconulid on the third molar is also of interest. Cases where the hypoconulid has been considerably reduced, though not reported here, are even more frequent.

Since the position and size of the hypoconulid constitute one of the principal elements determining the groove pattern of the lower molars, it readily appears that this pattern is much more variable in the gibbon than it is reported to be in other hominoids. In fact it was found by the writer that the usual groove system in the lower molars of the Chiengmai population did not conform exactly to the typical *Dryopithecus* pattern and, in many cases, approached somewhat the so-called plus-pattern, which was actually found at least once.

It has often been observed (Gregory, 1922; Steiner, 1949) that the gibbons present a number of features that are rather more primitive than those found in the other pongids. If this be true of the dentition it would follow that a pronounced buccal shifting of the hypoconulid on all lower molars may constitute a rather late development in the evolution of the hominoid dentition. This conclusion, the writer believes, is borne out by an attentive examination of the lower molars of *Limnopithecus* and *Proconsul*.

At any rate, the marked variability in the position and size of the hypoconulid calls for prudence in interpreting the phylogenetic significance of its position and of the *Dryopithecus* pattern of which it is an element. It may be recalled that the small size and the central position of the hypoconulid in the lower molars of *Oreopithecus* has caused some workers to deny the hominoid status of this form.

VARIABILITY IN THE MORPHOLOGY OF THE FIRST LOWER PREMOLAR

In respect of the total crown morphology, the anterior lower premolar doubtless represents the most variable tooth in the dentition of the Chiengmai population. As in all non-human hominoid genera the anterior lower premolar of gibbons is characterized by its sectorial aspect: the crown is enlarged and compressed laterally to form a mesial oblique cutting edge which, in occlusion, shears against the high upper canine. The variability observed in the Chiengmai gibbons concerns chiefly the degree of lateral compression of the crown. Beside the common or elongated type of crown another type was recorded which is best defined as triangular (Figs. 2 and 3). In the latter, a strong development of the disto-lingual portion of the tooth causes the crown to assume a triangular outline. The width index of the crown is thereby considerably increased and the tooth can no longer be described as "compressed". This variation, however, does not seem to alter the sectorial character of the crown. Moreover, no lingual cusp was ever found to occur on the expanded distal part, but the latter is often supported by a third root. This root originates lingually and somewhat mesial to the normal distal root which is thereby displaced slightly buccally (Fig. 4). The third root may be developed in various degrees, ranging from a short bud to a root nearly as long as the normal distal root.

Because of the number of forms intermediate between the compressed and the triangular type, it is hard to determine statistically the respective frequency of each type. The most objective criterion appears to be the presence of the third root just described. It is easily identifiable because of its lingual or mesio-lingual inclination which causes it to indent the lingual alveolar border of the jaw. Table V indicates the frequency of the three-rooted type of anterior lower premolar in the Chiengmai population.

TABLE V

NUMBER OF DENTITIONS WITH TREE-ROOTED P_3 IN THE CHIENGMAI POPULATION OF *Hylobates lar*

	N	P_3
Males	56	26 (+3)†
Females	40	12 (+1)

†Numbers within parentheses indicate doubtful cases to be added to the total of clearly determined occurrences.

In the course of further investigations on the gibbon dentition, the writer had the opportunity to examine 358 dentitions of *Hylobates* and *Symphalangus*. A number of gibbon species occasionally present the triangular type of premolar, though it is by no means as frequent as in the Chiengmai population. However, in only 2 instances was a three-rooted lower premolar observed. Both specimens belong to the subspecies *Hylobates lar*

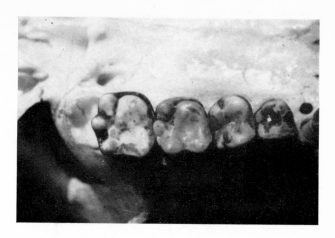

FIG. 1. Right upper permanent molars with divided hypocone. M. C. Z. (Harvard), 41491.

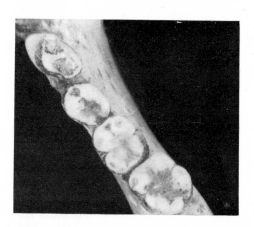

FIG. 2. Oblong type of anterior lower premolar (left mandible). M. C. Z. (Harvard), 41473.

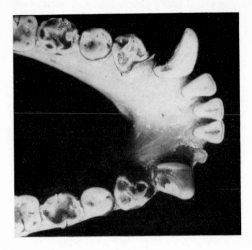

FIG. 3.   Triangular type of anterior lower premolar.
M. C. Z. (Harvard), 41448.

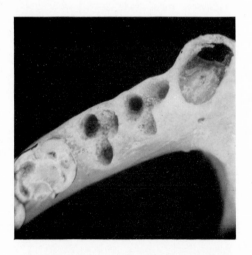

FIG. 4.   Alveoli of left lower premolars showing three-rooted
condition. M. C. Z. (Harvard), 41447.

pileatus and originate from the same locality which is represented in the collections of the National U.S. Museum (Washington, D.C.) by 5 males and 4 females. It is therefore not unlikely that the frequency of the three-rooted premolar is as high in that locality as it was found to be in Chiengmai. Most surprising, however, is the apparent complete absence of this variation in all other gibbon species examined. The limitation of this particularity to a few restricted populations may well account for the fact that the feature has never, to our knowledge, been reported in the literature.†

The significance of these observations lies chiefly in that they stress the high morphological plasticity of the anterior lower premolar. There seems to be sound evidence that this great variability also occurs in other hominoids and even in man. In what is perhaps the only available study on the recent evolution of the pongid dentition, Hooijer (1948) compares the dentition of the Pleistocene, subfossil and modern orangs from Sumatra. Among other changes that differentiate the subfossil from the recent form, he notes a marked reduction in the size of the anterior lower premolar, while the posterior premolar has remained practically unchanged.

The data gathered by Selma Thomsen (1955) on the dentition of the people of Tristan da Cunha point in the same direction. The dimensions of the anterior lower premolars have higher coefficients of variation in both sexes than is the case for the posterior lower premolar. In males, the anterior lower premolar is even shown to be the most variable of all the lower cheek teeth, including the third molar.

It is of interest to recall, in this connection, that in man the first deciduous molar, i.e. the precursor of P3, has also been found to be more variable than the second deciduous molar (Dahlberg, 1949; Hanihara, 1956).

That at least some of the variable characters of the anterior lower premolar are closely connected with genetic factors is

†The only mention of a somewhat similar occurrence is found in Bennejeant (1936) who, in his extensive study of dental anomalies and variability in Primates, reports a single case of a supernumerary root on the posterior lower premolar of a chimpanzee.

C

clearly indicated by the restriction of the three-root pattern to what are most likely strongly inbred populations. Since changes in the morphology of this tooth are among those that would characterize an hypothetical transition from a pongid to an hominid type of dentition, it seems important to realize that such changes can occur and spread rather widely within one limited genetic pool.

CONCLUSIONS

The few variable features examined in this paper underline the importance of obtaining a correct estimate of the dental variability characteristic of a given hominoid genus or species. Such an estimate is particularly needed in view of a more rational definition of fossil species and genera. If, for instance, anterior lower premolars of the oblong and triangular types described above had been found separately in some fossiliferous deposit, the chances are great indeed that they would have been attributed to distinct species, if not genera.

Again, the marked variability in structures such as the hypoconulid's position and size calls for prudence in interpreting the phylogenetic significance of these features.

The presence of pronounced interspecific differences further stresses the need for re-evaluating some of the commonly accepted views. The data contained in Remane's (1921) standard work on the hominoid dentition, and which are constantly referred to in the literature, were found to be at variance with all three sets of observations here reported for the Chiengmai population. As mentioned above, it is interspecific differences, rather than the personal bias of each observer, that almost certainly account for the discrepancies. It thereby becomes evident that the true nature of the gibbon dentition will be known only after adequate samples of each species, and preferably of each subspecies, have been examined. This conclusion, it is suggested, holds equally for other hominoid genera.

Finally, although the type of morphological variation observed in the anterior lower premolar of the Chiengmai population does not point in the direction of a two-cusped or non-sectorial tooth, the considerable plasticity evidenced by this tooth may have a bearing on the origin of the two-cusped premolar of hominids, the more so in that this plasticity does not seem to be restricted to the gibbon but extends to other hominoid genera. In the light of observations such as these it would seem particularly valuable to make a systematic study of the variability of this tooth in forms like *Proconsul* and *Oreopithecus* of which large fossil samples are now available.‡

REFERENCES

BENNEJEANT, M. C. (1936) *Anomalies et Variations Dentaires chez les Primates*. Paris.

DAHLBERG, A. A. (1949) The dentition of the American Indian. In W. S. LAUGHLIN (ed.) *The Physical Anthropology of the American Indian*, 138–176. Viking Fund, New York.

GREGORY, W. K. (1922) *The Origin and Evolution of the Human Dentition*. Williams and Wilkins, Baltimore.

HANIHARA, K. (1956) Studies on the deciduous dentition of the Japanese and Japanese-American Hybrids. III: Deciduous lower molars, *J. Anthrop. Soc. Nippon*, **64**, 95 (in Japanese with English summary).

HOOIJER, A. D. (1948) *Prehistoric Teeth of Man and of the Orang-utan from Central Sumatra, with Notes on the Fossil Orang-utan from Java and Southern China*. Leiden.

JOERGENSEN, K. D. (1956) The deciduous dentition. A descriptive and comparative anatomical study, *Act. Odont. Scandin.* **14**, suppl. 20.

MOORREES, C. F. A. (1957) *The Aleut Dentition*. Harvard U.P., Cambridge.

PEDERSEN, P. O. (1949) The East Greenland Eskimo dentition, *Meddelelser om Gronland*, **142**, Copenhagen.

‡This article was about to be sent to the editor when I came across the article by de Jonge (1961) (Gedanken über die Wurzeldifferenzierung des vorderen unteren Praemolaris, *Z. Morph. Anthrop.* **51**, 20) on root differentiation in the anterior lower premolar. de Jonge remarks on the presence of a three-rooted P_3 in a few modern human dentitions. The brief description given in the article corresponds rather well with the condition observed in *Hylobates*. Further references to isolated occurrences of this feature in fossil hominids are of interest since they may provide indications on the phylogenetic significance of this particular root-conformation.

REMANE, A. (1921) Beiträge zur morphologie des anthropoiden gebisses, *Arch. f. Naturgesch.* **87**, 1.

SCHULTZ, A. H. (1944) Age changes and variability in gibbons *Am. J. Phys. Anthrop.* N.S. **2**, 1.

SCHULTZ, A. H. (1956) *Significance of Recent Primatology for Physical Anthropology.* Selected Papers of the Fifth International Congress of Anthropological and Ethnological Sciences. Philadelphia.

SCHUMAN and BRACE, C. L. (1955) Metric and morphologic variations in the dentition of the Liberian chimpanzee; comparison with anthropoid and human dentitions. *In* J. A. Gavan (ed. *The Non-Human Primates and Human Evolution,* pp. 61–90 Wayne U.P., Detroit.

SELMER-OLSEN, R. (1949) *An Odontometrical Study on the Norwegian Lapps.* Det Norske Videnskaps-Akademi, Oslo.

STEINER, H. (1949) Beobachtungen über das brutbiologische Verhalten des Gibbons. *Archiv der J. Klaus-Stiftung für Vererbungslehre.* **24**, 217–236.

THOMSEN, S. (1955) *Dental Morphology and Occlusion in the People of Tristan da Cunha.* Det Norske Videnskaps-Akademi, Oslo.

WASHBURN, S. L. (1954) An old theory is supported by new evidence and new methods, *Amer. Anthrop.* **56**, 436.

OCCLUSION AND MALOCCLUSION OF
THE TEETH OF PRIMATES

by J. R. E. MILLS

Institute of Dental Surgery, London

THE teeth of the non-human primates have been studied chiefly by palaeontologists, for comparison with those of fossil material. Since the latter are usually fragmentary, little attention has been paid to their occlusion. Elliott (1913) describes the dentition of most genera of recent primates without mentioning their occlusion or function, while Warwick James (1960) pays it only passing reference, although he illustrates the skulls of most genera with their teeth in occlusion.

The occlusion of the teeth may be considered as either a static or a dynamic condition. Static occlusion is the relation of the teeth to each other, when the jaws are firmly closed in their normal centric position. It has been illustrated for certain primates by Cope (1889) and Gregory (1922, 1934). Dynamic occlusion is the corresponding relation of the teeth to each other when the jaw is carrying out normal chewing movements. Ryder (1878) describes this, somewhat subjectively, for a wide range of mammals, while Gregory (1920) illustrates the molar function of the fossil lemurs *Notharctus* and *Adapis*, basing his findings on the wear facets produced on the teeth by their opponents in chewing. By examining these facets it is possible to ascertain the part of the opposing tooth which has produced the facet. When this process is repeated for a number of facets, on different teeth, it is possible to infer the movements of the lower jaw which take place in function, and the relationship of the lower to upper teeth in chewing. This technique was elaborated in a study of the Perissodactyls by Butler (1952), and was applied to the recent primates by Mills (1955), and to

29

certain fossil members of the order by Butler and Mills (1959).

It is proposed to describe first the occlusion of the teeth in the gorilla, and then to use this for comparison with the other primates. The shapes of the individual teeth are not unlike those of man, except that the canines are very much larger, especially in the male. The incisors are spatulate, and the uppers slightly overlap the lowers vertically when newly erupted. This vertical overlap usually disappears with wear, leaving an edge-to-edge incisor relation. The enlarged canines project above the general level of the remaining teeth and become inter-locking, as indicated in Fig. 1. This has caused many comparative odontologists to deny the possibility of any lateral jaw movement in the great apes, and to state that chewing consists of a purely vertical, champing action. In fact, as Gregory (1916) and Mills (1955) have pointed out, lateral chewing takes place quite normally in the gorilla, as in all the primates. It will be seen in this figure that the upper canine slides between the lower canine and first premolar, while the lower canine similarly passes in a diastema between the upper

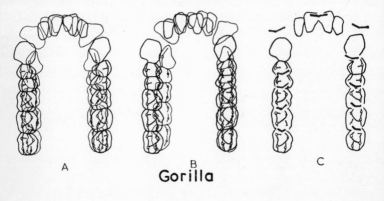

A B C
Gorilla

I

FIG. 2. Occlusal view of upper and lower dentitions of the gorilla, superimposed. A, In centric occlusion. B, With the mandible displaced to the right. C, Shows the paths of certain parts of the lower dentition during lateral chewing.

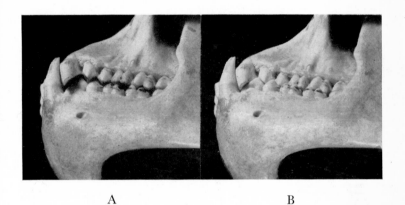

A   B

FIG. 1.   Lateral view of the teeth of the gorilla in occlusion. A, In centric occlusion; B, With the mandible displaced to the left. (*Reprinted by permission of the 'Dental Practitioner'.*)

second incisor and canine. The effect of these canines is to limit such movement to a single narrow path.

The premolars and molars occlude much as in man; the upper teeth overhanging the lowers. The lower buccal cusps occlude in the longitudinal groove between upper buccal and lingual cusps, while the upper lingual cusps fit into the corresponding groove in the lower teeth. Antero-posteriorly the

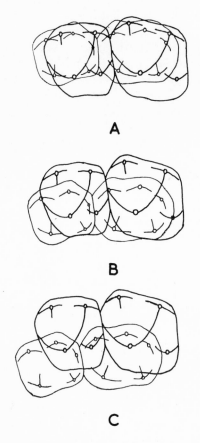

Fig. 3. Upper and lower first and second molars of the gorilla, superimposed. A, During buccal occlusion; B, In centric occlusion; C, During lingual occlusion.

upper and lower cusps also alternate, so that each cusp occludes in a fossa between four of its antagonists. This is shown again in Fig. 2A, which has been produced by superimposing accurate scale drawings of the upper and lower dentitions, as seen from above. The upper teeth are indicated by a thick and the lowers by a thinner outline, and the diagram also shows the principal cusps and ridges of the teeth.

Figure 3 shows an enlarged view of the first two molars, Fig. 3B indicating their relation in centric occlusion. It will be noted that the disto-buccal cusp or hypoconid of the lower molar fits into the centre of the main basin of the upper molar, while the mesio-lingual cusp or protocone of the upper molar similarly fits into the central basin of the lower tooth. Both these relations are quite constant throughout the mammals as are, indeed, many quite minor details of the occlusal relationships of their teeth.

Dynamic occlusion may be divided into two phases. The buccal phase commences with the lower jaw displaced laterally, as indicated for the molars in Fig 3A. It continues until the lower teeth reach the centric position shown in Fig. 3B. During this phase each of the cusps of the lower teeth shears along a groove between two opposing cusps. This cusp-in-groove action would serve to cut or slice the food. From this centric position the lower teeth continue to move medially, towards the opposite side of the mouth, until they reach the position seen in Fig. 3C. I have called this the lingual phase. During this phase the lower buccal cusps slide across the upper lingual ones, producing a grinding action analogous to a millstone, which is somewhat different from the cutting action seen in the buccal phase.

This is illustrated for the whole dentition in Fig. 2. In Fig. 2A we see again the centric relation of the teeth. In Fig. 2B the mandible has been displaced to the right, so that the teeth on the right of the mouth are at the beginning of the buccal phase. It will be noted that those on the left are at the end of the lingual phase; the buccal phase on one side is coincident with the lingual phase on the other, producing a balanced occlusion. This may help to reduce the stress on the mandibular joint.

Figure 2c was produced by first drawing the outlines of the upper dentition. The lower dentition was then drawn, to the same scale, on tracing paper. This tracing was superimposed on the upper dentition in the centric position, as in Fig. 2A, and points transferred to the diagram corresponding to the mesio-buccal cusp, or protoconid, of each molar, the buccal cusp of the lower premolars and canines, and the mid-point between the lower first incisors. The centre of the mandibular condyle had been marked on the tracing, and this was also transferred to the diagram. The tracing was then repositioned so as to correspond to the situation depicted in Fig. 2B, with the mandible displaced to the right. The same points were again transferred to the diagram. Finally the tracing was repositioned so that the outlines of the lower teeth were those seen when the mandible was displaced to the left; a mirror-image of the picture in Fig. 2B. Again the same points were transferred to the diagram. The three positions of each cusp, and of the centre of the condyle, were then joined together, and the resultant thick lines indicate the paths of these structures during chewing.

During the buccal phase of occlusion there is no translatory movement of the ipsilateral condyle; the mandible rotates about this condyle, with a posterior movement of the contra-lateral condyle. As the teeth pass through the centric position into the lingual phase, the ipsilateral condyle begins to move forward, with the contralateral condyle taking over the function of rotation. Chewing therefore consists of rotation about the two condyles alternately.

I would emphasize the path of the lower canine during this chewing action. In the buccal phase it moves between the upper canine and second incisor, while during the lingual phase it moves so that its tip passes over the lingual surface of the second incisor. It may produce a small facet in this area, but the low lingual surface of the tooth does not interfere with the movement of the canine.

A similar type of balanced occlusion is seen in the other great apes, and the condition is little changed in the New World monkeys, as shown in Fig. 4, for *Cebus*. There is again little difference in most of the Prosimii. Figure 5 shows the condition

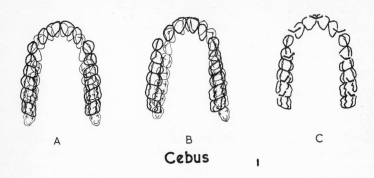

A   B   C

Cebus

FIG. 4.   Occlusal view of superimposed upper and lower
dentitions of *Cebus*.

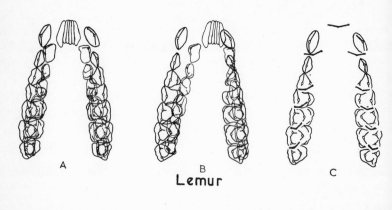

A   B   C

Lemur

FIG. 5.   Occlusal view of superimposed upper and lower
dentitions of *Lemur*.

in *Lemur*, and Fig. 6 in *Indri*. In the latter the occlusion is not
completely balanced. As shown in Fig. 6B, the buccal phase
commences with the contralateral teeth out of occlusion, and
they only come into contact for the last part of the buccal
phase.

In considering the most primitive members of the order,

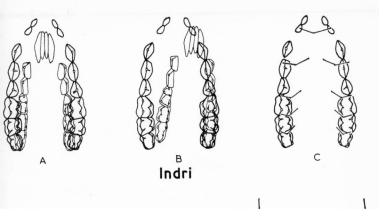

Indri

FIG. 6.   Occlusal view of superimposed upper and lower
dentitions of *Indri*.

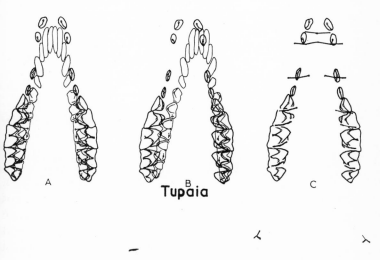

Tupaia

FIG. 7.   Occlusal view of superimposed upper and lower
dentitions of *Tupaia*.

such as the tree-shrew, *Tupaia*, and the tarsier, we find an essentially similar occlusal relationship, although the shape of the teeth, and especially the molars, is very different from that of the more advanced primates. The cusps are higher and more pointed, but lateral chewing still takes place, although movement of the lower jaw has a greater vertical component as its teeth slide across the uppers. Figure 7 illustrates this in *Tupaia*, and it will be seen that the cuspal relations remain essentially the same. There are, however, differences in the movement of the mandibular condyles; in the buccal phase, the ipsilateral condyle moves antero-medially, in addition to rotating. It can be shown that the movement of the contra-lateral condyle is a combination of a translatory movement parallel to that of the ipsilateral condyle, as shown by the dotted line, and a posterior movement resulting from the rotation about the centre of the ipsilateral condyle. The resultant of these two forces produces movement in the postero-lateral direction as shown. The situation in *Tarsius* shown in Fig. 8 is essentially similar, but here the translatory component is almost directly medial. It is suggested that this type of jaw movement, with translation combined with rotation, is more primitive than that seen in the higher primates and man.

The molar occlusion of the Old World monkeys is somewhat different from that considered so far, although the occlusion of the more anterior teeth is essentially similar to that seen in the gorilla. The occlusion of the first two molars is shown in Fig. 9. On the left are shown those of an Old World monkey, while those of gorilla are shown for comparison on the right. The outline of the molars is rectangular, instead of the rhomboidal outline seen in *Gorilla*. Consequently the lingual cusps are directly internal to the buccal ones, instead of being internal and slightly posterior, as in the apes. The buccal phase of occlusion is essentially similar in the two groups. The lingual phase of occlusion is somewhat reduced in the Old World monkeys, although less so than in *Indri*, and coincides with the latter part of the buccal phase. The cuspal relations during this lingual phase are also different from those seen in other primates. In the gorilla, as in most other primates, the lingual

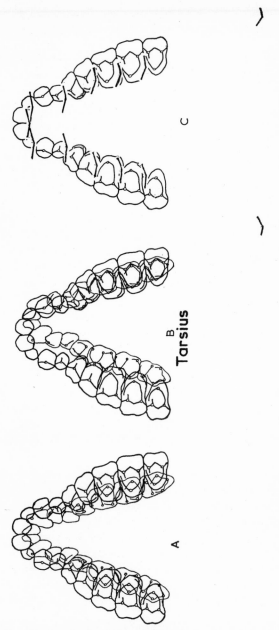

FIG. 8.   Occlusal view of superimposed upper and lower
dentitions of *Tarsius*.

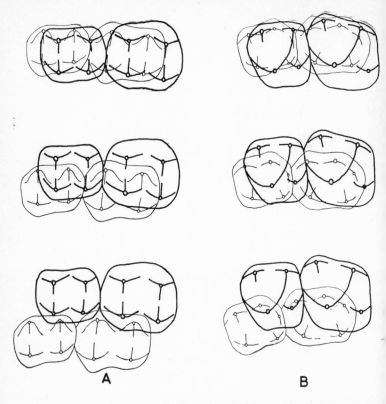

FIG. 9. A, Upper and lower first and second molars of *Macaca* superimposed during buccal occlusion, in centric occlusion and in lingual occlusion. B, Comparable view of first two molars of the Gorilla.

face of the lower buccal cusp slides across the buccal face of the upper lingual one, as shown in Fig. 9B. In the Old World monkeys, each lower buccal cusp passes between two upper lingual ones, as shown in Fig. 9A. The lingual phase thus duplicates the buccal phase, producing a cutting rather than a grinding action. This is perhaps more suited to a purely herbivorous diet. The jaw movement consists of medial translation combined with rotation, as in *Tupaia* and *Tarsius*. This is illustrated in Fig. 10.

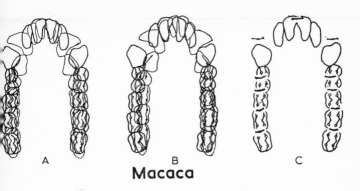

Fig. 10.   Occlusal view of superimposed upper and lower
dentitions of *Macaca*.

We see in man a marked reduction in facial prognathism,
when compared with the other primates. As a result of this the
dental arches lie nearer to the condylar axis, while the condyles
are displaced laterally due to the increase in brain size and
reduction in size of the dental arches. The latter are also somewhat changed in shape; in the apes the posterior teeth are
parallel on the two sides of the mouth, or even diverge anteriorly. In man the outline is rounded, and MacConaill and
Scher (1949) have suggested that it takes the form of a catenary
curve. Nevertheless both the jaw movements and the cuspal
relations remain similar to those seen in the apes as shown in
Fig. 11. Because of the change in the shape of the dental
arches, if the cuspal relations are to remain the same in dynamic
occlusion, changes are necessary in the shape of the molar
teeth. It may be that the change in shape of the human lower
molar from the so-called *Dryopithecus* pattern to the "plus"
pattern is an adaptation to this change in the direction of jaw
movement.

Probably the most noticeable difference between the dentition of the great apes and that of man lies in the reduction in
size of the canines in the latter. This is usually considered to be
due to their replacement by the hands in fighting. While this

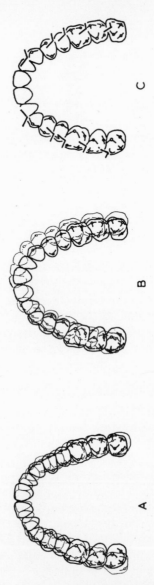

FIG. 11. Occlusal view of superimposed upper and lower dentitions of *Homo sapiens*.

nay be a factor, Butler and Mills (1959) have shown an occlusal eason for this change. It will be recalled that in the gorilla he lower canine, in the lingual phase of occlusion, moves so hat its tip passes across the low lingual region of the upper ncisor. In man, on the other hand, due to the rounding of the ental arch, the tip of the canine moves along the incisal edge f the second incisor, as shown on the left side of the mouth in 'ig. 11B and C. If the canine were enlarged such movement vould be impossible. It would therefore seem that the reduction n size of the canine is a remote result of the reduction of rognathism seen in man.

The occlusion of the teeth in primates, as in all mammals, orms a highly efficient machine for chewing the food, and it is nerefore rather surprising to find that malocclusion and rregularity of the teeth are by no means uncommon. Colyer 1931) has investigated the frequency of such malocclusion in a

TABLE I

Position Variations in the Different Orders (after Colyer)

Orders	No. of specimens	No. varying	Percentage of specimens varying
rimates	8148	2224	27·3
arnivora	4419	284	6·4
odentia	1819	12	0·7
ngulata	1335	162	12·1
yracoidea	300	37	12·3
arsupialia	2344	75	3·2

rge series of mammals, and his findings are given in Table 1. will be noted that malocclusion in the non-human primates as a considerably higher incidence than in any other order. a a further publication (1936) he has considered the various oups of primates individually and these are summarized in able II. The first column indicates the number of skulls amined in each group. The second column gives the per-

TABLE II
INCIDENCE OF MALOCCLUSION IN PRIMATES (AFTER COLYER)

Super-family	Genus, etc.	No. of speci-mens	Per-centage varying	Ditto less pm	Cl. III
Apes	Gorilla Pan Pongo	689 465 255	31·6 22 25	25 17 21·6	2·7 4·5 1·1
O.W. Monkeys	Colobinae Cercopithecinae	2319 2725	40·6 30·3	31·3 18·1	24·1 0·3
N.W. Monkeys	Cebidae Hapalidae	2122 211	17·7 9·5	N.A. N.A.	11·7 Nil
Prosimii		650	12	N.A.	N.A.

centage of skulls exhibiting abnormalities in the position of t
teeth. Many of these abnormalities were quite slight, and in t
apes and Old World monkeys many of the irregularities we
confined to very slight rotations of the premolars, so slight as
be insignificant. The third column therefore shows the pe
centage of irregularity in these two groups when such cas
were excluded.

The final column gives the percentage of cases in which t
lower incisor teeth occlude in front of the uppers; the rever
of the usual relationship. This does not arise in the Prosim
since most of the lemurs have no functional upper incisors.

Angle (1907) evolved a classification of malocclusion in m
which I propose to use in the present description. It is based
the antero-posterior relation of the dental arches. Thus, Class
constitutes those cases in which the posterior teeth, a
specifically the first molars, are in normal antero-posteri
relation. Class II consists of those individuals in whom t
lower posterior teeth (and usually also the lower jaw) were in
post-normal relation to their antagonists—in such cases t
upper incisors were frequently prominent. Class III is t
reverse of this, where the lower posterior teeth are prenorm
in their relation to the uppers, and the lower incisors usua

occlude in front of the uppers. The last group are represented in the final column of Table II.

The irregularities which Colyer describes are of three types. Many cases of mild irregularity of the incisors, premolars and molars are apparently due to a shortness of the tooth-bearing areas of the jaws—that is, to crowding. They are usually mild, and affect the occlusion but little. They fall into Angle's Class I, and similar conditions are seen in man, where the condition is often more severe. Secondly cases are seen in which the teeth are displaced bodily, in the absence of crowding. Such cases are rare. They are also occasionally seen in man, and it is assumed that the tooth-germ in such cases develops in an abnormal position, although the aetiology is unknown. Thirdly we see cases in which the lower incisors occlude in front of the uppers; analogous to Angle's Class III condition. The incidence of this varies considerably between different groups. Thus in the Old World monkeys, such a condition is seen in 24 per cent of the sub-family Colobinae, whereas in the other sub-family, the Cercopithecinae, the incidence is only 0·3 per cent. Within the species *Colobus polykomos* there is a marked variation between sub-species, from 20·2 per cent in *C. polykomos satanas* to nil in *C. polykomos caudatus*, with other sub-species lying between these extremes. In the genus *Presbytis* the incidence of this type of malocclusion rises to 77·2 per cent. Similarly in the New World monkeys, the incidence of Class III malocclusion varies from 36 per cent in *Brachyteles* to 1·5 per cent in *Cebus* and nil in *Pithecia*, *Cacajao*, *Saimiri* and *Aotus*. Colyer remarks that in the chimpanzees it is particularly common in individuals from the Batouri district of the Cameroons, where it is found in 16·6 per cent of 60 individuals, compared with 4·5 per cent of 312 individuals from other localities. Turning to man, Moorrees (1957) has investigated the teeth of the inhabitants of the Aleutian Islands. These may be divided into two communities, East and West Aleuts, which form "breeding isolates", although both are of Eskimoid origin. In his study he found a Class III incisor relation in 13·2 per cent of individuals, but all these affected individuals had at least one parent from the Eastern group; the condition was never seen in the pure West Aleut.

He suggests that it could be the result of a single gene. It would seem that this particular malocclusion has little effect on the efficiency of the dentition, and where it arises—possibly as a mutation—it is likely to be perpetuated.

It is notable that in Colyer's work, apart from those individuals with this Class III type of malocclusion, none of the conditions appears to be due to a disharmony of the parts of the skull. In particular, there are no instances of Angle's Class I malocclusion.

In general, it would appear that malocclusion is more common among the higher primates than in the relatively primitive Hapalidae and Prosimii. It is high in the Old World monkeys, but Colyer remarks that such malocclusions are usually less severe than in the great apes. The incidence of malocclusion would seem to bear an inverse relation to the height of the cusps of the posterior teeth. It would seem that a minor occlusal variation in the apes would be compensated by wear of the teeth, and would have little effect on function, while, with the high interlocking cusps of more primitive

TABLE III

COMPARATIVE INCIDENCE OF MALOCCLUSION IN WILD AND CAPTIVE PRIMATE
(AFTER COLYER)

Super-family	Genus	Wild State		Captive State	
		No. of specimens	Percentage varying	No. of specimens	Percentage varying
Apes	*Pan*	367	23·4	22	45·6
	Hylobates	248	21·0	29	31·0
O.W. Monkeys	*Macaca*	398	30·7	305	38·7
	Cercopithecus	1095	27·0	338	25·4
	Erythrocebus	35	25·7	45	44·4
	Papio	221	29·4	153	45·1
N.W. Monkeys	*Cebus*	493	19·7	98	30·6
Prosimii		602	15·9	85	21·2

genera, such a malocclusion would either be self-righting or would make chewing impossible.

Colyer (1931) also considers the effect of captivity on the incidence of malocclusion, and his figures are summarized in Table III. Variations of position of the teeth are apparently more common in the captive than in the wild state, in most genera. Colyer further remarks "the abnormalities seen in the captive animal are similar in type to those seen in the animal from the wild state but more marked, as a rule".

Turning to man, we find conditions of crowding and displacement of the teeth within the jaws, similar to those seen in the other primates. We also find a considerable number of malocclusions which are due to abnormalities in the relationships of the jaws to each other. These are primarily those which fall into Angle's Classes II and III, although the abnormality may also be vertical or lateral in direction. Apart from Class II abnormalities, these are not apparently seen in the non-human primates. Bjork (1947) has used lateral skull radiographs of living individuals, taken under standardized conditions, to study the dimensions of the component part of the face and of the cranial base. By comparing those of children exhibiting malocclusions with average figures obtained from a large random group, he has been able to identify the site of abnormalities which produce malrelationship of the jaws. These may involve the relative size and shape of the two jaws, but frequently the abnormality lies in other regions of the skull. Such abnormalities have the effect of increasing or decreasing the distance between the glenoid fossa and the maxilla, so that a mandible of normal size may be displaced forwards or backwards relative to the upper jaw. Class III malocclusion is most frequently associated with an abnormally large mandible, while in Class II malocclusion the abnormality more often lies in a posterior position of the mandibular joint.

Estimates of the incidence of malocclusion in man vary, from 2·4 per cent (Krockow and Winkler, 1932) to 91·4 per cent (Huber and Reynolds, 1946). The subject has been reviewed by Seipel (1946) and Brash, McKeag and Scott (1956). This wide variation is probably chiefly due to a difference of definition of normal and abnormal occlusion, although differences of race and age in the samples may be a contributing factor Smyth and Young (1932), in a study of some 20,000 English school-children, estimate the incidence of malocclusion at about 92 per cent, and if one accepts the very rigid standard set by Colyer for the primates, such a figure would not seem unreasonable. Seipel considers the relative frequency of the different types of malocclusion according to Angle's classification. In a review of the literature he finds the incidence of Class II malocclusion to vary between 4·1 and 26·6 per cent of the population, presumably as a result of differences of definition. Class III malocclusion remains fairly constant around an average figure of 2·8 per cent. His figures for his own Swedish sample are 10 and 4 per cent respectively.

Malocclusion is widely believed to be a disease of civilization and to be largely confined to recent man of Western European

TABLE IV

INCIDENCE OF MALOCCLUSION IN VARIOUS RACES (AFTER HELLMAN)

Race	Total no.	Percentage varying
Ancient Amerind	16	6·25
Modern Amerind	35	8·6
Eskimo	14	50
"Hindu"	39	35·9
Japanese	12	66·67
Chinese (Borneo)	14	91·4
Buriat	32	15·6
Tasmanian	11	27·3
Australian	14	28·6
Negro (East Africa)	33	21·2
Negro (South Africa)	10	Nil
Negro (West Africa)	76	32·9
Negro (W.R.U.)	43	6·98
White (W.R.U.)	62	32·26
White (Demko-Hegy)	41	34·2
White (Keszo-Hidegkut)	108	44·5
White (Szarazd)	42	33·33

escent. Table IV gives the incidence of malocclusion in
arious populations. It has been prepared from figures given by
Iellman in the discussion of a paper by Hrdlicka (1935), but
have combined the figures which he gives separately for the
wo sexes, and have omitted all groups in which the total
umber of skulls falls below ten. Even so his numbers are small,
ut they have the advantage that all the observations were
nade by the same individual, presumably using the same
riteria of normality. He does not indicate the origins of the
kulls beyond the fact that they came from "several museums".
hey would apparently indicate a relatively high incidence of
nalocclusion in those of European origin, although it is
qualled or exceeded by several other groups.

Begg (1954) examined some 800 skulls of Australian aborigines
ating from before the British occupation of Australia, and
ound an incidence of Class II malocclusion of 13 per cent, and
f Class III malocclusion of 3 per cent. These figures do not
iffer greatly from Seipel's figures for modern Swedes.

Clinch (1951) compares the occlusion of "primitive"
borigines, living under natural conditions in Northern
ustralia, with those of a "civilized" group from a mission
tation, and her findings are given in Table V. There is, of
ourse, a possibility of racial mixture in the latter group, but it
vould appear that the incidence of normal occlusion is over
hree times as great in the "primitive" group, although it is
nder 10 per cent in both.

It remains to consider the effect of civilization on the denti-
ions of the European races. Smyth (1933) examined 39 skulls
om a sixth-century Saxon burial ground at Bidford-upon-
Avon, and found only 5 skulls which had normal or nearly
ormal occlusion, while malocclusion was present in 34 or
7 per cent, although very mild in 13 (33 per cent). Class II
nalocclusion was present in 6 of 25 cases considered, and
Class III malocclusion in 2 of these 25 individuals. Examples
f these skulls are illustrated by Miss Smyth herself and by
rash (1956). Although one or two cases exhibit moderately
evere malocclusions, the majority are confined to a slight
rowding or irregularity of the incisors. Keith (1924) examined

skulls of various periods in the museum of the Royal College of Surgeons. He was concerned with what he described as a "contracted palate", presumably associated with crowding of the teeth. He states that it occurs sporadically in the Roman period, but is otherwise not found widely until the eighteenth and nineteenth centuries. He compared the measurements of palatal width and length in 50 pre-Norman English skulls with 50 buried in the eighteenth and nineteenth centuries. He ignores the possibility of racial difference. He found that on average the more modern skulls were about 1 mm narrower and shorter than the ancient group, but indicates that the variation was wider in the former group.

Lundstrom and Lysell (1953) describe a craniometric investigation of 121 skulls from a Danish medieval graveyard. They compare their findings with those for Swedish medieval skulls and with Seipel's figures for modern Swedes. It would appear that the medieval dentitions are on average about 2 mm wider in the premolar region, and 4·0 mm wider in the molar region, than present-day material. They also find a greater dispersion of "relative spacing"—that is, of crowding or spacing—in the modern sample. The incidence of Angle's Class II and III malocclusion is approximately the same in the medieval skulls as in the modern material, but the condition is seldom severe in the former group. On the other hand Cooke and Rowbotham (1958) find malocclusion in only 7·2 per cent of 300 Romano-British skulls.

Brash, McKeag and Scott (1956) review the incidence of malocclusion as reported by numerous authors, considering both historical and racial factors. The incidence of both varies widely for different authors, but it is noticeable that where the investigation has been carried out by a specialist orthodontist the incidence is very much higher than in other cases. This would corroborate an impression which I have received from illustrations in these articles, that many of the malocclusions are so slight as to be negligible to all but the specialist.

It would seem, then, that malocclusion occurs throughout the primates, to a greater degree than is usually realized, and that it is greatest in those animals whose posterior teeth have low cusps, and in which, therefore, it will be least likely to interfere with function. The incidence is highest in man, and is somewhat higher in some racial groups than in others. While severe malocclusions occur in all primates, their incidence is much increased in man, and especially in civilized man.

There are three possible reasons for this. Firstly the admixture of populations which takes place in an industrialized country. This is probably responsible for the malocclusions which are caused by discrepancies in the parts of the skull, and for the greater dispersion of crowding and spacing of the teeth, due to a discrepancy in size of teeth and jaws. It could also be responsible for the increase of malocclusion in animals bred in captivity.

Secondly we have the effect of an increased survival rate in a civilized community, or in animals in captivity. Thus an individual with a severe malocclusion is more likely to survive, and to perpetuate his malocclusion. In addition, there is a greater likelihood that the weaker members of the community, generally, will survive, and these would be more likely to have crowded arches.

Thirdly there is the possibility of environmental factors in the condition of captivity or of civilization which would cause malocclusion. Colyer (1936) remarks that "lemurs in the captive state seem peculiarly liable to develop abnormal conditions of the bone, and these conditions are often associated with irregularities in the position of the teeth". This is also true, according to the same author, of baboons. In these abnormal bone conditions, the teeth are grossly misplaced, and either fail to erupt, or erupt ectopically. A similar condition is seen in man in the group of diseases known as the osteodystrophies, which are genetically controlled. There is considerable evidence that environmental bone diseases such as rickets do not affect the dentition.

There remains the decrease in dental arch size in modern communities, as compared with medieval ones. Brash (1924) states that the narrow, contracted arch was found in the Middle Ages, and that it is only the incidence of such which has increased. It may be due to a racial difference in the samples, or to the effect of "survival of the unfit". It is probably analogous to the decreased stature seen in industrialized communities, and the aetiological factors may be similar.

TABLE V

INCIDENCE OF MALOCCLUSION IN "PRIMITIVE" AND "CIVILIZED" AUSTRALIA (AFTER CLINCH)

	Total number	Percentage varying
Primitive	108	93·23
Civilized	54	98·15

REFERENCES

ANGLE, E. H. (1907) *Treatment of Malocclusion of the Teeth*, 7th ed. p. 628. S.S. White Dental Mfgr. Co., Philadelphia.

BEGG, P. R. (1954) Stone Age Man's dentition, *Amer. J. Orthodont.* **40**, 462.

BJORK, A. (1947) The face in profile, *Svensk tandlak. Tidskr.* **40** No. 5B, 180.

BRASH, J. C. (1924) The genesis and growth of deformed jaws and palates. In *The Growth of the Jaws, Normal and Deformed, in Health and Disease*, p. 30. Dental Board of the U.K., London.

BRASH, J. C., MCKEAG, H. T. A. and SCOTT, J. H. (1956) *The Aetiology of Irregularity and Malocclusion of the Teeth*. 2nd ed., p. 503. Dental Board of the U.K., London.

BUTLER, P. M. (1952) The milk molars of the Perissodactyla, with remarks on molar occlusion, *Proc. zool. Soc. Lond.* **121**, 777.

BUTLER, P. M. and MILLS, J. R. E. (1959) A contribution to the odontology of *Oreopithecus*, *Bull. Brit. Mus. (nat. hist.)* **4**, No. 1, 1–26.

CLINCH, L. M. (1951) The occlusion of the Australian aborigines, *Trans. europ. orthod. Soc.* 80.

COLYER, J. F. (1931) *Abnormal Conditions of the Teeth of Animals in Their Relationship to Similar Conditions in Man*, p. 151. Dental Board of the U.K., London.

COLYER, J. F. (1936) *Variations and Diseases of the Teeth of Animals*, p. 750. Bale and Danielsson, London.

COOKE, C. C. and ROWBOTHAM, T. C. (1958) A craniometric and dental investigation of 301 Romano-British skulls and jaws circa 150 A.D., *J. dent. Res.* **37**, 753.

COPE, E. D. (1889) The mechanical causes of the development of the hard parts of Mammalia, *J. Morph.* **3**, 137.

ELLIOTT, D. G. (1913) *A Review of the Primates*, 3 vols. Amer. Mus. Nat. Hist., New York.

GREGORY, W. K. (1916) Studies on the evolution of the primates, *Bull. Amer. Mus. nat. Hist.* **35**, 239.

GREGORY, W. K. (1920) On the structure and relations of *Notharctus*, an American Eocene primate, *Mem. Amer. Mus. nat. Hist.* N.S. **2**, 51.

GREGORY, W. K. (1922) *The Origin and Evolution of the Human Dentition*. Williams and Wilkins, Baltimore.

GREGORY, W. K. (1934) A half-century of trituberculy, *Proc. Amer. phil. Soc.* **73**, 169.

HRDLICKA, A. (1935) Normal variation of teeth and jaws and orthodonty, *Int. J. Orthod.* **21**, 1099.

HUBER, R. E. and REYNOLDS, J. W. (1946) A dento-facial study of male students in the University of Michigan, *Amer. J. Orthodont.* **32**, 1.

JAMES, W. W. (1960) *The Jaws and Teeth of Primates*. p. 328. Pitman Medical Publishing Co., London.

KEITH, A. (1924) Concerning certain structural changes which are taking place in our jaws and teeth. In *The Growth of the Jaws, Normal and Abnormal, in Health and Disease*, p. 14. Dental Board of the U.K., London.

KROCKOW, I. and WINKLER, R. (1932) Sozial-und rassebiologische Untersuchung zur Frage der Verbreitung und Entstehung von Biss-und Stellungsanomalien, *Forts. der Orthodontik* **2**, 303.

LUNDSTROM, A. and LYSELL, L. (1953) An anthropological examination of a group of medieval Danish skulls, with particular regard to the jaws and occlusal conditions, *Acta odont. Scandinavica* **11**, 111.

MACCONAILL, N. A. and SCHER, E. A. (1949) The ideal form of the human dental arcade, with some prosthetic application, *Dent. Rec.* **69**, 285.

MILLS, J. R. E. (1955) Ideal dental occlusion in the Primates, *Dent. Practit.* **6**, 47.

MOORREES, C. F. A. (1957) *The Aleut Dentition*, p. 196. Harvard Univ. Press, Cambridge, Mass.

RYDER, J. A. (1878) On the mechanical genesis of tooth forms, *Proc. Acad. nat. Sci. Philad.* 45.

SEIPEL, C. M. (1946) Variation of tooth position, *Svensk. Tandlak. Tidskr.* **39** suppl. 1.

SMYTH, K. C. (1933) Some notes on the dentitions of Anglo-Saxon skulls from Bidford-on-Avon, with special reference to malocclusion, *Trans. Brit. Soc. Orthodont.* 21.

SMYTH, K. C. and YOUNG, M. (1932) *Facial Growth in children*, p. 8. H.M. Stationery Office, London.

PHYLOGENETIC AND INTRA-SPECIFIC VARIATIONS IN TOOTH SEQUENCE POLYMORPHISM

by STANLEY M. GARN and ARTHUR B. LEWIS

Department of Growth and Genetics
Fels Research Institute, Yellow Springs, Ohio

INTRODUCTION

The sequence of eruption of the permanent teeth shows a remarkable shift through the order primates. At one end, in the insectivores, the posterior or molar teeth add themselves to the dental arcade before the deciduous anterior teeth even begin replacement. At the other end, typified by the "textbook" European, the deciduous anterior teeth are largely replaced by their permanent successors before the second and third molar teeth extend the effective size of the dental arch. Once the molar teeth led the eruption parade, $M_1 M_2 M_3$. . . . Now the anterior teeth are scattered among them, $M_1 \ldots M_2 M_3$, or even $M_1 \ldots M_2 \ldots M_3$ (Grewel, 1935; Schultz, 1935, 1940, 1944, 1949, 1950, 1960; Clements and Zuckerman, 1953; Senyürek, 1955, 1956).

This distinction in eruption order between early primate and modern man is paralleled by a less dramatic but comparable difference between ape and man. In the great apes, as in the original primate pattern, the second molars commonly precede the second premolars, as typified by the notation $M_2 P_2$. In modern man, or more specifically European whites, the second premolars are presumed to erupt before the second molars, hence $P_2 M_2$. Presumably again, the difference between the $M_2 P_2$ order of monkeys and apes and the $P_2 M_2$ sequence in modern man marks a taxonomic chasm (Weidenreich, 1937).

53

The discovery, therefore, of immature paleoanthropic hominids directed attention to their still-developing if fossilized teeth. The question at hand was whether the fossils would prove $P_2 M_2$ (supposedly like us) or $M_2 P_2$ (like the apes). From his analysis of but two juvenile specimens of *Homo erectus*, and after reviewing earlier monographs on European Neanderthaloids, Weidenreich assigned the $M_2 P_2$ eruption order to the thick-skulled European and Asiatic fossils (Weidenreich, 1937). There appeared to be a neat developmental difference that put paleoanthropic man in one eruption set and neanthropic man in another, except perhaps for the copper-age Greeks (Senyürek, 1956).

But this neat differentiation between fossil and modern hominids, based on the presumed order of eruption in a few juvenile fossil mandibles, and the average age at eruption from norms for Europeans, proved to be one of the credible but incorrect myths of our time. It assumed, to begin with, that the tooth eruption sequence in individuals is fairly represented by massed-data tabulation. It assumed that the order of emergence through the alveolus is necessarily the same as the sequence of eruption through the gums. And it further assumed that estimates of the tooth eruption sequence could be made from fossils in various stages of tooth calcification and movement without prior familiarity with the course of tooth formation and eruption in contemporary children.

PROBLEMS IN DETERMINING THE ERUPTION SEQUENCE

To consider the first point, means or medians are notoriously poor indicators of the usual sequence of events. Without knowing both the extent of variability (σ) and the correlation between events (r), the fact that tooth X precedes tooth Y on the average scarcely tells us how often tooth X actually precedes tooth Y. Using Hurme's eruption norms (Hurme, 1948, 1949) the one-year lead separating P_2 from M_2 on the average, is obviously small compared to the eruption variability for each of the two teeth in question. And, in fact, Koski observed the $M_2 P_2$ eruption sequence in 16 per cent of his Finnish children

(Koski and Garn, 1957). Hurme (1957) found a 13 per cent incidence of the $M_2 P_2$ order of emergence in Boston boys and girls. While Senyürek (1956) was probably correct in attributing the far higher proportion of the $M_2 P_2$ sequence suggested in British children by Clements et al. (1953) to premature loss of teeth, the fact remains that the $M_2 P_2$ sequence of gingival eruption is no rarity in contemporary whites. As for other populations, the $M_2 P_2$ sequence may be observed in 48 per cent of contemporary Pima Indians (cf. Koski and Garn, 1957, p. 482) and it appears to have been the majority sequence in Apache and Pima Indians examined a half-century ago (Hrdlička, 1908).

Next, there is the inevitable discrepancy between alveolar eruption and gingival eruption, between the order in which the teeth appear above the alveolar border and the sequence in which they pierce the gum. This distinction is of major importance, because "eruption" in fossils and skulls has generally been determined in relation to the bone, whereas the gum is the reference line for eruption in the living. Randall (1943/1944) attempted to reconcile the two eruptions, by recording as "erupted" only those gorilla teeth which, in his opinion, would have been well above the gum line (see also Krogman, 1930, p. 307). Most workers, however, seem to have taken alveolar eruption and gingival eruption as equivalent if not identical, whether working with monkeys or men.

In actual fact, a large proportion (nearly 40 per cent) of American white children are of the $M_2 P_2$ eruption sequence in alveolar eruption (Garn, Koski and Lewis, 1957). But the majority of the very same boys and girls are of the $P_2 M_2$ or "modern" order of eruption when emergence through the gingiva is the criterion of use, and less than 20 per cent are then $M_2 P_2$. Clearly, alveolar eruption and gingival eruption cannot be used interchangeably in comparative studies!

The fact that a child may be $M_2 P_2$ in alveolar eruption, yet $P_2 M_2$ in gingival eruption is simpler to comprehend if the developmental course of the two teeth is retraced. M_2 forms immediately below the alveolar border. After 7 or 8 years it attains alveolar eruption and then remains relatively static for

1 to 2 years before gingival emergence. P_2, on the other hand, forms below the roots of dm_2. When M_2 is already above the alveolar border, P_2 may still be capped by dm_2 (hence the $M_2 P_2$ sequence of alveolar eruption). But once dm_2 is exfoliated, P_2 moves rapidly along the clear-channel so provided, while M_2 may still remain unerupted clinically. Thus, an $M_2 P_2$ sequence of alveolar eruption frequently becomes $P_2 M_2$ in gingival emergence.

While these descriptive facts explain how an $M_2 P_2$ order of alveolar eruption is transformed into the $P_2 M_2$ sequence in appearance through the gingiva, they only partly describe the hazards of estimating the probable eruption sequence in specific fossils. The comparative positions of the follicles of M_2 and P_2 may lead to erroneous estimates of the probable eruption sequence, as was true in Weidenreich's case. The relative degree of calcification of the developing germs of these two teeth may again suggest an eruption sequence that might not, in fact, obtain (see Fig. 1). At the other extreme, as the teeth come into approximation, the investigator unfamiliar with the developmental course of tooth movement might assign a $P_2 M_2$ eruption sequence retrospectively when the true order was $M_2 P_2$ in that particular specimen (cf. Broom and Robinson, 1951).

Determining the "eruption" sequence from dried specimen or fossilized skulls unquestionably remains a problem. Where the cusps or crowns of a tooth are just barely above the alveolar border, it is proper to use the term "alveolar eruption", but alveolar eruption should not be equated with gingival emergence. But for fossils or skulls where cusp calcification has barely begun or where nearly all teeth are effectively in occlusion, speculation on the true sequence of alveolar eruption is obviously hazardous. And guessing at the probable course of clinical eruption where no teeth have even broken through the alveolus remains an unacceptable procedure.

THE ERUPTION SEQUENCE IN MODERN MAN

To return to the tooth eruption sequence in modern man, or more specifically the order of emergence through the gingiva,

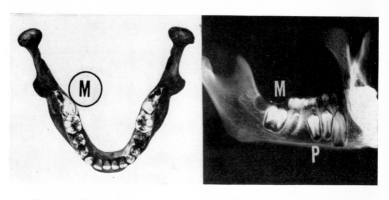

FIG. 1. Photograph (*left*) and radiograph (*right*) of a preadolescent mandible showing unerupted M_2 in crypt. Superficially, since dm_2 is still in place, the $M_2 P_2$ eruption sequence would be suggested. Actually, as shown in the radiograph, root formation of P_2 is well ahead of M_2. The calcification sequence is clearly $P_2 M_2$. Clinically, both teeth are far from gingival eruption.

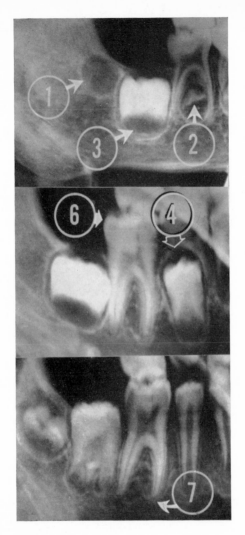

FIG. 2. Radiographs showing: (1) the follicle stage of M_2; (2) cusp calcification of P_2; (3) root formation of M_1; (4) alveolar eruption of P_2; (6) occlusal attainment of M_1; and (7) apical closure of M_1. As shown above, P_2 may attain alveolar eruption while still "capped" by its deciduous predecessor, thus further differentiating alveolar from gingival eruption.

a rough indication of order can be obtained from the mean (or median) values for eruption timing as has frequently been done. Hurme's data, for example (Hurme, 1948, 1949), suggest the order M_1 I_1 I_2 P_1 P_2 C M_2 M_3 for the permanent maxillary teeth in both sexes, and M_1 I_1 I_2 C P_1 P_2 M_2 M_3 for the mandibular teeth in boys and girls alike. The Japanese means of Okamoto (1934) as given by Hurme (1957) yield a not too dissimilar order, including the relatively earlier eruption of the permanent canine in the lower teeth.

However good the agreement between the order of eruption as taken from various published means, mean or average values are not individual values. As Hurme neatly put it, "even if it is assumed that the statistics . . . are reasonably reliable, it is still necessary to remember that, since they are statistics on *pooled* observations, or data on *groups*, they cannot furnish much information on the sequence of tooth eruption in isolated individuals" (Hurme, 1957, p. 380).

And, in fact, variability in the actual eruption order of M_1 and I_1 is well known. Whereas the mean values in most tabulations give a slight precedence to the first or "six-year" molar, in a goodly proportion of children the central incisor is first to erupt instead. Therefore, the sequence M_1 I_1 as given above must be bracketed (M_1 I_1) as Schultz (1940, 1944) did, to indicate variability or reversal of sequence. And, as we have already pointed out, the P_2 M_2 order suggested by the means must be rewritten (P_2 M_2) by virtue of our inability to discern precedence in some cases, and because M_2 P_2 is the eruption order in other cases.

Moreover, it is not necessarily true that the first premolar always precedes the second premolar, or even the second molar. There are situations in normal children where P_1 actually follows M_2, as Koski observed in 4 per cent of the children in the Finnish Growth Study (Koski and Garn, 1957). Similarly the . . . P_2 sequence strongly suggested by the averaged values for the mandibular teeth and previously claimed to be characteristic of modern man, may be replaced by the M_2 . . . C or even the P_2 . . . C order of eruption. This is not frequent, to be sure; Koski observed it in only 2 per cent of his Finnish children.

But in Dahlberg and Epling's observational data on Pima Indians (Koski and Garn, 1957), the $M_2 \ldots$ C order of eruption attained a frequency of 7 per cent. Thus, while the $P_2 \ldots$ C or $M_2 \ldots$ C sequences are not common today, the C M_2/M_2 C eruption polymorphism does not invariably distinguish man from ape (see also Clements and Zuckerman, 1953, p. 323).

In view of the equivocations given above, the permanent tooth eruption sequence is not simply $M_1 I_1 I_2 P_1 P_2 C_1 M_2 M_3$ but may be rewritten as:

$$(M_1 I_1) I_2 (P_1 C P_2 M_2) M_3 \text{ (Table I)}.$$

TABLE I

FORMULAS FOR THE ERUPTION SEQUENCE OF THE PERMANENT TEETH IN WHITES

Source	Formula
1. Hurme (1949) means	$\dfrac{M_1 I_1 I_2 P_1 P_2 C M_2 M_3}{M_1 I_1 I_2 C P_1 P_2 M_2 M_3}$
2. Schultz (1944)	$(M_1 I_1) I_2 (P_1 C P_2) M_2 M_3$
3. Schultz (1960)	$(I_1 M_1) I_2 (P C P) M_2 M_3$
4. Koski and Garn (1957)	$(M_1 I_1) I_2 (P_1 C P_2 M_2) M_3$†

†Based primarily on mandibular teeth. Bracketed teeth indicate variability of sequence.

In this sequence, previously given by Koski and Garn (1957), the relative precedence of M_1 and the late appearance of M continues to hold. While the order $\ldots M_1 \ldots M_2 M_3$ more or less describes the sequence of eruption of the molars, M varies in order of appearance, preceding the premolars and canines in some children and following them in others.

The eruption sequence given above, with all of its qualifying brackets, covers the majority of known eruption sequences reported for individuals, primarily Europeans. The possibility of other sequences, however, continues to exist and there is no reason to rewrite the previous formula $(M_1 I_1 I_2 P_1 C P_2 M_2) M$ to include the I_1/I_2 polymorphism known to exist (cf. the mean of Okamoto, 1934). Even the extreme M_3 C sequence remains within the realm of possibility, at least for populations in Eas

Africa where M_3 eruption has been reported as early as the 13th year (Chagula, 1960).† Therefore, the complete descriptive formula for the tooth eruption sequence in modern man may well put all of the permanent teeth within brackets as (M_1 I_1 I_2 P_1 C P_2 M_2 M_3) or at least (M_1 I_1 I_2) (P_1 C P_2 M_2 M_3).

The descriptive formula obtained from mean values for tooth eruption remains a first approximation when individual tooth eruption sequences are not available. Where raw data are given, however, or where eruption sequences are detailed *in extenso*, a more encompassing formula can then be written. But the more inclusive the formula, the more it includes all of the eruption sequences known to occur, the more it becomes a generalization of increasingly limited use. Of far greater importance is the frequency of the various eruption sequence polymorphisms, for these, as will shortly be shown, appear to be inheritable and therefore make it possible for us to put comparative eruption studies on a genetic basis.

THE SEQUENCE OF FORMATION OF THE POSTERIOR TEETH

But the order in which the teeth appear above the alveolar border, and the sequence of eruption through the gums are by no means the only sequential phenomena that may be studied in the developing dentition. Various discrete stages of calcification and movement can be discerned on radiographs, both of the living and of skeletalized material. Indeed, the eruption sequence of fossils can often be investigated through the medium of radiography as readily as in contemporary children.

Of the many possible "stages" of dental development, the following recommend themselves for radiographic appraisal (as shown in Fig. 2).

1. Stage of the follicle.
2. Beginning calcification of the cusps.
3. Crown completion and beginning root formation.

†While it is true that Weidenreich claimed the M_1 M_2 M_3 C eruption sequence for the Mousterian youth described by Klaatsch and Hauser, the original report clearly stated that neither C nor M_3 had erupted (Koski and Garn, 1957).

4. Alveolar eruption.
5. Gingival eruption (in the living).
6. Attainment of the occlusal level.
7. Apical closure.

These seven stages of tooth formation and movement have been used in our studies to date (Garn and Lewis, 1957; Garn, Lewis, Koski and Polacheck, 1958; Lewis and Garn, 1960). Other workers, of course, have made use of additional or intermediate stages of tooth development including estimates of the amount of root formation (Bengston, 1935; Saito, 1936; Gleiser and Hunt, 1955; Boulanger, 1958; Weishaupt, 1959). One or more of these supplementary stages of tooth development may well be useful in paleodontology, though in fossil populations estimates of the degree of pulp maturity and the fraction of ultimate root length attained must, of course, be made with caution.

From serial radiographic studies of the developing dentition, there appears to be surprisingly little variability in the order of beginning calcification of the teeth M_1, P_1, P_2, M_2 and M_3. M_1 appears to be first to calcify of these five, P_1 is always second and M_3 always last to calcify. P_2 and M_2, however, exhibit the same sequence polymorphism in beginning calcification and in about the same proportions that these two teeth show at the time of gingival eruption (Table II). Thus of 191 boys and girls for

TABLE II

THE ORDER OF BEGINNING CUSP CALCIFICATION OF THE PREMOLAR AND MOLAR TEETH IN OHIO CHILDREN[†]

Mandibular tooth	Order of calcification						
	1	2	3	3 or 4*	4	5	No.
	% of cases						
M_1	100	.	.	.	.	.	293
P_1	.	100	.	.	.	.	202
P_2	.	.	38	39	23	.	184
M_2	.	.	24	37	39	.	196
M_3	.	.	.	.	.	100	140

[†]Combined-sex data from Garn, Lewis and Shoemaker (1956).
*"bunched" calcification order.

whom the *entire* tooth calcification sequence could be ascertained radiographically:

1. 40 per cent were $P_2 M_2$ in calcification order.
2. 38 per cent were $(P_2 M_2)$ in calcification order.
3. 22 per cent were $M_2 P_2$ in calcification order (Garn, Lewis, and Shoemaker 1956).

Nevertheless, the proportion of children with the various formation sequences of P_2 and M_2 varies considerably from one formation stage to another. Whereas 30 to 40 per cent were $P_2 M_2$ at the time of beginning cusp calcification (Garn, Lewis and Shoemaker, 1956, Table II), 74 per cent proved to be $P_2 M_2$ at beginning root calcification (Garn, Koski and Lewis 1957, Table I). Virtually all of the children studied by us were $P_2 M_2$ in the order of apical closure of the second molar and second premolar. On the other hand, the proportion of $P_2 M_2$ children proved to be at its lowest at the time of alveolar eruption (34 per cent) whereas the incidence of the $M_2 P_2$ sequence was absolutely highest (37 per cent) at that particular stage of tooth movement (see Fig. 3).

These shifts in the proportion of $P_2 M_2$ and $M_2 P_2$ children at different stages of dental development are not due to

TABLE III

CHANGES IN P_2 AND M_2 PRECEDENCE DURING DENTAL DEVELOPMENT†

Stages of development	No. of individuals	% changed in precedence	% unchanged in precedence
Beginning cusp and root formation	105	59	41
Root formation and alveolar eruption	45	60	40
Alveolar eruption and occlusal level	34	47	53

†Data from Garn, Koski and Lewis (1957), Table II. See also Garn and Lewis (1957).

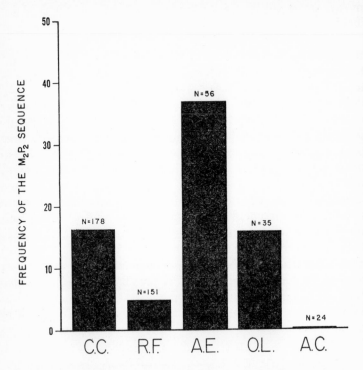

FIG. 3. Shifting frequencies of the M_2 P_2 sequence through five successive stages of tooth formation and movement. Least common of the three sequence polymorphisms in tooth calcification, the M_2 P_2 order is actually the majority sequence at the time of alveolar eruption (compare with Table III).

sampling, for they can be demonstrated in serial longitudinal observations. Children who are M_2 P_2 in beginning calcification tend to shift to the P_2 M_2 sequence in root formation: rarely is the reversal in the other direction. On the other hand, of individual children P_2 M_2 in beginning root formation, a substantial proportion shift to the M_2 P_2 sequence during the stage of alveolar eruption. Thus it may be demonstrated that the shifting frequency of sequence during tooth formation and movement is not illusory, but a real phenomenon indeed (see Table III).

Clearly, the $P_2 M_2/M_2 P_2$ polymorphism characteristic of the posterior dentition during alveolar and gingival eruption is found throughout most of the developmental course of the teeth in question. Sequence polymorphism is fundamental to the dentition during its development and not merely a phenomenon of eruption alone. Nevertheless it should be apparent that the sequence characteristic of one stage cannot be projected forward or backward to a subsequent or preceding stage of tooth development. Since there are changes in both the absolute frequencies of these sequences (or orders) and there are intra-individual shifts as well, the fact that a given order of dental development may be observed at one stage is of relatively poor predictive value in estimating what the sequence might have been at another stage. In comparing fossil to modern man, contemporary populations to contemporary primates or contemporary human populations to each other, odontological comparisons should in all cases involve the same stages of tooth formation or tooth movement using comparable procedures throughout.

THE FAMILIAL NATURE OF TOOTH SEQUENCE POLYMORPHISM

The simple existence of the $P_2 M_2/M_2 P_2$ tooth sequence polymorphism at most stages of tooth formation and movement indicates that this variability in developmental sequence is a fundamental property of the human dentition. Population differences in the frequency of the $P_2 M_2$, $(P_2 M_2)^*$ and $M_2 P_2$ sequences of gingival eruption further hint at the possibility of genetic control. The question, then, is whether the genetic contention can be supported by family-line data.

To provide a preliminary answer to this question we sorted our subjects into the three sequences $P_2 M_2$, $(P_2 M_2)$ and $M_2 P_2$ at cusp calcification and then compared the incidence of these

*The bracketed sequence $(P_2 M_2)$ here refers to cases where precedence cannot be determined (cf. Garn, Lewis and Shoemaker, 1956).

three developmental sequences in the siblings of the index cases so categorized. In the total group, as previously mentioned, the $P_2 M_2$ sequence of beginning tooth calcification obtained in 40 per cent. However, out of 39 siblings of index cases with the $P_2 M_2$ calcification sequence, 67 per cent were of the same $P_2 M_2$ order. With respect to the $M_2 P_2$ order of cusp calcification (observed in 22 per cent of the total group) the incidence of the $M_2 P_2$ order in siblings of $M_2 P_2$ index cases was 46 per cent. For both of the unequivocal sequences, then, $P_2 M_2$ and $M_2 P_2$, the siblings of the index cases tended to the same calcification sequence—suggesting genic control (Table IV).

TABLE IV

TOOTH CALCIFICATION SEQUENCES IN 104 SIBLINGS OF $P_2 M_2$ ($P_2 M_2$) AND $M_2 P_2$ CHILDREN[†]

Cusp calcification sequence in index cases	Sequence in their siblings		
	$P_2 M_2$	($P_2 M_2$)	$M_2 P_2$
		%	
$P_2 M_2$	67	26	8
($P_2 M_2$)	42	30	28
$M_2 P_2$	27	27	46

[†]Data from Table III in Garn, Lewis and Shoemaker (1956).

Such indications of familial similarity in the $P_2 M_2/M_2 P_2$ sequence polymorphism does not mean that there are genes specifically labelled "sequence". The evidence to date points to genetic control of the formation timing of *individual* teeth (Garn, Lewis and Polacheck, 1960; Garn, 1961) and it is likely that family-line, sibling and twin similarities in formation and eruption sequence exist through the medium of differential timing of the individual teeth or clusters of teeth.

These findings, however, suggest that other tooth sequence polymorphisms should be explored on a family-line basis, beginning with the common $M_1 I_1/I_1 M_1$ eruption orders. In fact, the sequence polymorphisms $M_1 I_1/I_1 M_1$ and $P_2 C/C P_2$ point to pairs of teeth where genetically-determined differences in formation timing presumably exist and may be demonstrated within populations.

M_3 AGENESIS AND THE TOOTH FORMATION SEQUENCE

The suggestion that genetic determination of formation timing underlies various sequences of tooth calcification and tooth eruption is abundantly confirmed when the presence or absence of the third molar tooth is taken into account. For agenesis of one or more third molars is not just a simple anomaly. Absence of the mandibular left third molar tooth is

TABLE V

The Effect of M_3 Agenesis on Calcification Timing of the Posterior Teeth†

Mandibular tooth	1. Children lacking $\overline{M}_3$	2. Unaffected siblings of No. 1	3. Unaffected children from unaffected sibships
	Cusp calcification T-scores		
P_1	53	56	48
P_2	54	53	49
M_1	52	52	48
M_2	59	52	48
M_3	—	57	49

†Data from Garn, Lewis and Bonné (1961); differences significant at $p = 0.05$ or better for P_1, M_2 and M_3.

consistently associated with late formation timing of the remaining posterior teeth, both in affected children and their siblings. And the mandibular second molar tooth is particularly affected when $\overline{M}_3$ is missing (Garn, Lewis and Bonné, 1961, and Table V of this paper). See also *J. Dent. Res.*, **41**, 717, (1962).

Since the formation of M_2 is especially delayed when the third molar is missing, one might anticipate an excess of $P_2 M_2$ children in such cases. And conversely one might assume that the rarer $M_2 P_2$ sequence would be unusually common when the third molar tooth is present. These expectations are fully realized when children lacking M_3 are compared with progeny from unaffected sibships. Children lacking the third molar tend disproportionately to be of the $P_2 M_2$ sequence both in tooth calcification and tooth movement. In unaffected sibships, on the other hand, the $M_2 P_2$ order of calcification and eruption is relatively more common (Fig. 4).

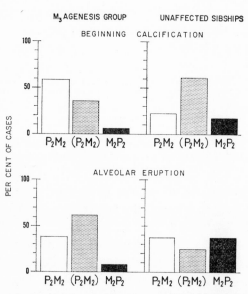

FIG. 4. P_2/M_2 sequence polymorphism in children with M_3 agenesis (*left*) and unaffected children from unaffected sibships (*right*). Both in calcification and eruption, the $P_2 M_2$ order tends to be more common where one or more third molar teeth are missing while the $M_2 P_2$ sequence of calcification and eruption is considerably more common in unaffected sibships.

To some extent, therefore, the $P_2 M_2/M_2 P_2$ sequence polymorphism is related to the presence or absence of M_3. Where M_3 is absent, the $P_2 M_2$ order is more common. In the presence of the third molar tooth, the $M_2 P_2$ sequence has a higher frequency in turn. The relationship is not obscure, but operates through delayed timing of the posterior teeth, particularly M_2. In theory, moreover, one might expect the population frequencies of the $P_2 M_2/M_2 P_2$ sequences to vary with the incidence of M_3 agenesis. And such polymorphisms as the $M_2 C/C M_2$ sequences could also be explained if in certain groups M_2 formation were especially delayed in the absence of the third molar tooth. Both theoretical possibilities are susceptible to direct investigation.

DISCUSSION

The simple descriptive fact remains that the second and third molar teeth are relatively delayed in modern man as compared with many primates, thus yielding the $M_1 \ldots M_2 M_3$ or $\ldots M_1 \ldots M_2 \ldots M_3$ eruption sequences. But the delay in molar eruption is variable, and somewhat different for the upper and lower jaws, involving not only the $P_2 M_2/M_2 P_2$ sequence polymorphism and the $M_2 C/C M_2$ sequence polymorphism, but also other sequence polymorphisms in which I_1, I_2 and P_1 vary in the order of emergence.

For this reason, the all-encompassing tooth eruption formula $(M_1 I_1) I_2 (P_1 C P_2 M_2) M_3$ or even $(M_1 I_1 I_2 P_1 C P_2 M_2) M_3$ is only slightly more informative than an eruption formula derived from mean values in the literature. Such a formula does show which teeth more frequently exhibit sequence polymorphism and it does show that the mean order is not an invariable order. But one formula, no matter how beset with brackets to indicate sequence reversals, cannot show the relative frequency of the various sequence polymorphisms within populations. Nor can it reveal population differences in eruption sequence frequencies.

But more than the notation used to show eruption sequence is at fault. The necessary data on the tooth eruption sequence are almost entirely lacking. Only for a few groups are estimates of the $M_2 P_2/P_2 M_2$ and $P_2 C/C P_2$ frequencies available. For the most part reported eruption orders are derived from means, or comparisons of variabilities (cf. Gödény, 1955, Tables III and IV). It is a welcome relief to return to Hrdlička's 50-year-old paper where individual observations are printed in full

(Hrdlička, 1908). Yet contemporary longitudinal growth studies in many lands could provide far more complete serial, longitudinal data on individual eruption sequences, at least in summary form. (See Sturdivant *et al.* 1962; Hurme *et al.* 1953.)

Moreover, the primate data we have quoted so far are also far from complete, but not from lack of work. Zuckerman (1928), Clements and Zuckerman (1953), and Schultz (see bibliography) have published extensive, individual records on gorilla and chimpanzee tooth eruption sequences. Mention should also be made of the studies of Baume and Becks (1950) on the Macaque. But these studies are complicated by an overly-elastic definition of the term "eruption". For most specimens, reported eruption sequences have of necessity been based on skulls, but the estimates have not always been limited to alveolar eruption (cf. Randall, 1943/1944 and Krogman, 1930). In living apes, or preserved specimens, gingival eruption has been the point of record. Available data and data summarizations thus combine alveolar eruption, gingival eruption, estimates of eruption order based on the relative heights of the erupted teeth, and radiological assessments. That these various definitions of eruption cannot be pooled for man we have already demonstrated. At the present time we may question their equivalence in apes.

In the course of this paper, and following Schultz, we have assumed the $M_2 P_2$ eruption order in anthropoids. But this is not strictly true, for the order $P_1 P_2 M_2$ does occur in the chimpanzee (Clements and Zuckerman, 1953, p. 316). And in the gorilla which appears to be somewhat less variable than the chimpanzee in eruption order, the $M_3 C/C M_3$ sequence polymorphism apparently exists. Krogman, it may be noted, favoured the $P_2 M_2$ order for both of the African great apes, possibly because of the more elastic definition of eruption he (of necessity) used. But broken down into individual cases, tooth sequence polymorphism unquestionably obtains in the anthropoids. The polymorphism frequencies, more than the "typical" eruption sequences may prove useful in the future, especially as domestication or zooification apparently affects the eruption sequence in the great apes.

A decade ago the prospect of determining eruption sequences on fossils seemed bright (Garn, 1952, p. 175). Weidenreich had reported on the "Sinanthropus" and Neanderthal groups, and Broom and Robinson (1951, 1952) gave tooth eruption orders for a variety of the South-African fossils examined by them. In retrospect our early optimism was unwarranted. Weidenreich made several major mistakes, as we have shown (Koski and Garn, 1957). Like Drennan, he was simply unfamiliar with the ordinary radiographic picture of tooth formation. And Broom and Robinson, in their honest efforts to interpret broken, crushed and incomplete jaw fragments, guessed at the "likely order of eruption" of still unerupted teeth. Thus the distinct formulae for various South African "Australopithecines" cannot be entered in the listing of established information on tooth eruption. In fact, except perhaps for the Teshik-Tash juvenile from Uzbekistan (Rohklin, 1949), there is scarcely a fossil child whose stated eruption sequences fully bear scrutiny (cf. Garn and Koski, 1957). Were the Asiatic representatives of *H. erectus*, and the South African megadonts more like us or more like the apes? We simply do not know.

And yet, there is an incredible amount of information on the sequence of tooth formation and tooth movement potentially available for our use. The thousands of primate skulls in museums beg to be reviewed, using radiographs to extract the maximum amount of information on cusp and root calcification and apical closure. There are millions of routine dental films on children and adolescents, nearly cost-free, but with priceless data on tooth formation sequences. There are primate colonies, rapidly proliferating under the monetary stimulus of National Health programmes.

And toward the future, when the sequences of tooth formation and eruption are all worked out for local and geographical races of men and for wild-shot, museum-collected and colony-reared primates, there will come the problem of explaining the various sequences.

Generic differences in the sequence of tooth eruption within the primates and intra-specific differences in the frequencies of the various sequence polymorphisms in the living, inevitably raise the question of causation. What adaptive value may be associated with late eruption of the accessional teeth? What genetic mechanisms maintain tooth sequence polymorphisms within contemporary populations? In the case of biochemical polymorphisms we now look for competing directions of selection or, alternatively, for an adaptive advantage associated with the heterozygotic state. The $M_2 P_2/P_2 M_2$ and $C M_2/M_2 C$ eruption polymorphisms are certainly maintained at different levels within contemporary populations, yet we have not the slightest hint of conditions that favor one sequence or the other. In the absence of evidence pertaining to modern and urbanized man, where differential survival may not be demonstrable, we may well investigate the tooth eruption sequence in particular primate species that have become adapted to new ecological zones and different dietaries. Population differences in eruption sequence frequencies would then provide an operational clue to the adaptive nature of the tooth sequence polymorphisms themselves.

ACKNOWLEDGEMENTS

The research on the sequence of tooth formation and movement and its relationship to third molar number polymorphism was supported in part by research grants M–1260 and D–1294 from the United States Public Health Service.

We are pleased to acknowledge the technical assistance of Demarest L. Polacheck and Batsheva Bonné, and the editorial and statistical assistance of Joan H. Vicinus in the course of the manuscript preparation. Lois A. Conklin assisted in the manuscript completion. We are grateful for the valuable comments of Dr. Peter Adler and Professor Adolph Schultz and regret our inability to reprint them here.

REFERENCES

Baume, L. J. and Becks, H. (1950) The development of the dentition of Macaca mulatta, *Amer. J. Orthodont. and Oral Surgery* **36**, 723.

Bengston, R. G. (1935) A study of the time of eruption and root development of the permanent teeth between six and thirteen years, *Northwestern U. Bull.* **36**, 3.

Boulanger, G. (1958) La calcification des prémolaires et molaires et ses relations avec l'âge chronologique et squelettique chez les enfants de 6 à 11 ans. Thesis submitted for Doctor of Dental Medicine, University of Zurich, Juris-Verlag, Zurich.

BROOM, R. and ROBINSON, J. T. (1951) Eruption of the permanent teeth in the South African fossil ape-men, *Nature* **167**, 443.

BROOM, R. and ROBINSON, J. T. (1952) Swartkrans ape-man *Paranthropus crassidens, Pretoria: Transv. Mus. Mem.* No. 6.

CHAGULA, W. K. (1960) The age at eruption of third permanent molars in male East Africans, *Amer. J. Phys. Anthrop.* N.S. **18**, 77.

CLEMENTS, E. M. B. and ZUCKERMAN, S. (1953) The order of eruption of the permanent teeth in the Hominoidea, *Amer. J. Phys. Anthrop.* N.S. **11**, 313.

CLEMENTS, E. M. B., DAVIES-THOMAS, E. and PICKETT, K. G. (1953) Order of eruption of the permanent human dentition, *Brit. Med. J.* **1**, 1425.

GARN, S. M. (1952) Physical growth and development, *Amer. J. Phys. Anthrop.* N.S. **10**, 169.

GARN, S. M. (1961) The genetics of human growth. In *De Genetica Medica*, Vol. II (edited by L. Gedda), Gregor Mendel Institute, Rome.

GARN, S. M. and KOSKI, K. (1957) Tooth eruption sequence in fossil and recent man, *Nature* **180**, 442.

GARN, S. M. and LEWIS, A. B. (1957) Relationship between the sequence of calcification and the sequence of eruption of mandibular molar and premolar teeth, *J. Dent. Res.* **36**, 992.

GARN, S. M., KOSKI, K. and LEWIS A. B. (1957) Problems in determining the tooth eruption sequence in fossil and modern man, *Amer. J. Phys. Anthrop.* N.S. **15**, 313.

GARN, S. M., LEWIS, A. B. and BONNÉ, B. (1961) Third molar polymorphism and the timing of tooth formation. *Nature* **192**, 989. See also *J. Dent. Res.* **41**, 717 (1962).

GARN, S. M., LEWIS, A. B. and POLACHECK, D. L. (1960) Sibling similarities in dental development *J. Dent. Res.* **39**, 170.

GARN, S. M., LEWIS, A. B. and SHOEMAKER, D. W. (1956) The sequence of calcification of the mandibular molar and premolar teeth, *J. Dent. Res.* **35**, 555.

GARN, S. M., LEWIS, A. B., KOSKI, K. and POLACHECK, D. L. (1958) The sex difference in tooth calcification, *J. Dent. Res.* **37**, 561.

GLEISER, I. and HUNT, E. E. (1955) The permanent mandibular first molar: its calcification, eruption and decay, *Amer. J. Phys. Anthrop.* N.S. **13**, 253.

GÖDÉNY, E. (1955) Die typische Zahnformel zu verscheiden Zeiten während der Wechselgebissperiode, *Zeitschrift für Altersforschung* **8**, 284.

GREWEL, F. (1935) *De Doorbraaktijd van het Blijvend Gebit*. Scheltema and Holkema's Boekhandel, Amsterdam.

HRDLIČKA, A. (1908) Physiological and medical observations among the Indians of Southwestern United States and Northern Mexico, *Bureau Amer. Ethnol. Bull.* No. 34.

HURME, V. O. (1948) Standards of variation in the eruption of the first six permanent teeth, *Child Developm.* **19**, 213.

HURME, V. O. (1949) Ranges of normalcy in the eruption of permanent teeth, *J. Dentistry for Children* **16**, 11.

HURME, V. O. (1957) Time and sequence of tooth eruption. Symposium on the human dentition in forensic medicine, *J. Forensic Science* **2**, 377.

HURME, V. O. and VAN WAGENEN, G. (1953) Basic data on the emergence of deciduous teeth in the monkey, *Proc. Am. Phil. Soc.* **97**, 291.

KOSKI, K. and GARN, S. M. (1957) Tooth eruption sequence in fossil and modern man, *Amer. J. Phys. Anthrop.* N.S. **15**, 469.

KROGMAN, W. M. (1930) Studies in growth changes in the skull and face of anthropoids. I. The eruption of the teeth in anthropoids and Old World apes, *Amer. J. Anat.* **46**, 303.

LEWIS, A. B. and GARN, S. M. (1960) The relationship between tooth formation and other maturational factors, *Angle Orthodontist* **30**, 70.

OKAMOTO, K. (1934) A statistical study of variation in the emergence ages of permanent teeth, *Shikwa Gakuho* **39**, 139.

RANDALL, F. E. (1943/1944) The skeletal and dental development and variability of the gorilla, *Hum. Biol.* **15**, 236; **16**, 23.

ROHKLIN, D. G. (1949) Certain data from a roentgenological examination of the child skeleton from the cave of Teshik-Tash, Southern Uzbekistan. In *Teshik-Tash: Palaeolithic Man.* pp. 109–13. (Edited by M. A. Grematski), Moscow State University Press, Moscow.

SAITO, H. (1936) Radiological studies on the development of the third molar, *Kokubyo Gakkai Zasshi* **10**, 366.

SCHULTZ, A. H. (1935) Eruption and decay of the permanent teeth in primates, *Amer. J. Phys. Anthrop.* **19**, 489.

SCHULTZ, A. H. (1940) Growth and development of the chimpanzee, *Contributions to Embryol.* Carnegie Inst. Wash. Publ. No. 518, **28**, 1.

SCHULTZ, A. H. (1944) Age changes and variability in gibbons, *Amer. J. Phys. Anthrop.* N.S. **2**, 1.

SCHULTZ, A. H. (1949) Ontogenetic specializations of man, *Arch. Julius Klaus-Stift.* **24**, 197.

SCHULTZ, A. H. (1950) The physical distinctions of man. *Proc. Amer. Phil. Soc.* **94**, 428.

SCHULTZ, A. H. (1960) Age changes in primates and their modification in man. In *Human Growth*, Symposia of the Society for the

Study of Human Biology, vol. III, pp. 1–20. (Edited by J. M. Tanner), Pergamon Press, New York.

SENYÜREK, M. (1955) A review of the order of eruption of the permanent teeth in fossil hominids, *Türk Tarih Kurumu Belleten* **19**, 407.

SENYÜREK, M. (1956) Order of eruption of the permanent teeth in the Chalcolithic and Copper Age inhabitants of Anatolia, *Türk Tarih Kurumu Belleten* **20**, 1.

STURDIVANT, J. E., KNOTT, V. B. and MEREDITH, H. V. (1962) Interrelations from serial data for eruption of the permanent dentition, *Angle Orthodont.*, **32**, 1.

SWINDLER, D. R. (1961) Calcification of the permanent first mandibular molar in Rhesus monkeys, *Science* **134**, 566.

WEIDENREICH, F. (1937) The dentition of *Sinanthropus pekinensis*: A comparative odontography of the Hominids. *Palaeontologica Sinica* N.S. D, No. 1.

WEISHAUPT, H. (1959) Die Verkalkung der Schneide und Eckzähne in Relation zum chronologischen Alter und Skelettalter bei Kindern von 6 bis 11 Jahren. Thesis submitted for Doctor of Dental Medicine, University of Zurich, Juris-Verlag, Zurich.

ZUCKERMAN, S. (1928) Age-changes in the chimpanzee, with special reference to the growth of the brain, eruption of teeth, and estimation of age; with a note on the Taungs ape, *Proc. Zool. Soc. Lond.* Part 1, 1–42.

F

A RADIOGRAPHIC STUDY OF THE NEANDERTHAL TEETH FROM KRAPINA, CROATIA

by JURAJ KALLAY [*]

Zagreb, Jugoslavia

THE application of radiographic techniques in the study of fossil hominid remains, particularly teeth, is by no means a recent facet of palaeontological studies. Gorjanović-Kramberger (1906) in his original work on the Krapina remains, and Schoetensack's (1908) study of *Homo heidelbergensis*, both include radiographic details. In the classic work by Henri Martin (1923) on the neanderthal skeletons from La Quina, radiographic aspects of the teeth are also discussed.

In the following analysis, it is hoped to give some idea of the extent of the additional information which can be obtained from a detailed consideration of the radiographic data for a series of teeth, in this case representing a neanderthal population from Croatia in Jugoslavia. On the basis of remnants of jaws and fragments of ascending ramus, it is possible to say that the Krapina finds probably represent 28 individuals, of which 23 are quite certain. First of all, consideration will be given to erupted teeth and their radiographic characteristics.

THE INCISORS

X-rays were taken in the mesio-distal direction, as it is only in this way that the incisors display characteristics which are not typical of recent man. The usual radiograph taken in the labio-oral direction (Fig. 1a), shows a uniform shape of the pulp chamber of the teeth in function which narrows down in

[*]Present address: Zagreb III, Lašćinska 63, Jugoslavia.

the corono-apical direction. In Fig. 1b can be seen the upper incisors of maxilla C which are still developing, showing unusually wide pulp chambers which are not found in recent man. There is also a very strong dental palatinal cusp in the shape of a flame. The difference in the width of the pulp of teeth which are now functional and those which are still developing is evident, and it is indeed surprising how quickly the pulp appears to narrow during the completion of growth and its functional life, particularly when taking into account the short life span of these Krapina people. Considering the radiograph in the mesio-distal direction a different picture is seen (Fig. 1c), showing the so-called lancet form in its final stage of development (c_1). This is particularly visible on an upper lateral incisor (described already by Gorjanovic-Kramberger (1906)) where the dental cusp is considerably developed. This shape is now termed the margoid form and shows a narrow projecting pulp horn (Fig. 1c). This lancet type represents the final form in the development of the tooth from the basic shape of the growth of the pulp chamber, which is very wide (Fig. 1c, 3, 4). The more developmentally complete a tooth is, the more the pulp chamber narrows to take the shape of the root and the crown of the tooth. Sometimes a narrowing down of the pulp chamber can be seen on the upper third of the root and in this way edgeless "dentine-spurs" are formed; these are particularly well developed in the case of upper premolars (Fig. 3g). With abraded teeth the occlusal point of the pulp is edgeless, because the chamber itself has been reduced in size by the formation of secondary dentine. Major differences between the upper mesial incisors (Fig. 1d), the lateral incisors (Fig. 1c) and the lower incisors (Fig. 1f) do not exist. The width of the pulp chamber may vary from 1 to 3 mm, depending on the duration of the function of the tooth and on age. The difference between the lower incisors, as compared with the upper ones, lies only in the fact that the cervical part of the pulp of the lower teeth was not so well developed as in the upper ones. The lancet form also appears in the Ehringsdorf group (Virchow, 1920), whereas in recent man this form is occasionally only slightly indicated. The upper central incisor, found at a depth of 2·90 m in a cave of the Franches-Montaignes (Swiss Jura), described by Koby (1956), shows in its form the classical Neanderthal characteristics, but with the root canal in the shape of an oval which is considerably larger in the labio-lingual than in the mesio-distal direction and without the lancet form of the pulp chamber.

In the case of the permanent incisors of Krapina there is absolutely no evidence of the double root canal variant, which can be found in recent populations of man.

The deciduous incisors do not display any marked radiographic differences in comparison with recent teeth. It is worth mentioning, however, that there exists a separate twin-incisor with a very wide pulp chamber, extending along the whole length of the root (Fig. 1g).

THE CANINES

The configuration of the canines is similar to that of the incisors, although the cervical narrowing of the pulp is somewhat prolonged. The canines show in their morphology greater variations, although the lancet form prevails. Generally, the width of the pulp chamber depends on the size of the tooth, which again is quite variable. The canines display especially well the development of the pulp chamber (Fig. 1b), where, on the upper canine (extreme left), the chamber reaches the width of 7-8 millimetres and has a somewhat "taurodont" appearance. In the remaining two teeth in the figure, the chamber is narrower—this depending on the size of the tooth. The final shape in the development of the tooth is shown as a lancet form on both the upper and the lower canines (Fig. 2a). This can also be seen in the premolarization on the upper canine (Fig. 2b, the upper right tooth and the lower teeth). Comparing the hypoplastic lower incisor (the right-hand in Fig. 2c), the lower canine (the left tooth in Fig. 2c) and the hypoplastic upper canine, it can be seen that certain variations appear in the width of the pulp. In recent canines, such configurations of the pulp are far from common.

THE PREMOLARS

As the premolars differ in the number of roots present, the one-rooted lower premolars will be discussed first. In the majority of cases, the configuration of the coronal part of the pulp in the mesio-distal direction is comparable with that seen in the canines and sometimes even in incisors. This is best seen in Fig. 2d (upper row), where the pulp narrows down in the apical direction after the completion of the dental development, whereas, with the still open apical foramen, the pulp has an almost uniformly wider canal than in the fully developed tooth (the third tooth in the row). This partially developed tooth does not show any pronounced coronal pulp horns, as can be seen on the recent lower second premolar in the same figure.

An unusual, and perhaps "transitional" form to be seen in the Krapina series, is a lower premolar with two roots. In this specimen at about half way along the root, the wide and long pulp chamber divides to form two narrow branches (Fig. 2e). The canals are placed buccally and lingually. This two-rooted lower first premolar from Krapina can be regarded, I think, as belonging to a morphologically intermediate stage between the *Pithecanthropus pekinensis* and the classic Neanderthal types.

Something similar to the Krapina premolar form may occasionally be noted in recent man, as for example shown by the dental radiographs of a modern child of 11 years in Fig. 2d (lower row). In this case the growing second premolar has a uniformly wide pulp canal and an unclosed apex, similar to the third Krapina tooth in the same figure (2d, above). This radiograph was also taken in the bucco-oral direction. In the same way a recent first premolar, which shows two roots, mesial and distal, was examined. This modern tooth is considerably smaller than that of its Krapina counterpart seen in Fig. 2e, but shows the bifurcation of the roots at a relatively low level, and the formation of supraradicular taurodontism on the lower premolar, just as in the two-rooted Krapina lower P_1.

Upper premolars have usually two roots and two canals. Of the 17 premolars, only one of them has a cuneiform and broad root which ends with a well-developed pointed apex. Its pulp chamber is uniformly wide and narrows down only slightly in the apical direction (Fig. 3b, 3rd tooth). This shows the tendency towards the formation of a broad canal analogous to radicular taurodontism in molars.

When these premolars are examined radiographically, it is seen that three forms are evident during the formation of the roots and therefore also three forms of the pulp chamber. The first type can be primarily located coronally. The pulp is here predominantly low (Fig. 3, as in the 2nd and 3rd teeth of *a* and the 1st and 3rd ones in *c*) and may be termed corono-cervical. The second form is that where the bifurcation of the canal of the root is placed considerably lower so that we can already speak of a supraradicular taurodontism of the pre-molars (Fig. 3, as in the 1st tooth of *a* and the 2nd and 3rd ones of *f*). Finally there is the third form which is a well defined radicular taurodontism as described already (the 3rd tooth in *b* of Fig. 3). If we compare these Krapina teeth with those of recent men (Fig. 3d, i, j) various similarities may be noted, suggesting but little evolutionary divergence as regards the morphology of this tooth form.

PERMANENT MOLARS

Much has been written on the permanent molars from Krapina and their affinities are still not without controversy.

Radiographs will be considered of all the loose molars at this site, namely, 24 of the upper and 24 of the lower jaw. These had all erupted and were functional. Besides these, there were also 5 upper and 4 lower molars loose which were not yet functional. There were also 84 permanent molars contained in jaw fragments, there being 35 of the upper jaw and 49 of the lower jaw.

The best radiographic projections to be employed in studies of molars are in the bucco-lingual direction, as in the case of premolars. Further information can be obtained from radiographs in the mesio-distal plane. In Fig. 4, bucco-lingual views are shown of upper molars (first and second rows) and the lower ones ones (third row). These clearly show that the pulp chamber above the bifurcation of the roots, is broader than usually found in recent human molars. Variations in the level of the bifurcation and in the height of the pulp chamber itself also occur. The size of the chamber is such that it extends not only into the crown, but also into the root area of the teeth. Because of this, the term "supraradicular" taurodontism is the only suitable term for this morphological form.

Supraradicular taurodontism can exist only in teeth with several roots, and then only above their bifurcations. In this it differs from radicular taurodontism where the broad pulp chamber extends along the entire undivided root (the so-called "prismatic" form). Typical radicular taurodontism is not present in all the prismatic Krapina teeth.

J. C. Shaw (1928) introduced the terms "hyper-, hypo- and mesotaurodontism". These terms are not precise enough however to indicate the relative position of the enlarged and lengthened pulp chamber. This is clearly demonstrated in Fig. 5, where a series of molar teeth are radiographically shown in the bucco-lingual plane. The pulp chamber is seen to extend through the crown of the tooth and along the whole length of its uniform root. In this kind of taurodontism the term "radicular" indicates precisely the location, whereas "hypertaurodont" does not have the same accuracy of definition. It is also incorrect to speak generally about extreme taurodontism, as Fischer (1961) has, in view of the very different shapes of the pulp chamber. Indeed in one and the same jaw, molars may be found which display both radicular and supraradicular taurodontism (Fig. 10 e, f). Furthermore, supraradicular taurodontism is not always associated with the "prismatic" or "pyramidal" lower roots but can be found even on the upper molars of recent men. (Tratman, 1950; Miles, 1954; Dahlberg, 1945 and Pedersen, 1949.) Dahlberg (1960) also mentions a "mild degree of taurodontism" in Neolithic Jarmo molars, but from this description it is not known what form of taurodontism is involved. However, in his Fig. 7 examples can clearly be seen of supraradicular taurodontism on the first two molars of the same picture. This again demonstrates the need to distinguish one form from the other.

In order to differentiate clearly between the forms of taurodontism, it is necessary to take radiographs in both directions.

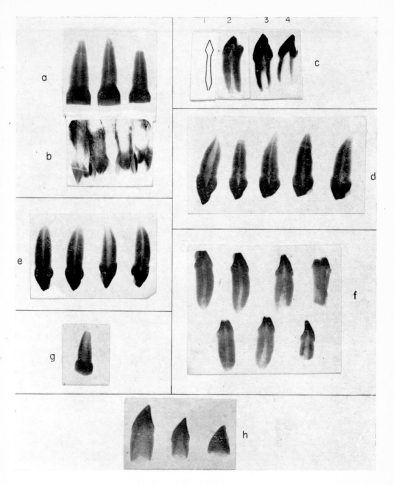

Fig. 1(a) Krapina upper incisors (labio-lingual direction).
(b) Incisors from maxilla C. (c) Incisors with pulp chambers
of: 1, lancet form; 2, margoid form; 3 and 4, basic form.
(d) Upper mesial incisors (mesio-distal direction). (e) Upper
lateral incisors (mesio-distal direction). (f) Lower incisors
(mesio-distal direction). (g) Deciduous twin upper incisor
(labio-lingual). (h) Development of the pulp chamber of
canines (mesio-distal direction).

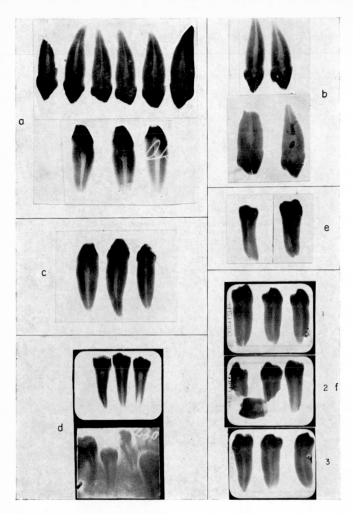

Fig. 2(a) Lancet-form of upper (upper row) and lower canines (lower row) (mesio-distal direction). (b) Premolarization of canines. (c) Lower canine, hypoplastic canine, hypoplastic lower incisor. (d) Lower Krapina premolars (mesio-distal direction, upper row); recent premolars (lower row). (e) Lower first premolar with two roots, P_1 inf. cum duabus radicibus by Kallay, from Krapina (left is bucco-lingual, right is mesio-distal direction). (f) Lower premolars of Krapina showing lancet form (mesio-distal direction).

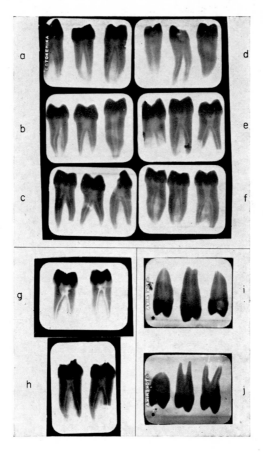

FIG. 3(a), (b), (c), (e), (f) Krapina premolars (mesio-distal direction). (d) Recent premolars (mesio-distal direction). (i) and (j) Recent first premolars (mesio-distal direction). (g) and (h) Krapina premolars with "dentine spurs" (upper row) and hypoplasia (lower row).

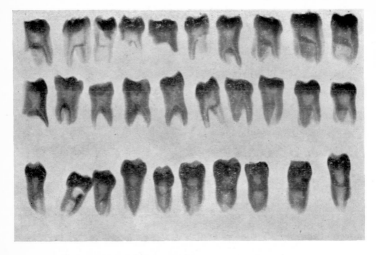

Fig. 4. Upper molars (upper and middle row) and lower molars (lower row) from Krapina (bucco-lingual direction).

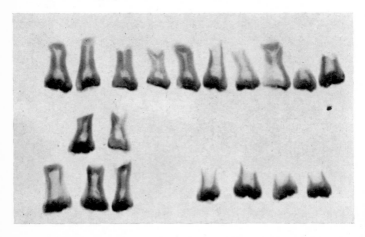

Fig. 5. Krapina molars (bucco-lingual direction).

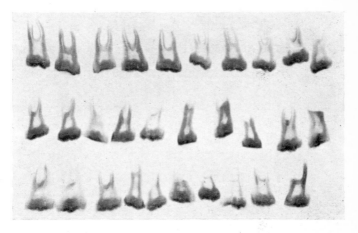

FIG. 6.   The same teeth as in Fig. 4, only in the mesio-
distal direction.

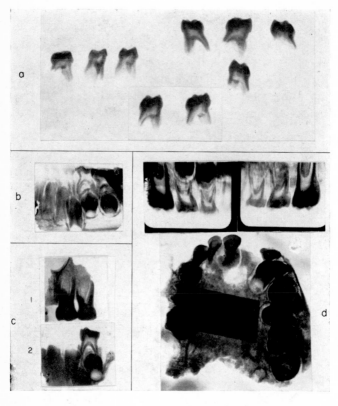

FIG. 8(a) Deciduous molars of Krapina (bucco-lingual direction). (b) Recent teeth. (c) Teeth of: 1, the maxilla A; 2, mandible A. (d) Teeth of maxilla B.

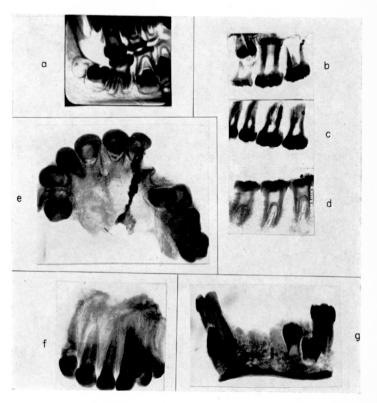

FIG. 9(a) Chimpanzee, immature specimen. (b) Teeth of maxilla C. (c) Teeth of maxilla D. (d) Teeth of mandible G. (e) Teeth of maxilla C, vertical radiograph. (f) Teeth of maxilla E. (g) Teeth of mandible B.

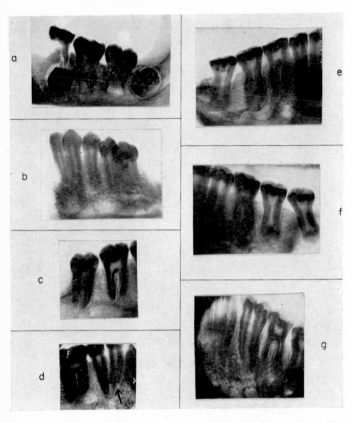

Fig. 10(a) Teeth of mandible C. (b) Teeth of mandible D. (c) and (d) Two views of mandible E. (e), (f) and (g) Views of mandible H.

Thus we have in Fig. 6 the same teeth taken in the mesio-distal plane as were taken in the bucco-oral direction in Fig. 4. Comparing these two radiographs it will be seen,

(a) that in the mesio-distal direction the teeth are broader; and accordingly the pulp chambers are also larger than in the bucco-oral direction (Fig. 4);

(b) from this it follows that the upper molars should be primarily taken in the mesio-distal direction;

(c) lower molars should be primarily taken in the bucco-oral direction (Fig. 4) in order that the roots situated mesially and distally are not obscured.

In considering the formation of "prismatic" roots it is necessary first to review some terms and processes which play a certain role here. Gorjanovic-Kramberger (1906) was of the opinion that only in certain cases did fusion or coalescence of Krapina molar roots take place (Fig. 6, first and last three teeth in the first row), whereas in others, this did not occur at all. My own studies (1958) fully support this view.

The term "fusion" of two roots is only truly a reality when there exists a crown broader than normal, and we can conclude that these are two elements, like twins. The root which is formed for this double crown shows a wide canal, whose walls are the product of Hertwig's sheath of both the crowns as exemplified in Fig. 1g. Thus, fused roots must have a common canal, and accordingly, a common pulp chamber. If they do not have this characteristic, then coalescence will have taken place. Coalescence of two or more roots can be distinguished by the fact that they have two or more canals. For instance, two buccal roots of upper molars can be connected by cement.

In an entirely similar way—by considering the action of Hertwig's sheath of a normal crown—we can imagine the anomalous origin of "prismatic" roots and accordingly of radicular taurodontism, because the formation of the bridge of Hertwig's sheath was not completed in due time.

The origin and development of the cap which closes the bottom of a prismatic root apically can only be explained by the fact that the Hertwig's sheath, which seems unable to form the root bridge, nevertheless protects the pulp by means of this late developing cap. Such a conclusion is clearly demonstrated by examining schematic pictures of taurodontic teeth (Fig. 7)

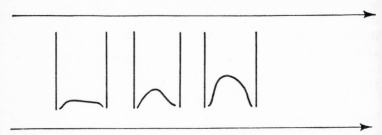

FIG. 7.   Schematic picture of taurodontic teeth.

based on radiographs. Here we may distinguish a stage where the formation of roots can only be anticipated, then the stage of the pyramidal cap, and finally, the stage of the even cap. It is characteristic of all these stages that a space is present between the cap and the wall of the root, that is to say, there is a canal which serves as the passage for veins and nerves.

Of a total of 85 molars from Krapina which were available for study, 32 upper molars and 45 lower molars (in all 77 permanent molars) were examined radiographically.

The following Table I gives the results of this investigation.

TABLE I

Teeth	Normal		Suprar. taurodont.		Radic. taurodont.		Cuneiform	"Unclassified"	Total
	Loose teeth	Teeth in jaws	Loose teeth	Teeth in jaws	Loose teeth	Teeth in jaws	type	type	
Upper molars	—	2	17	2	9	2	—	—	32
Lower molars	1	4	10	7	10	9	1	3	45
Total	1	6	27	9	19	11	1	3	77

Expressed in per cent of the 73 normal and taurodont teeth (but without the cuneiform and "unclassified" types), only 9·6 per cent can be classified as normal, whereas 90·4 per cent of this sample were taurodont (about 49 per cent being supraradicular and something over 41 per cent being radicular).

Although but few deciduous molars are available, it was thought of value to study their radiographic appearance, at least in the mesio-distal direction (Fig. 8a). The sample consists of 3 first upper molars and of 6 second molars. Although the coronal part of the pulp chamber is slightly more accentuated in these milk teeth, similar to that found in recent deciduous teeth (Fig. 8b), nevertheless, it was not possible to assign any of these Krapina teeth to one or other taurodont category.

As well as the general morphological features of the Krapina teeth which can be determined radiographically—as described above—a number of other variations were noted. These seem more satisfactorily dealt with according to the jaw fragment involved.

Maxilla A (Fig. 8c, upper). Both teeth have thin and slightly bent roots, with signs of taurodontism. The germs of the premolars cannot be seen in the radiograph owing to an artifact.

Maxilla B (Fig. 8d) is a child's jaw containing deciduous molars without signs of taurodontism, but which are associated with first permanent molars which show the partly developed supraradicular type. Congenital absence of both the left premolars can also be seen.

If the permanent molars of this child are compared with those of a young chimpanzee (Fig. 90) it will be seen that these teeth also show a similar supraradicular type of taurodontism, but on the other hand the deciduous molars of the chimpanzee have a very narrow coronal pulp. This pulp is much smaller than that found in modern deciduous teeth of man. (Fig. 8b.)

Maxilla C (Fig. 9b) shows a developing second left premolar, with the second left deciduous molar above it displaying root resorption. The first molar displays radicular taurodontism with a well formed cap (which might be termed *total* taurodontism) and the second is clearly similar although still developing. The vertical radiograph (Fig. 9e) of the same jaw shows particularly the narrow socket of 4 between the second right premolar and the canine; also the broad pulp chamber of the incisors.

Maxilla D (Fig. 9c) is the left fragment only, with teeth generally similar to recent man, except for the second molar.

Maxilla E (Fig. 9f) is interesting in that at the mesial side of the left medial incisor, the outline of the otherwise sharp alveolar outline is blurred. This suggests the beginning of a chronic apical infection (Kallay (1951)).

Mandible A (Fig. 8c, bottom view) probably belongs with maxilla A. The first deciduous molar is well developed and with a pulp chamber which is non-taurodont.

Mandible B (Fig. 9g). The left first molar shows a moderate degree of supraradicular taurodontism.

Mandible C (Fig. 10d). Around the second deciduous molar, a follicular cyst is in formation (Kallay, 1952).

Mandible D (Fig. 10b). In the first premolar, the pulp chamber is clearly of lancet form, noticeable here because the tooth is rotated in the buccal direction.

Mandible E (Fig. 10c) shows two molars of which the first one has —relative to its size—a normal pulp chamber, whereas the second one shows supraradicular taurodonty. In Fig. 10d, the second premolar is not in a normal vertical position, but is directed slightly backwards, so that its apex is nearer to the first premolar and its crown to the first molar. The root of the first premolar in this jaw is seen to be anomalous (Kallay, 1949). It is several millimetres shorter than the neighbouring P_2. The pulp cavity of this P_1 is fairly wide in its upper part, but narrows down towards the centre of the root and then widens considerably towards the apical part of the root. It could well be that this represents a new premolar variant tending to simulate the prismatic shape of the molar root.

Mandible G (Fig. 9d, bottom view). The three molars present show clearly a well-marked gradient for supraradicular taurodontism from the first to the third molar. A similar example is to be seen in the Heidelberg jaw, although here the M_2 has the narrowest coronal pulp chamber and none of the teeth has such a large chamber as that found in mandible G.

Mandible H (Fig. 10e, f and g) also shows interesting variations in molar root form. The first molars have roots which are normally developed. The second left molar is a typical prismatic tooth with a uniform root which has a low cap, the right second molar being very similar. The third molars also show marked radicular taurodontism. This jaw also displays an anomalous first left premolar (10g). A detailed analysis (Kallay, 1949) of the radiograph showed that the root canal of this tooth can be divided, according to its length, into three parts; the upper two thirds of the root comprise a relatively broad canal but towards the apex, dentine narrows the canal. At the end of this apical area of the root is a small ball (2 mm in diameter), possibly made of dentine. This ball has according to the radiographic evidence, no connection with the tooth, or at any rate not a substantial one. The last third of the root is certainly far from normal, and might perhaps be some sort of hamartoma. The ball is neither a denticle nor a "dens in dente". It is possible that it represents an unsuccessful attempt to create a prismatic root by means of a hamartoma, or else a deficiency of Hertwig's sheath.

Mandible I is the best preserved jaw of all. At the right side there is an entirely normally developed first molar with two relatively long bifurcated roots; an identical one being situated on the left side. The right second molar has a cuneiform simple root with a narrow canal, a form also to be found in recent man. This root ends with a pointed apex. The left second molar also has only one root, but in this case there is radicular taurodontism, although the canal is narrow. The right third molar shows a still more developed form of radicular taurodontism. Thus in one and the same jaw, three quite different forms of molar structure can be seen. From the condition of the alveolar bone about the roots, the individual clearly had some degree of periodontal infection.

From the foregoing detailed analysis of the Krapina teeth, it is hoped that the extent of additional information to be revealed by radiography will be obvious. The dental variability to be seen in the Krapina group—as revealed by X-rays—certainly indicates that similar detailed studies of other fossil human teeth would be very worthwhile.

REFERENCES

DAHLBERG, A. A. (1945) The changing dentition of man. *J. Amer. Dent. Ass.* **32**, 676.

DAHLBERG, A. A. (1960) The dentition of the first agriculturists (Jarmo, Iraq). *Amer. J. Phys. Anthrop.* **18**, 243.

FISCHER, H. (1961) Die "prismatischen" Molaren von Krapina/ Kroatien im Lichte rezenter Funde. *Dtsch. Zahnarztl. Zschr.* **16**, 1.

GORJANOVIC-KRAMBERGER, K. (1906) *Der diluviale Mensch von Krapina in Kroatien. Ein Beitrag Zur Palaoanthropologie.* Kreidel, Weisbaden.

KALLAY, J. (1949) Some anomalies of the lower premolar roots of Homo primigenius from Krapina in Croatia. *Fol. Stomatol. Zagreb.* **10**, 1.

KALLAY, J. (1951) Healed tooth fractures in a Krapina Neandertal. *Amer. J. Phys. Anthrop.* **9**, 1.

KALLAY, J. (1952) Follikularzyste im Krapina Unterkiefer C. *O.Z. Stom.* **49**, 2.

KALLAY, J. (1954). New report of the jaws of Krapina men. *Iz hrvatske medicinske proslosti.* Zagreb, 125–137.

KALLAY, J. (1955) Krapinaunterkiefer I und Paradentose im Pleistozoen. *O.Z. Stom.* **52**, 58.

KALLAY, J. (1958) Dentale Anthropologie und Neandertalproblem. In: *Ber. 6 Tag. dtsch. Ges. Anthrop. Kiel.* pp. 191-202. Mutersch-midt-Verlag. Gottingen.

Koby, F. E. (1956) Une incisive néandertalienne trouvée en Suisse. *Verh. Naturf. Ges.* **67**, 1.

Martin, H. (1923) *L'Homme Fossile de la Quina.* Doin, Paris.

Miles, A. E. W. (1954) Malformations of the teeth. *Proc. roy. Soc. Med.* **47**, 817.

Pedersen, P. O. (1949) *The East Greenland Eskimo Dentition. Med delelser om Gronland.* **142**, 1.

Schoetensack, O. (1908) *Der Unterkiefer des Homo heidelbergensis.* Engelmann, Leipzig.

Shaw, J. C. M. (1928) Taurodont teeth in South African races. *J Anat. Lond.* **62**, 476.

Tratman, E. K. (1950) A comparison of the teeth of people. Indo European racial stock with Mongoloid racial stock. *Dent. Rec.* **70**, 31, 63.

Virchow, H. (1920) *Die menschlichen Skelettreste aus dem Kamfschen Bruch im Travertin von Ehringsdorf bei Weimar.* Fischer, Gena.

MORPHOGENESIS OF DECIDUOUS MOLAR PATTERN IN MAN*

by **BERTRAM S. KRAUS**
Department of Orthodontics, School of Dentistry,
University of Washington, Seattle

DENTAL MORPHOLOGY AND EVOLUTION

There is no need, among anthropologists, to emphasize the role of the dentition in the study of human palaeontology. The monographs and general texts devoted to fossil man and the adaptive radiation of the primates could scarcely have been undertaken without serious attention to the morphology of the teeth, particularly the molars. The works of Gregory, Weidenreich, von Koenigswald, Vallois, and Le Gros Clark clearly illustrate how much of our knowledge of primate evolution stems from careful analysis of the dental structures. To a lesser degree is this true of the study of racial variation within the species of *Homo sapiens*, since we are copiously supplied with entire skeletons of recent man and may examine the whole body of living man.

It might be remarked, however, that there are certain limitations placed upon progress in the study of evolution by virtue of the fact that our concern has been largely restricted to the morphological features exhibited by completely calcified and erupted teeth. We justify this emphasis on the grounds that (1) the teeth are frequently the sole surviving parts of long-buried primates, (2) dental crown characteristics appear to be inherited, and (3) the teeth, particularly the molars, have been demonstrated to be relatively stable throughout long periods of

*This research was supported in part by Grant D-910 from the National Institute of Dental Research, United States Public Health Service.

evolution. As Le Gros Clark (1960) has pointed out, "the molar teeth in the different groups of Primates show far less deviation from the basic pattern than the other teeth often do . . . the molars usually retain their fundamental Primate characteristics".

Although we must agree that the evidence from twin, pedigree, and population studies overwhelmingly indicates the genetic control of morphological features of the individual molar crowns, it is at the same time apparent that the nature of this control has remained *in limbo*. Familiarity with phenotypic structure, combined with neglect of developmental anatomy, has perhaps been responsible for certain areas of widespread conjecture and disagreement in connection with the theory of the evolution of the dentition. For example, while the changes in molar morphology throughout primate evolution have, in some cases, been rather carefully charted, the explanations of how these changes occurred are sometimes perplexing. It is interesting to note that evidence which might settle the question one way or the other has been notably absent. For many years now, the presence of a new cusp in the enamel crown has been variously attributed to (1) an "outgrowth" on the side of an old cusp, (2) a folding of the side of the crown, (3) an "outgrowth" from the cingulum, or (4) a "splitting off" or "dichotomy" of the major cusp. Similarly, we note the apparent absence of a cusp on a molar crown and begin to speak of a "trend toward reduction" in the size of the tooth or in the number of cusps. We are all aware that the path toward morphogenetic reconstruction may be lined with pitfalls if our observations are based upon the gross structure alone. It is partly my purpose to suggest that such pitfalls really exist in the case of deductions drawn from gross dental morphology.

MOLAR CROWN MORPHOGENESIS AND EVOLUTION

The structure of the enamel molar crown that we so assiduously study is, of course, but the final phenotype resulting from a rather complex developmental history. Thanks to the

vestigations of Blechschmidt (1953), Lefkowitz, Bodecker,
nd Mardfin (1953), Glasstone (1938), Butler (1956), and
many others, we have considerable knowledge of some of the
major events in this history. Clearly the eventual morphology
f the molar crown is dependent upon at least two types of
rowth. The folding of the inner enamel epithelium, which is
self a phenomenon of differential rates of mitotic activity
von Ebner, 1922), may be regarded as the primary and most
undamental step in the ultimate determination of the crown
morphology. A secondary, but important, contributing process
o the final configuration of the crown is the deposition of
namel, which has been demonstrated to proceed at different
ates in different parts of the tooth (Schour and Poncher, 1937;
raus, 1959). Since growth rates are clearly under genetic
ontrol (Sinnott, Dunn, and Dobzhansky, 1950), by con-
centrating upon the growth aspects of molar crown morphology
e might expect to draw closer to the site and time of genetic
ction. In so doing we might hope to gain a fresh point of view
egarding the mechanics of dental evolution by observing the
mbryological stages through which the crown has passed to
chieve its ultimate morphology.

In the present paper we shall examine the molar crowns of
le primary dentition both in the soft tissue stage prior to
nitial calcification and in the various stages during the
alcification process. Our purpose is three-fold:

(1) To determine if there is a regular sequence of appearance
    of centers of calcification in each of the 4 primary molars.
(2) To ascertain if there is a discernible pattern of calcifica-
    tion for each individual molar and for all 4 molars as a
    whole.
(3) To establish whether the enamel crown accurately
    reflects the developing morphology of the soft tissue
    crown, based upon observations of the mesial marginal
    ridge of the maxillary second molar.

METHODOLOGY AND SAMPLE

The primary molars of 150 human fetuses, ranging in age
om 3 months to full-term, were extracted and stained with

alizarin red S. All teeth were then photographed under low magnification from the occlusal view in both color and black and-white. Higher magnification and other views were utilized when necessary. The great majority of specimens were Caucasoids; a small minority were either American Negroes or Caucasoid-Mongoloid hybrids. The fetuses were selected for absence of any gross malformation or pathology.

RESULTS AND DISCUSSION

Sequence of Appearance of Centers and Pattern of Calcification

In each the mesio-buccal cusp is the first to calcify, followed by the mesio-lingual cusp. This is ascertained by collecting all those molars having only one center calcified. Invariably this turns out to be the mesio-buccal cusp. When all molars with 2 centers of calcification are examined, the mesio-buccal invariably is present and presents the larger calcified area. This method is continued until the most likely sequence is established. It will be noted that in terms of number of deviations from the proposed sequence of appearance, the lower first molar is the most variable while the upper second is the most constant, there being no exceptions to the proposed sequence in the latter.

In terms of number of cusps, the upper first molar has 2 or at the most, 3 cusps—2 buccal and one lingual. The lower first and second molars are regularly 5-cusped teeth, although the first shows some interesting variations, as will be pointed out. The upper second molar, in terms of developmental cusps—that is, cusps having a separate center of calcification, generally has 7 cusps, and frequently as many as 9 or 10 cusps! The extra cusps include the Carabelli, when present, and those on the mesial marginal ridge, as will be discussed later. In the chart (Figs. 12, 13, 14, and 15) these extra cusps are omitted for the sake of clarity.

1. *Lower first molar.* Figure 1 shows a plaster cast of a first lower deciduous molar fully calcified and erupted, for purposes of comparison. Figures 2–11 picture this molar in various stages of calcification as seen from the occlusal. They indicate the ease with which the appropriate observations can be made

To avoid repetition both pattern of calcification and sequence of appearance of centers will be discussed together. Figure 12 shows diagrammatically the proposed sequence, the types of deviations from it, and the frequency distribution of the sample into the various stages. By "pattern of calcification" we refer to the obvious regularity with which calcification spreads in predictable fashion over the "soft tissue" or membranous crown. The following points may be noted:

(a) The sequence of centers:
　　First—protoconid
　　Second—metaconid
　　Third—hypoconid
　　Fourth—entoconid
　　Fifth—hypoconulid

(b) The 5 centers appear before "bridging" between cusps occurs.

(c) The sequence of bridging:
　　First—protoconid-hypoconid
　　Second—hypoconid-hypoconulid
　　Third—protoconid-metaconid
　　Fourth—hypoconulid-entoconid
　　Fifth—metaconid-entoconid

(d) The mesial marginal ridge is entirely the result of a calcified extension from the protoconid and does not unite with the metaconid until after the protoconid and metaconid are united. This is distinctive for the lower first molar.

(e) Although frequently the completed crown shows no hypoconulid or entoconid, the soft tissue crown shows both cusps. The entoconid may be very late in developing, or very close to the hypoconulid in position; or the hypoconulid may be very close to the hypoconid or entoconid, so that enamel deposition may obscure it entirely as a separate cusp. Time of appearance and place of appearance in the soft tissue crown are important factors in ultimate crown morphology.

2. *Lower second molar.* Figure 13 shows the proposed sequence

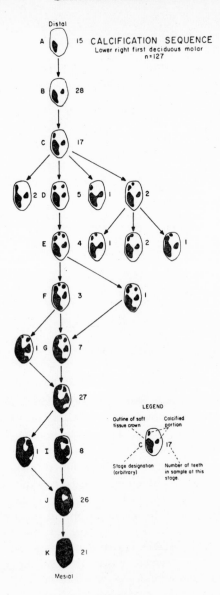

FIG. 12

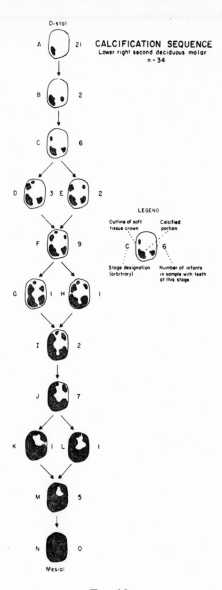

FIG. 13

of calcification. Certain differences between this and the lower first molar are noteworthy:

(a) The regularity of appearance of the hypoconulid and entoconid.

(b) The nature of formation of the mesial marginal ridge whereby both the protoconid and metaconid send out extensions.

(c) The protoconid-metaconid bridging does not take place as such.

At this point it is of interest to observe that in all 4 molars the first center of calcification to appear is the mesio-buccal cusp, followed by the mesio-lingual cusp. In rhesus monkeys, however, in the case of the lower first permanent molar, the second center to appear is the disto-buccal (Swindler, 1961).

3. *Upper first molar.* Figure 14 illustrates the striking differences in calcification pattern of this molar. *Note:*

(a) The absence of entocone, hypocone, or hypoconule as separate centers.

(b) The relatively infrequent presence of the metacone as a separate center. Possibly it calcifies independently but unites so quickly with the paracone that it is unusual to find a fetus in that stage before union of the metacone with the paracone.

(c) For the greater portion of the calcification period the upper first molar is morphologically and developmentally a bicuspid.

(d) There is great irregularity in the joining of buccal and lingual calcified moieties.

4. *Upper second molar.* Figure 15 shows the marked consistency in the sequence and pattern of calcification of the upper second molar if we consider only the 4 major cusps. *Note:*

(a) There are only 4 major cusps.

(b) The hypocone is very late in appearing on the soft tissue crown. It is preceded by a cingulum, and the hypocone develops only when the other cusps have already begun calcification.

(c) There are no deviations from the proposed sequence and pattern.

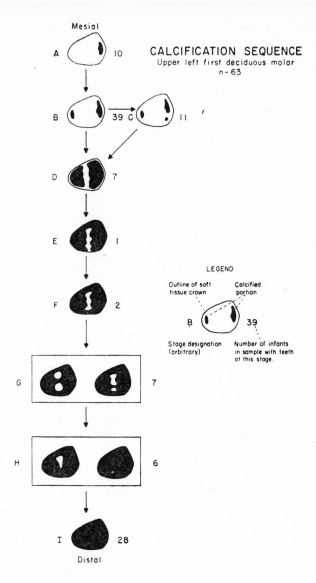

FIG. 14

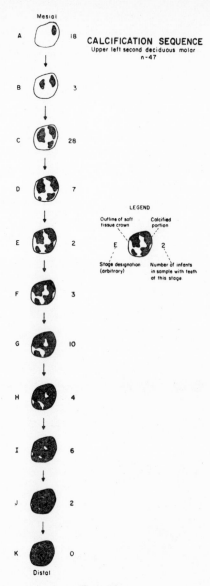

FIG. 15

(d) The hypocone is united to the rest of the calcified crown only after the oblique ridge has calcified.

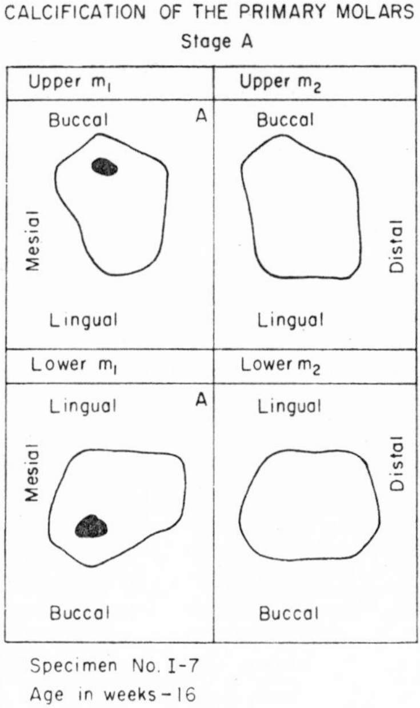

CALCIFICATION OF THE PRIMARY MOLARS
Stage A

Specimen No. I-7
Age in weeks – 16

Fig. 16

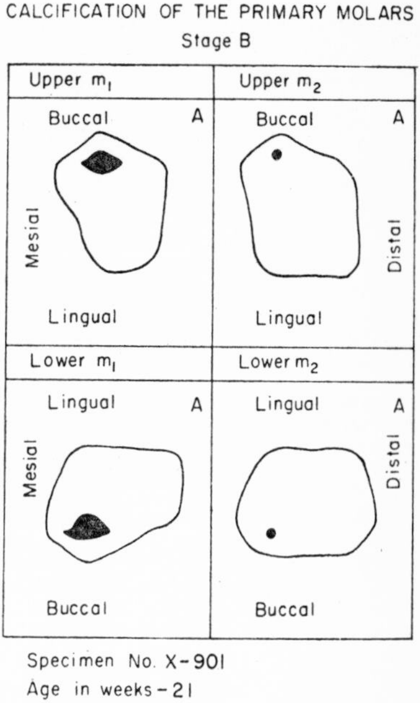

CALCIFICATION OF THE PRIMARY MOLARS
Stage B

Specimen No. X-901
Age in weeks – 21

Fig. 17

The 4 molars considered together. Figures 16–27 show diagrammatically the stages of cusp calcification when all 4 molars are taken together. Each figure represents 4 molars taken from a single specimen. For each stage represented there were several fetuses whose molars matched that particular stage of development. None of the 150 fetuses in the sample presented a situation other than that represented in the 12 figures shown. By using all 4 molars a much finer breakdown of the sequence of initial cusp calcification is permitted. For example, the first cusps to begin calcification are the mesio-buccal cusps of the upper and lower first molars; but the mesio-buccal cusps of the upper and lower second molars begin to calcify before the mesio-lingual cusps of the first molars. It can be seen that the last cusp to begin calcification is the hypocone of the upper second molar. The capital letter in the upper right corner of

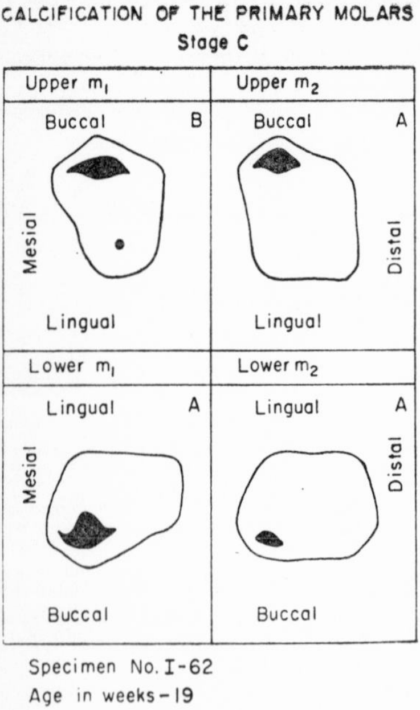

CALCIFICATION OF THE PRIMARY MOLARS
Stage C

Upper m_1		Upper m_2	
Buccal	B	Buccal	A
Mesial			Distal
Lingual		Lingual	
Lower m_1		Lower m_2	
Lingual	A	Lingual	A
Mesial			Distal
Buccal		Buccal	

Specimen No. I-62
Age in weeks – 19

FIG. 18

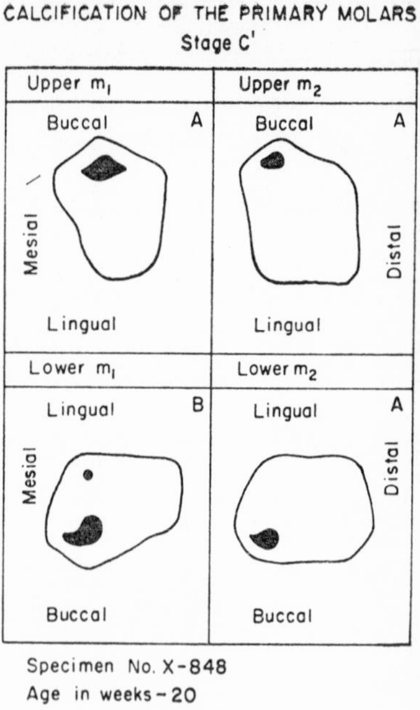

CALCIFICATION OF THE PRIMARY MOLARS
Stage C'

Upper m_1		Upper m_2	
Buccal	A	Buccal	A
Mesial			Distal
Lingual		Lingual	
Lower m_1		Lower m_2	
Lingual	B	Lingual	A
Mesial			Distal
Buccal		Buccal	

Specimen No. X-848
Age in weeks – 20

FIG. 19

each box indicates the stage of development for that particular tooth, corresponding to the sequences presented in Figs. 12–15. Stage J is omitted since no fetus occurred in this postulated stage, presumably because the transition from Stage I to Stage K takes place relatively rapidly. According to the ages of the specimens selected for illustration, calcification in the molars commences at 16 weeks and reaches Stage L by 28 weeks; however the other specimens in the sample indicate a considerable range of variation can be expected. For example, calcification of the mesio-buccal cusp of the first molar has been observed as early as 14 weeks (Kraus, 1959). We have intentionally avoided construction of a cusp sequence for all 4 molars since this should properly await a much larger sample in order that the frequencies of deviations from the usual sequence can be appraised.

Eventually there should be at least 3 important functions

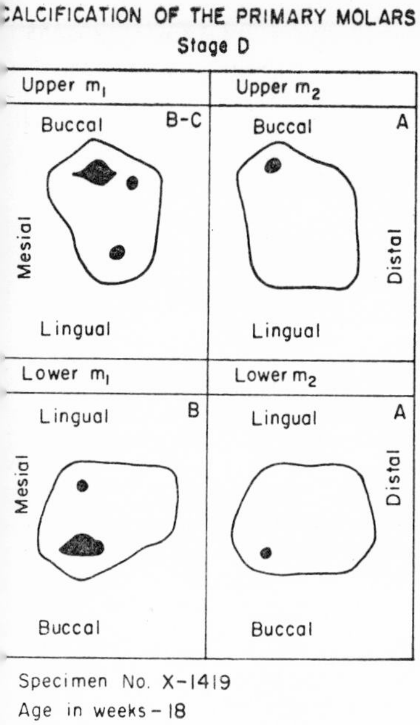

CALCIFICATION OF THE PRIMARY MOLARS
Stage D

Specimen No. X-1419
Age in weeks - 18
FIG. 20

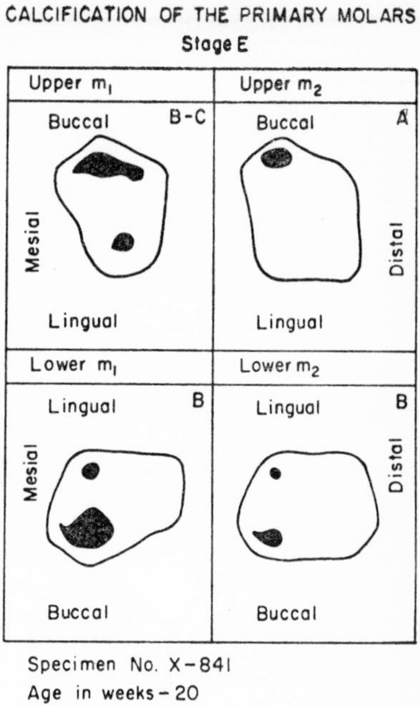

CALCIFICATION OF THE PRIMARY MOLARS
Stage E

Specimen No. X-841
Age in weeks - 20
FIG. 21

fulfilled by a statistically prepared probability chart of the sequence of initial cusp calcification for all 4 molars taken together. In the first place it will permit comparison of the dentitions of fetuses having congenital malformations with the norms for sequence and pattern of calcification. Secondly, fetuses of different ethnic stocks can be compared to determine if genetic differences in sequence and pattern of calcification occur at the racial level. And finally, the sequence and pattern common to *Homo sapiens* can be compared with that for various other primate groups to establish whether intra-primate differences can be detected in developmental traits of the dentition.

The Mesial Marginal Ridge of the Upper Second Molar. There is common agreement in the literature that the upper second deciduous molar consists generally of 4 primary cusps—paracone, protocone, metacone, and hypocone. An accessory fifth cusp—the Carabelli—often is present on the mesio-lingual

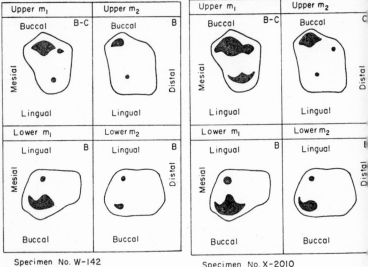

CALCIFICATION OF THE PRIMARY MOLARS
Stage F

CALCIFICATION OF THE PRIMARY MOLAR
Stage G

Specimen No. W-142
Age in weeks - 20

FIG. 22

Specimen No. X-2010
Age in weeks - 23

FIG. 23

aspect of the protocone. Most text-book descriptions of the molar pay little attention to the mesial marginal ridge beyond describing its presence. Jorgensen (1956), however, pointed out that the mesial marginal ridge may develop a "distinct cusplet", known in comparative odontology as the protoconule. Clinicians commonly refer to the irregularities of the mesial marginal ridge as "spillways". The embryology of the ridge has hitherto not been described.

Developmentally, in terms of separate centers of calcification, the upper second deciduous molar is regularly a 7–9-cusped tooth! In all molars examined there were at least 3, and in many cases as many as 5, cusp-like formations on the mesial marginal ridge prior to its calcification. Relative to the primary cusps they were small, but in many cases they began calcification as separate centers. In all cases calcification of the cusps of the mesial marginal ridge follows initial calcification of the primary cusps. Figure 28 presents an occlusal view of the

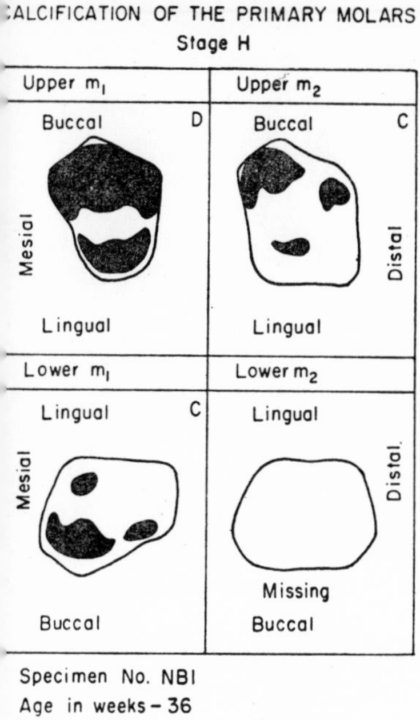

CALCIFICATION OF THE PRIMARY MOLARS
Stage H

Upper m₁		Upper m₂	

Specimen No. NBI
Age in weeks – 36

Fig. 24

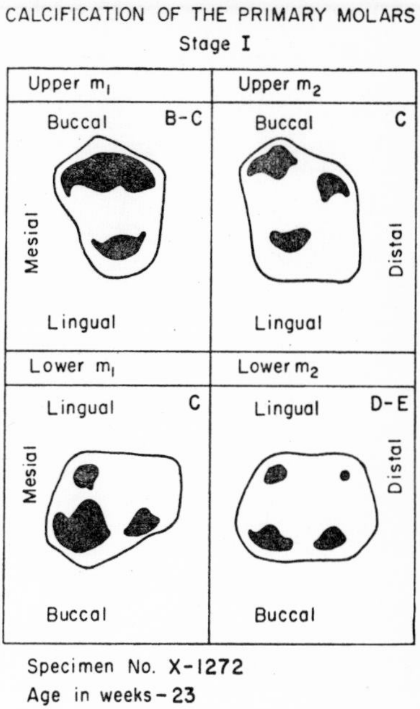

CALCIFICATION OF THE PRIMARY MOLARS
Stage I

Specimen No. X-1272
Age in weeks – 23

Fig. 25

mesial half of an upper right second deciduous molar, showing the most buccal cusp of the mesial marginal ridge commencing calcification as a separate center. A distal view of the same center, in greater magnification, is shown in Fig. 29. The adjoining soft tissue cusp on its lingual side is clearly evident. Figure 30 illustrates the same view of the upper left second molar from the same specimen, showing the high degree of bilateral symmetry. In the same figure can be seen two additional cusplets buccal to the separate calcification center and mesial to the paracone. It is apparent from the distribution of enamel thickness over these 2 cusplets that they did not calcify as separate centers but rather as an "overflow" from the paracone. This phenomenon is more clearly seen in Fig. 31 which provides a distal view of a left upper second molar in a more advanced stage of calcification. In the 3 cusps of the mesial marginal ridge it is evident that the 2 large cusps in the center

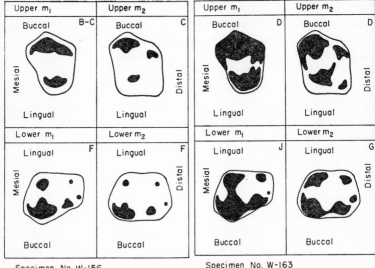

Specimen No. W-156
Age in weeks — 24

Specimen No. W-163
Age in weeks — 28

Fig. 26   Fig. 27

originated as separate centers. This is attested by the greater
enamel thickness over the tips of the cusps and the steadily
attenuated thickness coming down either side. On the other
hand, the cusplet on the extreme right of the figure shows that
it was calcified by extension of the calcification process from the
paracone, since the thickness of enamel diminishes regularly
from buccal to lingual. Figure 32 shows a distal view of another
left second molar in a slightly less advanced stage than that in
Fig. 31. Careful study (and measurement) of the enamel thickness throughout will indicate that the buccal cusp (on the right
of the figure) and the lingual cusp arose as separate centers of
calcification, but that the middle cusp was calcified as an
extension of the process ("overflow") from the buccal cusp.

Clearly we must exercise care in defining the term "cusp".
We might adopt a developmental point of view and regard as a
cusp any cone-shaped eminence of the soft tissue crown which

begins to calcify as a separate center; or we might go back earlier in the ontogenetic period and define a cusp as simply any cone-shaped eminence or protuberance that appears on the soft tissue crown before calcification occurs. In any event, it is necessary to distinguish between a developmental definition and a purely morphological one such as is in current usage with regard to the completed enamel crown. It is obvious that what are, developmentally, 3 to 5 cusps on the mesial marginal ridge, cannot be distinguished, morphologically, as cusps on the final completed crown. What happens to these cusps? We suggest, tentatively, that we must look to differential rates of enamel deposition as the "great leveler" (Kraus, 1959; Schour and Poncher, 1937). Although there is much food for thought here, it is best to await more exhaustive investigation into the embryology of molar development before indulging in further speculation. At any rate, it seems advisable to give pause before drawing too dogmatic conclusions regarding "trends toward reduction of cusps" or the "rise of a new cusp" when these are based solely upon the completed enamel crown morphology.

SUMMARY AND CONCLUSIONS

The primary molars of 150 human fetuses ranging in age from 3 months to full-term were extracted and stained with alizarin red S. The molar crowns, in various stages of calcification, were classified according to number of calcification centers present and number of inter-cuspal calcified unions effected. A most likely sequence of appearance of initial centers of calcification and pattern of subsequent calcification was drawn up for each of the 4 molars. In addition, stages of development were diagrammatically drawn up for all 4 molars taken together. Finally, particular attention was paid to the mesial marginal ridge of the upper second primary molar with regard to the number and nature of cusps occurring on this ridge during the process of calcification.

It was found that each molar presents a rather distinctive sequence and pattern of calcification, and that the number and kinds of deviations from the proposed developmental stages differ for each molar. Taken together, the 4 molars show a clear-cut pattern of appearance of the various cusp centers of calcification. Developmentally, the lower first molar is the most variable, the upper second the most constant. The upper first molar appears to be a 2 or 3 cusped molar, while the upper second, in terms of defining the cusp as a separate center of calcification, may be considered to possess 7 or more cusps. The lower molars are both 5-cusped teeth in this respect.

The development of the cusps on the mesial marginal ridge and their subsequent obscuration during the course of enamel deposition suggest that the ultimate crown morphology of the molars may not be entirely reliable criteria for the reconstruction of phylogenetic lines or the estimation of degree of taxonomic affinity.

REFERENCES

BLECHSCHMIDT, E. (1953) Die Entwicklung der Zahnkeime beim Menschen, zum Studium der Entwicklungsdynamik der menschlichen Embryonen, *Acta Anat.* **17**, 207.

BUTLER, P. (1956) The ontogeny of molar pattern, *Biol. Rev.* **31**, 30.

VON EBNER, V. (1922) Histologie der Zähne mit Einschuss der Histiogenese. *Scheff's Handbuch der Zahnheilkunde*, 4th ed., pp. 325–96. Hölder, Vienna.

GLASSTONE, S. (1938) A comparative study of the development *in vivo* and *in vitro* of rat and rabbit molars, *Proc. Roy. Soc. B.* **126**, 315.

JØRGENSEN, K. (1956) *The Deciduous Dentition.* Bianco Lunos Bogtrykkeri A-S. Copenhagen.

KRAUS, B. (1959) Differential calcification rates in the human primary dentition, *Arch. Oral Biol.* **1**, 133.

LEFKOWITZ, W., BODECKER, C. and MARDFIN, D. (1953) Odontogenesis of the rat molar; prenatal stage, *J. Dent. Res.* **32**, 749.

LE GROS CLARK, W. (1960) *The Antecedents of Man.* Quadrangle Books, Chicago.

SCHOUR, I. and PONCHER, H. (1937) The rate of apposition of human enamel and dentin as measured by the effects of acute fluorosis, *Amer. J. Dis. Child.* **54**, 757.

SINNOTT, E., DUNN, L. and DOBZHANSKY, Th. (1950) *Principles of Genetics.* McGraw-Hill, New York.

SWINDLER, D. (1961) Calcification of the permanent first mandibular molar in Rhesus monkeys, *Science* **134**, 566.

Fig. 1

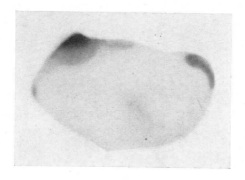

Fig. 2

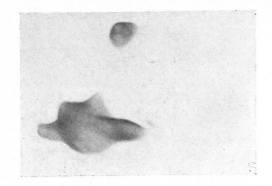

Fig. 3

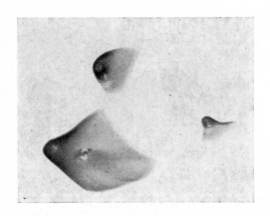

Fig. 4

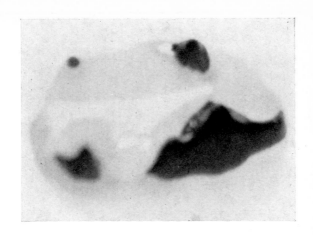

Fig. 5

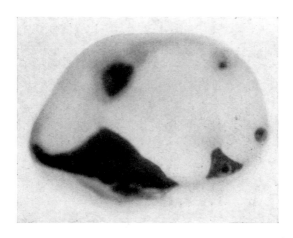

Fig. 6

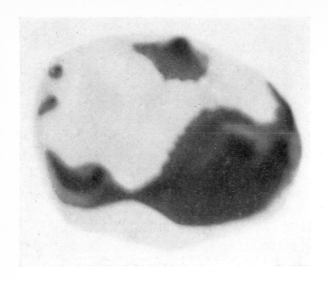

Fig. 7

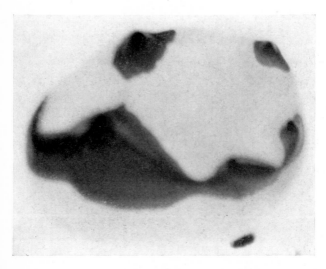

Fig. 8

FIG. 9

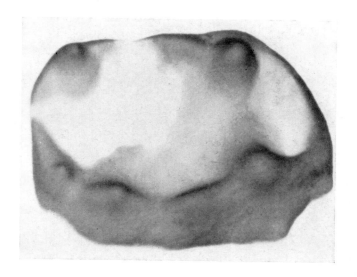

FIG. 10

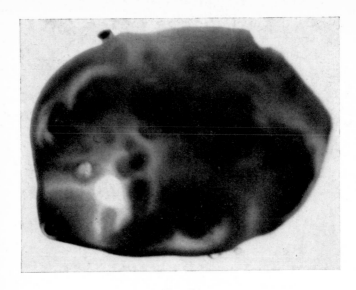

Fig. 11

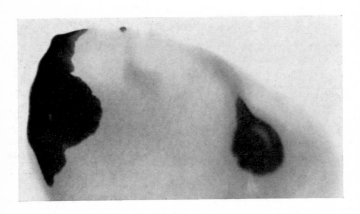

Fig. 28

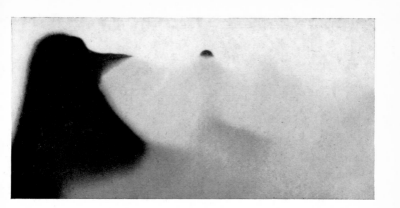

FIG. 29

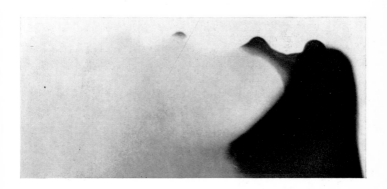

FIG. 30

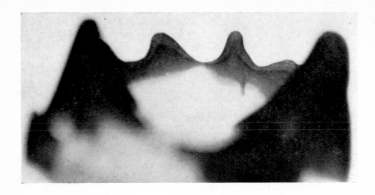

Fig. 31

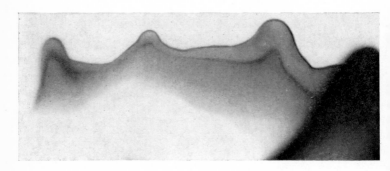

Fig. 32

CROWN CHARACTERS OF THE DECIDUOUS DENTITION OF THE JAPANESE–AMERICAN HYBRIDS

by **KAZURO HANIHARA**

Department of Legal Medicine, Sapporo Medical College, Sapporo

Since 1949 studies of the physical traits of Japanese-American hybrids have been carried out by the members of the Department of Anthropology, University of Tokyo, under the direction of Professor Suda.

The children studied were born of Japanese mothers and American fathers, including both Whites and Negroes, after World War II. They were brought up in one of the institutions for such orphans, the Elizabeth Sanders Home at Oiso, located some fifty miles south-west of Tokyo.

Anthropological studies of these children are being undertaken twice a year. In addition to recording anthropometric data, we are undertaking X-ray studies of hand and foot bones, skin colour tests, motor performance tests, dental studies, and psychiatric tests. My concern has been particularly with the morphology of their dentition, studied by means of plaster casts. Since the oldest children were born in 1946 the study is, at present, limited to the deciduous dentition. Limits of space do not allow me to give a detailed description of all the dental characters, so that a few selected traits of particular importance will be discussed here. The remaining characters, as well as measurements of the tooth crowns, will be given in a forthcoming paper.

MATERIALS AND METHODS

The materials used were plaster casts from children of 3 to 5 years of age. At the same time, casts from Japanese, American

TABLE I
MATERIALS USED

Racial group	Number of individuals		
	♂	♀	Total
Japanese–American White hybrid	53	26	79
Japanese–American Negro hybrid	23	23	46
Japanese	105	104	209
American White	28	33	61
American Negro	22	30	52

White, and American Negro children of almost the same age were also observed as a control. The control groups, except for the Japanese, were obtained in the University of Chicago, Western Reserve University, and Howard University. The numbers of specimens given in Table I were not necessarily fixed for each characteristic because some teeth were either badly worn or damaged by dental caries.

The classification of each crown character was based on the D-series Plaques (given as Figs. 1 to 6) prepared for the human deciduous dentition, a detailed description being given in previous paper (Hanihara, 1961).

DESCRIPTION OF CROWN CHARACTERS

1. *Shovel-shaped Character in the Deciduous Upper Central Incisors*

Hrdlička first described shovel-shaped incisors in 1920. Variations in this character result from differences in the mesial and distal marginal ridges, the cingulum and the concavity or nature of the surface between these elements.

The shovel-shaped character on the deciduous upper central incisors has been classified into four categories as illustrated in Fig. 1, in which each category is identified by numbers from 0 to 3. Thus 0 means no shovel shape, 1 semi-shovel shape, shovel shape, and 3 strong shovel shape.

Because of weakness of the lingual marginal ridges the

Table II

Frequencies of the Shovel-shaped Teeth in the Deciduous Upper Central Incisors (in %)

Racial group†	N	0	1	2	3
J	124	0·0	23·4	76·6	0·0
J-W	65	7·7	55·4	36·9	0·0
W	20	50·0	50·0	0·0	0·0
J-N	35	0·0	42·9	57·1	0·0
N	10	80·0	10·0	10·0	0·0

†Abbreviations: J, Japanese; J-W, Japanese-American White hybrid; W, American White; J-N, Japanese-American Negro hybrid; N, American Negro.

deciduous incisors are far exceeded by the permanent ones in the development of the shovel-shape character. The classification has, therefore, been based on the relative variability of the deciduous teeth and not with regard to the permanent incisors.

The frequencies of each category are given in Table II, both sexes being combined as the difference between them is statistically insignificant.

In general, the shovel-shape character is frequent and relatively well-developed in Japanese and the reverse is true for both Whites and Negroes. The hybrids, either Japanese-White or Japanese-Negro, show the intermediate form. In Table II, it can be seen that the majority of Japanese children show a well-developed shovel-shape character (class 2), while the frequencies of this class decrease in Whites and Negroes, with the hybrid groups showing intermediate values. On the other hand, the frequencies of class 0, or no shovel shape, increase in the same order.

The differences between the distributions are highly significant for each pair of groups, as seen in Table III, with the exception of the differences between Japanese and Japanese-Negro hybrids. This is mainly caused by the high degree of difference in class 0, namely, most of the White and Negro children have no shovel-shaped incisors whereas the reverse is true for Japanese and hybrid children.

TABLE III

CHI-SQUARE TESTS OF THE SHOVEL-SHAPED TEETH IN THE DECIDUOUS UPPER CENTRAL INCISORS

Pair of groups	0	1	2	3	Total (DF=3)
J : J-W	9·71†	13·24‡	10·19†	0·00	33·14‡
J : W	61·43‡	4·28	15·47‡	0·00	81·18‡
J-W : W	14·97‡	0·12	7·65	0·00	22·74‡
J : J-N	0·00	3·72	1·42	0·00	5·14
J : N	98·67‡	0·62	5·21	0·00	104·50‡
J-N : N	27·56‡	2·29	3·61	0·00	33·46‡

†Significantly different under the 5 per cent level.
‡Significantly different under the 1 per cent level.

In the present study no individual could be placed into the class 3 category. I have only found such a dental type in a few cases of the American Indians. As already pointed out by many authors, shovel-shaped permanent incisors are most frequently observed in the Mongoloids. The same condition is also recognized in the deciduous dentition.

With regard to the shovel-shaped condition, almost the same tendencies are found in the deciduous upper lateral incisors as well as in the deciduous upper and lower canines.

2. *Cusp Development on the Deciduous Upper First Molars*

Although cusp development of the deciduous upper first molars has so far been discussed by few authors, there are variations in the arrangement of the cusps in this tooth.

In Fig. 2 eight varieties are classified with regard to the number and the degree of cusp development. Each type is symbolized as follows.

(2) Only two cusps, protocone and paracone, are present. In this type two sub-groups are recognized; one which shows relatively simple crown pattern and the other a more complicated pattern with small ridges and accessory formations.

(3M1 and 3M2) The metacone is displayed in addition to the protocone and paracone, but there is no hypocone. The

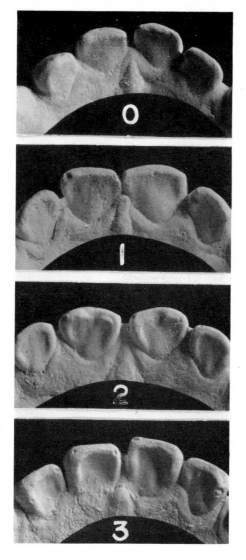

FIG. 1. Shovel-shape of the deciduous upper central incisors.

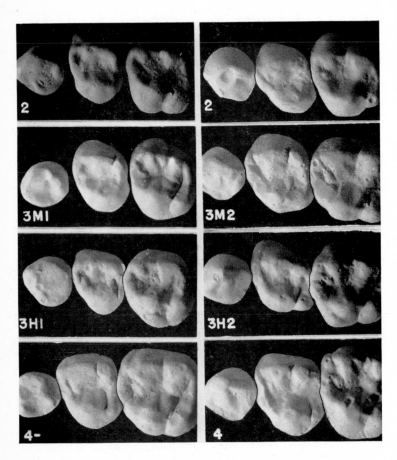

FIG. 2.   Crown pattern of the deciduous upper first molars.

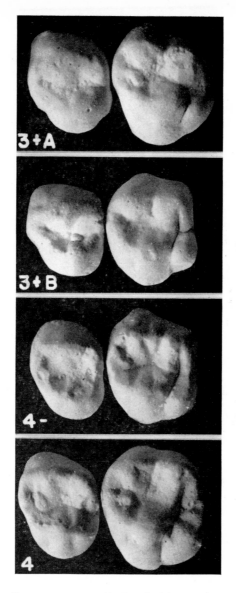

FIG. 3. Crown pattern of the deciduous upper second molars.

TABLE IV

FREQUENCIES OF EACH TYPE OF CUSP DEVELOPMENT IN THE DECIDUOUS
UPPER FIRST MOLARS (IN %)

Racial group	N	2	3M	3H	4— and 4
J	184	15·2	60·3	4·3	20·1
J-W	70	17·1	68·6	4·3	10·0
W	55	60·0	23·6	16·4	0·0
J-N	42	11·9	45·2	4·8	38·1
N	50	28·0	36·0	16·0	20·0

metacone is divided from the paracone by a shallow groove
and its size is always much smaller than the paracone. The
difference between 3M1 and 3M2 is due to the size of the
metacone, namely 3M1 carries a very small metacone and
3M2 a relatively well-developed one.

(3H1 and 3H2) The hypocone is present as the "third cusp"
and there is no metacone. The hypocone is separated from the
protocone by a shallow groove. 3H1 presents an extremely
small hypocone and 3H2 shows a well-developed one.

(4— and 4) All four main cusps are in evidence. 4— means
a tooth carrying a relatively small hypocone and 4 shows a
crown pattern such as is usually recognized in the permanent
upper molars.

In this study 3M1 and 3M2, 3H1 and 3H2, and 4— and 4
are combined with each other to simplify the discussion, so
that we have four classes for the cusp development of the
deciduous upper first molars.

It may be seen, in Table IV, that the Whites show the most
simple pattern of the crown, in which over half of the individuals carry the two-cusped type of teeth. On the other hand,
the three-cusped type is most common in the remaining groups.
It is of interest to note that, in the White and Negro groups, the
frequencies of the 3H type carrying the hypocone as the third
cusp are almost four times those of the Japanese and hybrid
children, although statistically no significant difference is
recognized.

TABLE V

CHI-SQUARE TESTS OF THE CUSP DEVELOPMENT IN THE DECIDUOUS UPPER
FIRST MOLARS

Pair of groups	2	3M	3H	4— and 4	Total (DF=3)
J : J-W	0·08	0·39	0·00	3·17	3·64
J : W	33·47‡	10·95†	8·66†	11·04†	64·12‡
J-W : W	15·71‡	12·68‡	4·62	5·56	38·57‡
J : J-N	0·33	1·63	0·00	4·26	6·22
J : N	3·88	3·87	7·90†	0·00	15·65‡
J-N : N	2·90	0·44	2·72	2·47	8·53†

†Significantly different under the 5 per cent level.
‡Significantly different under the 1 per cent level.

The differences in the distribution of each type are significant
between Japanese and Americans as well as hybrids and
Americans. The simplicity of the crown in White children is
very clearly shown in Table V. With regard to this character
both hybrid groups are rather similar to the Japanese and
practically no significant difference was found.

A few different descriptions have so far been given by
previous authors in respect of the standard number of cusps
on the deciduous upper first molars. For instance, Virchow
(1919) and Fujita (1956) stated that this molar crown was a
two-cusped type, Black (1902) and Jones (1947) considered
it to be three-cusped, and Wheeler (1950) described the
standard type as a four-cusped crown. We should now recognize,
however, that the so-called standard type or number of cusps
differs in various human populations and that the teeth of the
three- or four-cusped type show unexpectedly high frequencies.
This might reveal that the cusp differentation of this tooth is
still in an unstable condition.

3. *Crown Pattern of the Deciduous Upper Second Molars*

Dahlberg (1949) originally divided the crown pattern of the
permanent upper molars into four types: 3, 3+, 4— and 4, in
terms of the degree of development of the hypocone. I have

Table VI

Frequencies of Each Type of Crown Pattern in the Deciduous Upper
Second Molars (in %)

Racial group	N	3+A	3+B and 4—	4
J	191	1·6	27·7	70·7
J-W	72	1·4	33·3	65·3
W	57	1·8	24·6	73·7
J-N	43	0·0	30·2	69·8
N	51	0·0	9·8	90·2

followed this classification in considering the deciduous upper
second molars (Fig. 3), but with a slight modification. A
peculiar feature of this tooth is that the true three-cusped type
designated as type 3 by Dahlberg has never been observed.

Figure 3 illustrates the following four types:

(3+A) This type is exactly equal to the "3+" permanent
molar. The tooth has three main cusps and the hypocone is
represented as only a very small cusp located on the distal
side of the crown.

(3+B) This tooth is almost the same as the "4—" type, but
the distal marginal ridge connecting the hypocone with the
metacone is interrupted by a groove. It is such that the small
hypocone seems to be more or less attached independently to
the distal side of the crown.

(4—) The hypocone is very small in its relative size and the
distal marginal ridge continues to the tip of the metacone
without interruption.

(4) All of the four main cusps are well developed.

In the present paper types 3+B and 4— are combined
together to calculate their frequencies because they seem to
represent basically the same type of cusp differentiation.

As a whole, type "4" of the crown is the most common and
"3+A" is rare. The distribution shows almost the same
pattern in all of our five groups with the exception of the Negro
children who show a relatively high frequency of the type "4".

It is of interest to compare these findings with the data on
the permanent upper first molars. In the case of these teeth, a

Table VII

Chi-square Tests of the Crown Patterns in the Deciduous Upper
Second Molars

Pair of groups	3+A	3+B and 4−	4	Total (DF=2)
J : J–W	0·01	0·67	0·12	0·80
J : W	0·01	0·17	0·05	0·23
J–W : W	0·02	0·78	0·36	1·16
J : J–N	0·60	0·12	0·00	0·72
J : N	0·75	5·38	2·13	8·26†
J–N : N	0·00	4·94	1·32	6·26†

†Significantly different under the 5 per cent level.

few authors have studied various racial groups. For example, Dahlberg (1949) reported on the American Indians, Eskimos, American Whites and Melanesians, Pedersen (1949) on the East Greenland Eskimos and Suzuki and Sakai (1956b) on the Japanese. According to their data the frequency of the four-cusped type of the permanent upper first molar is almost invariable among the races, representing frequencies of between 96 and 100 per cent. Therefore, it may be concluded that, in both deciduous upper second molars and permanent upper first molars, no racial difference is present in this respect. The only distinction between these two teeth is that the frequency of the type "4−" is higher in the former than in the latter. This may be caused by the fact that the hypocone is significantly smaller in the deciduous teeth than in the permanent ones in its relative size (Hanihara, 1956b).

As has been previously pointed out, the cusp differentiation is still in a relatively unstable condition in the deciduous upper first molars, while it seems to have attained a more stable condition in the deciduous upper second molars.

4. *Carabelli's Cusp on the Deciduous Upper Second Molars*

Carabelli's cusp has been discussed by a number of authors and from various points of view. They have been concerned with the racial differences, genetic or evolutionary studies, the relationship between the so-called cusp and the pit, techniques of classification, and so forth. Most of them, however, consider the permanent upper molars, but very few the deciduous dentition.

Carabelli's cusp is not rare in the deciduous upper second molars and it shows some variability in its shape and development. Figure 4 illustrates three types of the so-called Carabelli's pit and four of the cusp. Each type is defined as follows.

(0) No Carabelli's cusp is recognized.

Carabelli's pit

(1) A shallow groove on the mesial side of the lingual surface suggests a trace of the pit.

(2) A shallow depression or groove exists without any change in the curvature of the lingual surface.

(3) The depression or pit is somewhat deeper than in type "2", but no bulge is observed on the lingual surface.

Carabelli's cusp

(4) The appearance is similar to that of type "3", but there is a slight eminence on the lingual surface of the protocone.

(5) The eminence becomes stronger than in type "4". However, the Carabelli's cusp extends smoothly to the rest of the lingual surface without interruption.

(6) Carabelli's cusp is completely encircled by a groove so that it seems to form a "5th cusp".

(7) Carabelli's cusp is strongly developed and, in some cases, it might be even larger than the hypocone.

In this paper types 2 and 3, 4 and 5, and 6 and 7 are combined respectively for ease of calculation as well as classification, so that we have five types: no Carabelli's cusp, two types of Carabelli's pit and two of Carabelli's cusp. The first types of either pit or cusp may be regarded as representing a trace or weak stage of development and the second types as a well-developed or strong one.

It is clear, from Table VIII, that the Carabelli's cusp shows a very high frequency in Whites and relatively low frequencies in the Japanese and Negro children. Both hybrid groups show

TABLE VIII

FREQUENCIES OF CARABELLI'S CUSP IN THE DECIDUOUS UPPER SECOND MOLARS (IN %)

Racial group	N	O	1	2+3	4+5	6+7
J	185	32·4	30·8	24·9	6·5	5·4
J–W	71	14·1	19·7	42·3	18·3	5·6
W	56	5·4	19·6	39·3	14·3	21·4
J–N	41	17·1	19·5	43·9	17·1	2·4
N	51	19·6	29·4	39·2	2·0	9·8

TABLE IX

CHI-SQUARE TESTS OF CARABELLI'S CUSP IN THE DECIDUOUS UPPER SECOND MOLARS

Pair of groups	0	1	2 + 3	4 + 5	6 + 7	Total (DF = 4)
J : J-W	6·53	2·43	4·93	7·10	0·00	20·99‡
J : W	11·85†	1·76	3·41	3·26	12·16†	32·44‡
J-W : W	2·28	0·00	0·07	0·28	6·35	8·98
J : J-N	2·62	1·43	4·47	4·64	0·61	13·77‡
J : N	2·42	0·05	2·68	1·60	1·13	7·63
J-N : N	0·11	1·01	0·09	5·84	1·95	9·00

†Significantly different under the 5 per cent level.
‡Significantly different under the 1 per cent level.

almost the same pattern of distribution representing somewhat closer resemblance to the Whites.

It has been pointed out that the Carabelli's cusp is, in the permanent upper molars, more commonly seen in the Caucasians than in the other racial groups. The same tendency is also true for the deciduous upper second molars. This is clearly shown in the higher frequency of the well-developed Carabelli's cusp in the White children. The pit, however, shows a somewhat different distribution with almost no racial difference, at least among our five groups. This may be regarded as demonstrating a different pattern of inheritance of the Carabelli's cusp and pit. A similar opinion is expressed by Gregory (1922) and Weidenreich (1937) who state that the pit repre-

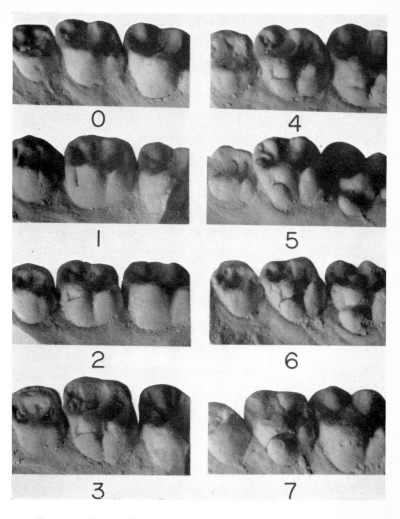

FIG. 4.   Carabelli's cusp on the deciduous upper second
molars.

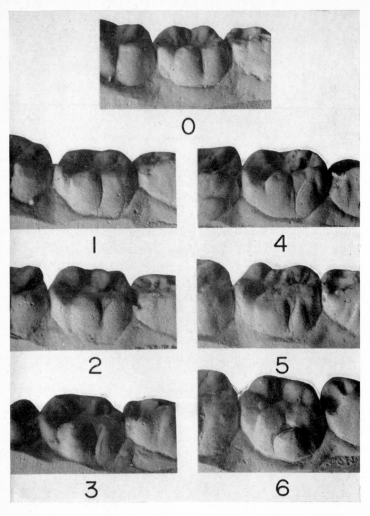

FIG. 5.   Protostylid of the deciduous lower second molars.

FIG. 6.   Central ridge of the metaconid on the deciduous
lower second molars.

sented a remnant of the cingulum and the cusp was an accidental variation without phylogenetic significance. Dahlberg (1949) also emphasized the heterogeneity of the cusp and the pit and stated that the latter was probably still confused with the former by some workers.

In the case of early fossil hominids no Carabelli's cusp has been found and, considering this fact, the opinion that the Carabelli's cusp is a relatively recent acquisition is widely accepted.

Carabelli's pit, on the other hand, has been found in many specimens of the Neanderthal group such as at Krapina (Gorjanović-Kramberger, 1906), in the Mousterian youth (Gregory, 1922), and both Tabūn and Skhūl types of Mt. Carmel (McCown and Keith, 1939). McCown and Keith even stated that the Carabelli's pit must have been a constant feature of the upper molars of the Neanderthal group. Furthermore, Robinson (1956) noted many instances of the Australopithecines displaying the Carabelli's pit and McCown and Keith found it also in *Dryopithecus rhenanus*. From this evidence it may be concluded that the pit has, contrary to the cusp, an early origin in the course of human evolution.

This kind of difference between the Carabelli's cusp and pit is very probably related to the difference in their distribution such as I have mentioned above.

Although further studies may still be required in regard to the distinction between the Carabelli's cusp and pit, comparative studies among various racial groups may supply information of special importance in this field.

5. *Central Ridge of the Metaconid on the Deciduous Lower Second Molars*

In Fig. 6 two types of central ridge on the metaconid of the deciduous lower second molars are illustrated, the distinction of which is entirely due to a difference in development or thickness of the ridge. Each type is designated as follows.

(1) The central ridge of the metaconid is similar in size and prominence to that of the other cusps.

(2) The central ridge is very well developed and thick on the

Table X
Frequencies of the Deflecting Wrinkle in the Deciduous Lower
Second Molars (in %)

Racial group	N	1 (none)	2 (present)
J	144	44·4	55·6
J–W	70	65·7	34·3
W	53	86·8	13·2
J–N	41	46·3	53·7
N	47	80·9	19·1

Table XI
Chi-square Tests of the Deflecting Wrinkle in the Deciduous Lower
Second Molars

Pair of groups	1	2	Total (DF=1)
J : J–W	3·87†	4·61†	8·48‡
J : W	12·26‡	15·88‡	28·14‡
J–W : W	1·81	5·22†	7·03‡
J : J–N	0·04	0·01	0·05
J : N	8·17‡	10·46‡	18·63‡
J–N : N	4·28†	7·09‡	11·37‡

†Significantly different under the 5 per cent level.
‡Significantly different under the 1 per cent level.

metaconid. In such a case the ridge is usually not only very wide and long but also expands its breadth at the trigonid basin. As a result, the ridge sometimes seems to curve distalward at its inner end.

The distribution of types 1 and 2 displays clear differences among our five groups (Tables X and XI). Type 2 shows a much higher frequency in Japanese than in White and Negro children, with the hybrids as intermediate groups.

Type 2 illustrated in Fig. 6 seems to be homologous with one which is described by Weidenreich (1937, 1945) as a "deflecting wrinkle". The wrinkle, according to the original author, emerges from the tip of the metaconid, extends in the direction of the protoconid, and there forms a right angle distally; it traverses the groove between the protoconid and the hypoconid and meets the mesial wrinkle of the entoconid approximately in the center of the occlusal surface.

Although a few papers describing this feature are published, no comparative study in recent man has so far been undertaken. However, the data reported by von Koenigswald (1952), Jørgensen (1956) and Suzuki and Sakai (1956a) agree with my results on the deciduous lower second molars, in that the type 2 or so-called deflecting wrinkle is much more frequently observed in the Mongoloids than in the other groups. For instance, I have found this type in approximately 84 per cent of the Pima Indians, 73 per cent of Eskimos and 55 per cent of Japanese, while the American Whites and Negroes show much lower frequencies as shown in Table X.

The deflecting wrinkle is also observed in some fossil material such as *Dryopithecus cautleyi*, *Gigantopithecus*, *Pithecanthropus pekinensis* and *P. modjokertensis*. On the other hand, this seems to have a morphological relationship with the distal trigonid crest defined by Weidenreich (1937). In this connection further studies of this feature should be carried out from an evolutionary point of view.

6. *Protostylid on the Deciduous Lower Second Molars*

The protostylid has been defined and described by Dahlberg (1950) as a primary character found on the buccal surface of the protoconid of lower molars. This feature is also found on the deciduous lower second molars, though less prominently.

In Fig. 5 seven categories are classified in terms of development of the protostylid.

(0) No trace of the protostylid.

(1) No protostylid is in evidence, but the beginnings of one is suggested by the curvature and branching of the buccal groove.

(2) The divergence of the buccal groove is barely recognizable.

(3) Two branches of the buccal groove can be noted. A small triangular area with its tip downwards is seen between the branches of the groove.

(4) A very shallow groove appears at the mesial corner of the

buccal surface. The area between this groove and the mesial branch of the buccal groove bulges slightly and gives a triangular shape with its tip upwards.   •

(5) The triangular area is decidedly more prominent.

(6) In this class the protostylid is strongly developed so that the tooth seems to have an extra cusp on the buccal side. In some instances, this may be confused with a supernumerary (paramolar) element which has been fused to the buccal surface.

In Tables XII and XIII the frequencies of the classes 0, 2 and 4 are shown in combination with that of the classes 1, 3 and 5, respectively, for ease of comparison. We have, therefore, four major classes, each of which may be characterized by the terms of (a) none or trace, (b) weak, (c) distinct, and (d) strong.

It is clear from Table XII that the individuals carrying the distinct protostylid are rare, and there are none at all in the class 6 as far as the present five groups are concerned. As a result, the differences are mainly observed in the class $2+3$, or weak protostylid. The frequency of this type of tooth is significantly higher in the Japanese than in the American Whites and Negroes. The hybrid groups show intermediate frequencies, although the differences between these and either the Japanese or American figures are statistically insignificant (Table XIII).

Dahlberg (1950) noted that the protostylid on the permanent lower first molars showed a frequency as high as 31 per cent in the Pima Indians and a very low frequency in the Whites. In their studies on the Japanese permanent dentition Suzuki and Sakai (1954) found the protostylid in 18·5 per cent of this same tooth. In regard to the high incidence in the Pima Indians, Dahlberg expressed the opinion that this might be explained by the reappearance of ancestral patterns in a highly inbred group. However, the fact that the Japanese also show a considerably high frequency of the protostylid suggests that this cusp represents one of the characteristics of the Mongoloid group.

In the deciduous lower second molars the frequency of the protostylid is usually higher than in the permanent molars.

Table XII

Frequencies of the Protostylid in the Deciduous Lower Second Molars (in%)

Racial group	N	0+1	2+3	4+5	6
J	152	55·3	41·4	3·3	0·0
J–W	70	71·4	24·3	2·9	0·0
W	54	87·0	13·0	0·0	0·0
J–N	42	69·0	31·0	0·0	0·0
N	47	83·0	14·9	2·1	0·0

Table XIII

Chi-square Tests of the Protostylid in the Deciduous Lower Second Molars

Pair of groups	0+1	2+3	4+5	6	Total (DF=3)
J : J–W	2·07	4·25	0·03	0·00	6·35
J : W	6·60	9·31†	1·76	0·00	17·67‡
J–W : W	0·63	2·19	1·64	0·00	4·46
J : J–N	0·87	1·05	1·41	0·00	3·33
J : N	4·03	7·53	0·14	0·00	11·70‡
J–N : N	0·53	2·60	1·00	0·00	4·13

†Significantly different under the 5 per cent level.
‡Significantly different under the 1 per cent level.

This may be explained by Dahlberg's results; he stated that whenever the protostylid was present on the permanent molars it was also found on the deciduous second molars if these teeth were present in the dentition, although the reverse was not always true.

Jørgensen (1956) noted an extremely low frequency of this cusp in the deciduous lower second molars of the Medieval Danes and modern Dutch. As far as can be seen from his description and figures, however, a weak cusp type such as class 2 (as shown in Fig. 5) does not seem to be regarded as the protostylid. Thus, the difference in frequencies between his

Danes and Dutch and my American Whites may be mainly caused by this kind of incongruity of classification.

DISCUSSION

In the previous pages, some crown features of Japanese-American hybrids have been described. I should now like to discuss some of the more general characteristics of the hybrids in terms of the deciduous dentition.

The hybrid groups generally show an intermediate pattern of distribution between the racial groups of their parents. In some characters, however, they show a closer resemblance or inclination to one of the parents.

Tables XIV and XV show the relationship between the hybrids, Japanese and Americans as revealed by the chi-square values. In most characters the differences between Japanese and Americans are highly significant, while the hybrid groups show a smaller degree of difference from the parent groups. The Japanese-White and Japanese-Negro hybrids also differ from each other in their morphological distance from the parent groups. The former, as a whole, occupies about the central point between Japanese and American-Whites, while the latter shows closer resemblance to the Japanese than to the American Negroes. This kind of difference may be partly caused by the difference of gene frequencies in the Whites and Negroes, although detailed analyses in this respect have not yet been made.

It is of interest to note that both hybrid groups are closer to the Japanese as regards the cusp development of the deciduous upper first molars, but on the other hand are nearer to the Americans when considering Carabelli's cusp in the deciduous upper second molars.

It is quite obvious that, in race-crossing, the gene frequencies of the parent groups are responsible for the frequencies of the phenotypes in the hybrid groups. Carabelli's cusp, for instance, appears to be under the control of a simple Mendelian dominant gene with incomplete penetrance (Tsuji, 1958). If this hypothesis is correct, the gene frequencies could be estimated from the figures shown in Table VIII. However, only

TABLE XIV

DIFFERENCES IN DISTRIBUTION OF EACH CROWN CHARACTER AMONG THE
JAPANESE, JAPANESE-AMERICAN WHITE HYBRIDS AND AMERICAN WHITES

Crown character	J : J–W	J–W : W	J : W	J–W closer to
Shovel-shape, i^1	XX	XX	XX	
Cusp development, m^1	—	XX	XX	J
Crown pattern, m^2	—	—	—	
Carabelli cusp, m^2	XX	—	XX	W
Deflecting wrinkle, m_2	XX	XX	XX	
Protostylid, m_2	—	—	XX	

TABLE XV

DIFFERENCES IN DISTRIBUTION OF EACH CROWN CHARACTER AMONG THE
JAPANESE, JAPANESE-AMERICAN NEGRO HYBRIDS AND AMERICAN NEGROES

Crown character	J : J–N	J–N : N	J : N	J–N closer to
Shovel-shape, i^1	—	XX	XX	J
Cusp development, m^1	—	X	XX	J
Crown pattern, m^2	—	X	X	J
Carabelli cusp, m^2	XX	—	—	N
Deflecting wrinkle, m_2	—	XX	XX	J
Protostylid, m_2	—	—	XX	

—, difference is insignificant, X, significantly differ under the
5 per cent level, XX, significantly differ under the 1 per cent level.

TABLE XVI

TOTAL CHI-SQUARE VALUES IN COMPARISON FOR THE JAPANESE, AMERICAN
WHITES AND AMERICAN NEGROES

DF	J : W	J : N	W : N
16	176·12‡	166·37‡	43·31‡

‡Significantly different under the 1 per cent level.

types 4, 5, 6 and 7 could be used for calculation, because types 1, 2 and 3 represent the pit which is regarded to be morphologically different from the cusp.

The frequency of the dominant gene responsible for the appearance of Carabelli's cusp is estimated to be 0·198 for Whites and 0·061 for the Japanese. Therefore the frequency of the gene in the Japanese-White hybrids is theoretically estimated to be 0·130 and that of the individuals carrying the Carabelli's cusp to be 0·243, which are very close to the figures obtained by direct observation. The same is also true for the Japanese-Negro hybrids. Although in this case the observed frequency seems to differ from the theoretical one, 0·118, there is no statistically significant difference between the two figures.

There seems little doubt that genetic analyses of tooth characteristics will be of considerable importance in the study of human variability as well as human evolution. Little work, however, has so far been undertaken in this field, and it is very desirable that more detailed studies on dental morphology should be carried out from the genetical point of view.

Finally I should like to add that the American Negroes, as a whole, show relatively close relationship to the American Whites (see Table XVI). This may be rather natural, if one takes account of the fact that the former is essentially a mixed race of the original Negroes and the American Whites to a greater or lesser degree. In this sense the American Negroes also should be regarded as representing one of the hybrid groups. Unfortunately, however, almost no work on the dental morphology of either the American or African Negroes is available, and it is to be hoped that such a study will be undertaken in the not too distant future.

ACKNOWLEDGEMENTS

My acknowledgements and thanks are due to Dr. Frank J Orland and Dr. Albert A. Dahlberg, Zoller Memorial Dental Clinic, and the Department of Anthropology of the University of Chicago for kindly inviting me to undertake special studies of the deciduous dentition. Also I am indebted to Mrs. Miki Sawada, director of the Elizabeth Sanders Home, Dr. Car

Francis and Mr. James R. Skelly, Western Reserve University, Dr. Leonard A. Altemus and Dr. Maria Silberkweit, Howard University, for their generous assistance in my studies. Finally I owe much to Professor Akiyoshi Suda, who recently retired from the University of Tokyo, for his direction of the studies on the Japanese-American hybrids.

REFERENCES

Black, G. V. (1902) *Descriptive Anatomy of Human Teeth*. White, Philadelphia.

Dahlberg, Albert A. (1949) The dentition of the American Indian. In W. S. Laughlin (ed.) *The Physical Anthropology of the American Indian*, pp. 138–76. Viking Fund, New York.

Dahlberg, Albert A. (1950) The evolutionary significance of the protostylid, *Amer. J. Phys. Anthrop.* **8**, 15.

Fujita, Tsunetaro (1956) *Anatomy of Teeth*. 3rd ed. Tokyo. (In Japanese.)

Gorjanović-Kramberger, K. (1906) *Der diluviale Mensch von Krapina in Kroatien*. Lieferg, Wiesbaden.

Gregory, W. K. (1922) *The Origin and Evolution of the Human Dentition*. Williams and Wilkins, Baltimore.

Hanihara, Kazuro (1954) Studies on the deciduous dentition of the Japanese and the Japanese–American hybrids. I. Deciduous incisors, *J. Anthrop. Soc. Nippon* **63**, 168. (This and following four papers written in Japanese with English summary.)

Hanihara, Kazuro (1955) Ibid. II. Deciduous canines, *ibid.* **64**, 63.

Hanihara, Kazuro (1956 a) Ibid. III. Deciduous lower molars, *ibid.* **64**, 95.

Hanihara, Kazuro (1956 b) Ibid. IV. Deciduous upper molars, *ibid.* **65**, 67.

Hanihara, Kazuro (1957) Ibid. V. General conclusion, *ibid.* **65**, 151.

Hanihara, Kazuro (1961) Criteria for classification of crown characters of the human deciduous dentition, *ibid.* **69**, 27.

Hrdlička, Aleš (1920) Shovel-shaped teeth. *Amer. J. Phys. Anthrop.* **3**, 429.

Jones, Hector G. (1947) The primary dentition in Homo sapiens and the search for primitive features. *Amer. J. Phys. Anthrop.* **5**, 251.

Jørgensen, K. D. (1956) The deciduous dentition, a descriptive and comparative study. *Acta Odont. Scand.* **14**, supplement 20.

Koenigswald, G. H. R. von (1952) Gigantopithecus blacki von Koenigswald, a giant fossil hominoid from the Pleistocene of

Southern China. *Anthrop. Pap. Amer. Mus. Nat. Hist.* **43**, pt. 4, 295.

McCOWN, T. D. and KEITH, A. (1939) *The Stone Age of Mount Carmel*, vol. II: *The Fossil Human Remains from the Levalloiso-Mousterian.* Oxford U.P.

PEDERSEN, P. O. (1949) The East Greenland Eskimo dentition, *Meddelelser om Gronland*, **142**. Copenhagen.

ROBINSON, J. T. (1956) *The Dentition of the Australopithecinae.* Transvaal Museum Memoir, 9. Pretoria.

SUZUKI, M. and SAKAI, T. (1954) On the "protostylid" of the Japanese, *J. Anthrop. Soc. Nippon* **63**, 81. (This and the following two papers are written in Japanese with an English summary.)

SUZUKI, M. and SAKAI, T. (1956a) On the "deflecting wrinkle" in recent Japanese, *ibid.* **65**, 49.

SUZUKI, M. and SAKAI, T. (1956b) On the occlusal surface patterns of cusps of maxillary molars in recent Japanese, *ibid.* **65**, 54.

TSUJI, TADASHI (1958) Incidence and inheritance of the Carabelli's cusp in a Japanese population, *Jap. J. Hum. Gen.* **3**, 21. (In Japanese with English summary.)

VIRCHOW, H. (1919) Die Milchwangenzähne des Menschen und anderer Primaten. *Z. Ethnol.* **51**, 260.

WEIDENREICH, FRANZ (1937) The dentition of Sinanthropus pekinensis: a comparative odontography of the hominids, *Palaeontol. Sinica*, n.s. D 1.

WEIDENREICH, FRANZ (1945) Giant early man from Java and South China, *Anthrop. Pap. Am. Mus. Nat. Hist.* **43**, pt. 1.

WHEELER, R. C. (1950) *A Textbook of Dental Anatomy and Physiology.* Philadelphia.

DENTAL MEASUREMENT: AN ASSESSMENT OF ITS VALUE IN ANTHROPOLOGICAL STUDIES

by **DENYS H. GOOSE**

Department of Preventive Dentistry, University of Liverpool

INTRODUCTION

Teeth may be missing, abnormal in form, and variable in size. In this paper it is only intended to consider the variability in what may be called the morphologically normal.

Measurements of skulls fell into disrepute for some time after the excess of papers produced in *Biometrika* and other journals in the first quarter of the century, partly because it was becoming largely an exercise in advanced mathematics divorced from reality, and partly because it was realized that comparisons of phenotypes as such were not necessarily very meaningful. In this connection Leakey (1953) stated, ". . . it must be remembered therefore that the measuring of skulls must remain the servant and not the master of the physical anthropologist".

Often in evolutionary studies of primates, the teeth and jaws play an important part. However, as Le Gros Clark (1950) pointed out, teeth should not just be measured and simple comparisons made, but rather various aspects of size, position, and morphology must be taken into account before conclusions can legitimately be drawn.

We may, I think, agree with Yates and Healy (1951) that although the field of measurement of teeth may be limited, nevertheless when there are no differences in basic anatomical features or easily recognizable differences in shape, the metrical approach is the only one possible.

It will be convenient to discuss the subject of dental measurement under three headings. Firstly, a review of what measurements can be made and some of the difficulties encountered in making them. Then a discussion of how these measurements may be analysed and presented. Finally, some examples are taken from the various fields of study in which dental measurements may play a part, for example, palaeo-anthropology, comparative odontology of recent man, and the more orthodontic problem of the relationship of the teeth to the jaws.

MEASUREMENTS

It is exceedingly difficult to measure teeth satisfactorily as there are several limiting factors of which the following are the most important:

(1) The shape is often rather complex, for example a molar has cusps of varying sizes, and surfaces of varying curvatures.

(2) Attrition may alter the size and shape.

(3) Tartar may obscure the actual tooth and add to its size.

(4) Measuring errors resulting from slight differences in technique can be high in some instances.

(5) Some measurements are made on plaster and these do not necessarily correspond to the original teeth.

Theorectically it might be possible to measure all the values involved in the shape of a tooth; however, in practice investigators have usually only described a limited number. Unfortunately the way in which they take their measurements is not always precisely described nor are the same criteria used by all authors. Basically three dimensions are given, that is, the mesiodistal diameter, buccolingual diameter, and crown height, although sometimes root height is also included if teeth, not imbedded in the jaws, are available.

The mesiodistal diameter (Fig. 1) is called "breadth" by some authors (Martin, 1928; Mijsberg, 1931; and Selmer-Olsen, 1949, "length" by some (Hrdlicka, 1952; Remane, 1927; and Senyürek, 1959), and "width" by others (Seipel, 1946; and Smyth and Young, 1932). However, as Moorrees (1957) suggests, the best term seems to be mesiodistal diameter, since this refers directly to the dental arch, whereas the other terms are used for other parts of the body. Even when the difficulties of terminology are cleared up there is still a variety of measurements that can be made in any one direction; for instance, Remane (1927) gives mean length, greatest length, external length, and length of the occlusal surface. Martin (1928), Pedersen (1949), Senyürek (1959) and Weidenreich (1937) take the maximum mesiodistal diameter. Others prefer to measure the diameter between the adjacent contact points—or where they would be —in the case of the cheek teeth (Hrdlicka, 1952; Selmer-Olsen, 1949; and Ashton and Zuckerman, 1950); but the maximum in the case of the incisors and canines. In many cases there will not be a serious discrepancy whichever way is chosen, but it seems better to follow the second method, since the contact points are a natural anatomical feature. In addition rotation of the teeth (which is common in modern populations) may give a spuriously larger maximum measurement (Fig. 2) (10·1 mm instead of 9·2 mm, for example).

The buccolingual diameter (Fig. 1) is generally taken at right angles to the mesiodistal one. Remane (1927) gives two, one in a plane which bisects the projective mesiodistal diameter, the other being the projective maximum. Ashton and Zuckerman (1950), for cheek teeth, measure maximum trigon (id) and talon (id) diameters perpendicular to the mesiodistal one and take the larger of the two. A further difficulty, not mentioned in the literature, is that some molar teeth have a bulge at the cervical margin which means that the size of the buccolingual diameter will be enlarged if it is included, but if it is not, it may be difficult to obtain a satisfactory measurement (Fig. 3).

The crown height is not so often employed as it is so frequently invalidated by the degree of attrition (Fig. 4). Some investigators try to correct for this in molars by measuring to the deepest point between the cusps (Martin, 1928).

A number of authors (Azouley and Regnault, 1893; Black, 1902; and Goose, 1956) have in addition given mesiodistal diameters at the necks of teeth and these are measured parallel to the normal mesiodistal ones.

Attrition is the normal wearing away of teeth during function, and has been discussed recently by several authors (Begg, 1954; Davies and Pedersen, 1955; Lysell, 1958a; Moses, 1959; and Murphy, 1959). Two types are to be distinguished, occlusal and approximal, the former affecting height measurements, and the latter mesiodistal diameters (Fig. 5). In the case of occlusal attrition several stages have been described (such as by Davies and Pedersen, 1955): 0, no attrition; 1, attrition of enamel; 2, dentine visible; and 3, exposure of secondary dentine.

It is, of course, possible to ignore all teeth showing wear, and not include them in metrical studies, but this can be rather wasteful, and in some cases can lead to very few, if any, being available. Consequently some authors appear to have ignored dental attrition in their metrical work, others have attempted to correct for loss of tooth substance (for example, Hrdlicka, 1952), while a few have tried to reduce any such biasing of the sample by separating the material into age groups (Ashton and Zuckerman, 1950). The difficulty is that an arbitrary correction cannot really be satisfactory, since it is too subjective, and an age correction may be too inaccurate for the comparison of different populations, since attrition is not only a function of age but is also dictated by the type of diet. George (1928), for instance, comments that in eighth- to sixteenth-century British skulls the teeth are worn down almost to the gum margin, with hard polished surfaces, while in seventeenth- to nineteenth-century ones only the tips of the cusps in molars were worn.

An estimate of approximal attrition was recently attempted by me in a series of Saxons, where the attrition did not often penetrate more than halfway into the enamel. It was therefore assumed that on average, a quarter of the enamel would be lost, which means that as much as 3·2 mm of the enamel substance may be lost from the premolars and molars combined (Goose, 1961a). Lysell (1958a) calculated an index

$$\frac{100 \times \text{buccolingual diameter}}{\text{mesiodistal diameter}}$$

for modern teeth, and by assuming that teeth from earlier

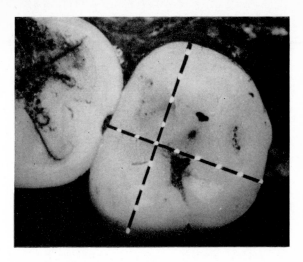

FIG. 1.   Maxillary second molar showing mesiodistal and
and buccolingual diameters.

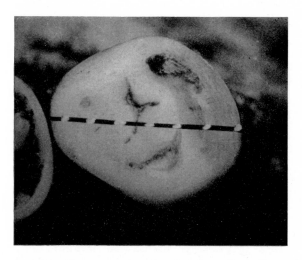

FIG. 2.   Maxillary second molar showing effect of rotation
from the normal position on mesiodistal diameter.

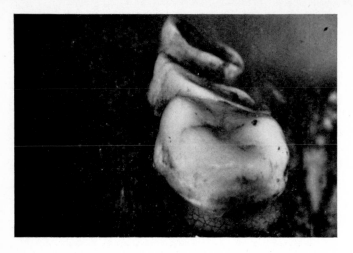

FIG. 3. Maxillary second molar showing bulge at the cervical margin.

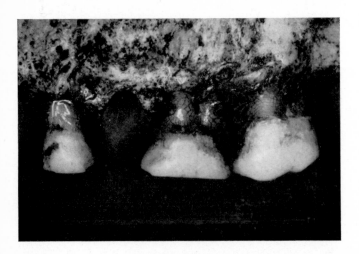

FIG. 4. The effect of attrition on crown height.

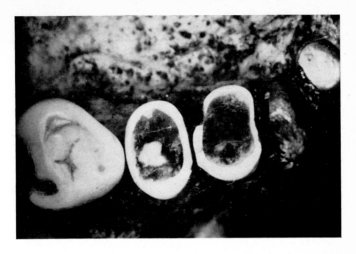

FIG. 5. The effect of attrition on the mesiodistal diameter.

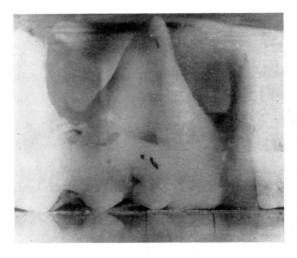

FIG. 9. Periphery photograph of a lower molar, crown downwards. The cusps are spread out in a flat plane.

periods had the same basic shape, he used this index to arrive at the "correct" mesiodistal diameters from the known bucco-lingual ones, the latter being unaffected by approximal attrition.

Two possible methods of avoiding this approximal wear error may be mentioned. Other measurements which are relatively less affected by attrition might be used in preference and by way of an example the cervical mesiodistal diameter was tested. Secondly, a sample of sound teeth of known size might be ground to simulate attrition and then be used as standards; the mesiodistal diameters of unknown teeth being calculated after reference to them.

Fortunately, errors of measurement do not usually seem high (Ashton and Zuckerman, 1950; Goose, 1961a; and Lundstrom, 1943). Testing for errors may be undertaken by an analysis of

TABLE I
ANALYSIS OF VARIANCE FOR ERRORS OF MESIODISTAL DIAMETER OF M′

	Sum. squares	DF	σ^2	F	P
Total	1·150	19	—	—	—
Between	0·758	4	0·1895	7·26	<0·01
Within	0·392	15	0·0261	—	—

variance (Table I), although some investigators have preferred the method of double determination, using the formula $S = \sqrt{\dfrac{Sd^2}{2n}}$; d being the difference between two determinations, and n the number of double determinations (Lundstrom, 1943; Lysell, 1958b).

Casts of fossil skulls are sometimes used for measurement when it is difficult to have access to the original, and since these are produced in plaster (often from a gelatine mould) some inaccuracy may result. Similarly, several investigations in dentistry have been conducted on plaster or stone models produced from impressions made in the mouths of living patients, and these again may be inaccurate. Lundstrom (1943) obtained slightly higher values from casts (1–2 per cent of the average width) than the measurements in the mouth. Hunter and Priest (1960) found that cast measurements were systematically 0·1 mm larger than the intraoral ones in the case of molars and pre-molars, but attributed this difference more to the difficulty of measurement in the mouth.

ANALYSIS

Some very elegant statistical methods have been evolved in the past for the consideration of tooth size and shape. However, these are not always necessary or possible, and in fact the type of analysis depends on the extent and accuracy of the data and the problems involved. For example, in orthodontics one is mainly interested in mesiodistal widths of teeth in relation to the available space in the jaws, and would not normally measure buccolingual diameters; in other cases as many measurements as can be made are desirable for multivariate analysis. It is, however, worth stressing that no amount of statistical refine-ment will be of any use, unless the basic data is sound. This is not always the case, unfortunately, and some earlier investi-gators were inclined to round off measurements to the nearest millimetre in spite of the fact that it is possible to measure to 0·1 mm. Also, as has been shown, attrition may make nonsense of some measurements, and so render comparisons between different groups invalid.

Individual measurements of teeth have been given by most authors at least in the first stages of presentation (Ashton and Zuckerman, 1950; Campbell, 1925; Middleton Shaw, 1931; Moorrees, 1957; Pedersen, 1949; and Selmer-Olsen, 1949). These are best given for one side only since correlations occur between the two sides. However, it may be necessary, owing to shortage of numbers, to employ some measurements from the opposite side of the jaw when the teeth are missing. It is often difficult to obtain sufficient measurements of incisors since they tend to fall out *post mortem*, thus limiting comparisons for these teeth.

Summated measurements may be useful in certain circum-stances and Hrdlicka (1952) mentions the length of the dental arch parallel to the median plane and in addition that of the nolar segments only. These are not very satisfactory as the curvature of arches varies. Goose (1961a), to obviate this difficulty, used the sums of the individual mesiodistal diameters of the cheek teeth (Pm^1–M^2 inclusive) in his comparisons between different historical populations in Britain. Pont (1909) used the sum of the mesiodistal diameters of the maxillary incisors in an index with dental arch width to assess prognosis in orthodontic patients, that is, to determine whether there would be enough room for all the teeth to erupt into their correct positions.

Azouley and Regnault (1893) instead of summating measurements computed a difference which they claimed was useful for distinguishing different races. This difference was the mesiodistal diameter less the cervical diameter taken at the neck of the tooth parallel to the former, and was highest in Negroes (2·39) and least in Europeans (1·61) and Indians (1·27).

Many different indices have been computed in the past, some less useful than others. The Dental Index is the distance between the most anterior point on the first premolar to the most posterior point on the third molar divided by the basi-nasal length, and expressed as a percentage. Although it has been used to compare races it is not very helpful, because it relates two variables which may or may not be correlated and in addition attrition and irregularities in the position of the teeth will change its value.

The Crown Module has been employed by several authors (De Terra, 1905; Pedersen, 1949; and Selmer-Olsen, 1949), and is the sum of the mesiodistal buccolingual diameters divided by two. It gives an overall picture of size, but not, of course, of shape. Robinson (1956) used the log–module, and plotted size relationships between different groups, stating that it has the advantage of indicating proportional differences as well as absolute ones. The Crown Index is also often used and is the ratio of the labiolingual to mesiodistal diameter expressed as a percentage. This gives some idea of shape difference and can be quite useful.

The Robustness Value is the product of the mesiodistal and buccolingual diameters (Pedersen, 1949; Senyürek, 1959; and Weidenreich, 1937), and gives some indication of the overall size, but again takes no account of shape differences.

Only one other index will be mentioned here, and that is the Step Index (Selmer-Olsen, 1949) in which the cheek teeth are each related separately to the first molar (since it is the least variable). This offers to be quite valuable in dental anthropology; for example, in the case of the human third molar

($\frac{M^3}{M^1} \times 100$) Selmer-Olsen (1949) gives an index of 90·7 for the

mesiodistal diameter. In *Paranthropus robustus*, using Robinson's (1956) figures the same index is 111·5 showing the considerable reduction in *Homo sapiens*.

Correlations have been calculated between teeth in the same jaw by various authors, and, for example, Gabriel (1955) found that in his Australian aboriginal skulls anterior teeth were positively correlated with one another, but negatively with the

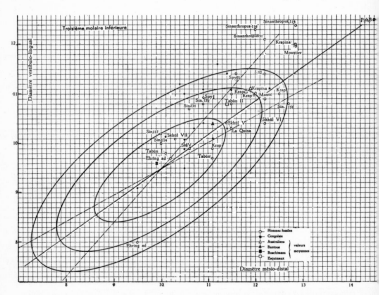

Fig. 6. The relation of mesiodistal and buccolingual diameters plotted graphically for the third mandibular molar, indicating in the ellipses 70, 95 and 99.9 per cent of the results (Twiesselman and Brabant, 1960).

posterior teeth. Lundstrom (1943) found no correlation ($r = +0.01$) between incisors and canines on the one hand and with premolars and first molars on the other. Selmer-Olsen (1949) notes that there are many positive correlations, and they are strongest between teeth within the same tooth group (incisors, molars, and so forth). He also observed that positive correlations may be established between upper and lower teeth in the same individual as previously indicated by other authors, for example, Bolton (1958) and Gabriel (1955). Tweisselman and Brabant (1960) plotted in graphical form the correlation between the mesiodistal and buccolingual dimensions for each tooth with ellipses around the mean representing 70, 95 and 99.9 per cent respectively of their results. This facilitates comparisons with other populations and also with fossil hominids, which they plot on the same graph (Fig. 6).

Multivariate analysis was suggested by Bronowski and Long (1951) to treat adequately a fossil specimen such as a tooth as a unit rather than a discrete assembly of independent measurements. They suggested that to discriminate between two genera or species it is necessary to construct a function $X = a_1x_1$ and a_2x_2 and a_3x_3 and a_4x_4 where the x's represent the different types of measurements, and the constants are calculated from the averages, variations and correlations of the measurements within both species. Hence X can be found for both series, and when an unknown fossil tooth is measured, its distance from the known groups may be computed. Bronowski and Long (1953) extended this work to include the idea of a generalized distance. This may be used to sum up in one quantity the divergence of the complete set of measurements of an unknown specimen from the means of the groups with which it is being compared. It is given by an expression of the type $S = (y_1 - 6.53)^2 + (y_2 - 11.96)^2$, etc., the y's being merely to produce uncorrelated values of x.

Ashton, Healy and Lipton (1957) carried the matter further by constructing a number of linear functions analogous to the discriminant function and spacing out the means of the groups. These may be surrounded by contours containing a given percentage of the results and the unknown fossils plotted too and their affinities estimated (Fig. 7). Even in multivariate

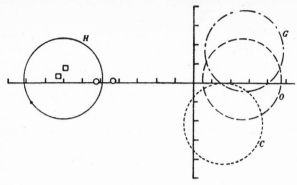

Figure 9. Milk lower canine. —— Man (mixed stock); —·—·— gorilla; ——— orang-outang ···· chimpanzee.

☐ *Pithecanthropus pekinensis*　　　○ *Australopithecus africanus*

Fig. 7. Multivariate analysis indicating graphically the relation between man and the anthropoid apes for the mandibular milk canine. The circles enclose 90 per cent of the results (Ashton, Healy and Lipton, 1957).

analysis when certain conclusions are reached with respect to one tooth it must be remembered that the other teeth in the jaws may give different results. Thus it may be possible to have the lower molars of an unknown hominoid fossil showing affinities with the chimpanzee on the one hand, but with the upper incisors nearer to *Homo sapiens* on the other.

Penrose (1954) suggested that more simplified methods might be appropriate in certain cases, especially when one is dealing with rather crude data and small samples. Based on a reconsideration of the "Coefficient of Racial Likeness" he separates out two components, namely, a size distance $\left[\overset{m}{\underset{1}{S(d)}}\right]^2 \Big/ m^2$, and a

shape distance $\overset{m}{\underset{1}{S(d^2)}} \Big/ m - \left[\overset{m}{\underset{1}{S(d)}}\right]^2 \Big/ m^2$ where d-values are differences between mean values expressed in terms of standard deviation units, and m is the number of characters involved. Brothwell has calculated these values for a series of Minoan teeth and compared them with others in the literature, using four dimensions (see Carr, 1960).

Shape can, of course, be described more specifically and Williams (1928), for example, said there were three types of maxillary incisor crowns: square, tapering, and ovoid. Later Reisenfeld (1956) estimated the different proportions of these types in various ethnic groups in the Pacific area.

Goose (1956) described how the labial surface of the maxillary first incisor could be regarded approximately as a trapezium

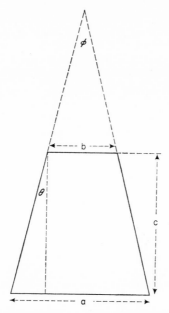

FIG. 8. Labial surface of maxillary first incisor: (a) maximum mesiodistal width, (b) cervical width, (c) maximum crown height, (d) angle of taper.

(Fig. 8) and that three fundamental quantities could therefore be calculated from the crown height, mesiodistal and cervical diameters. These are the surface areas in mm²

$$\frac{\text{height}}{2} \times \text{mesiodistal and cervical widths}),$$

the tooth width index

$$\frac{(\text{mesiodistal width} \times 100)}{\text{crown height}}$$

and the angle of taper calculated as

$$2\,\theta\ (\tan\theta = \frac{\text{mesiodistal—cervical width}}{\text{height} \times 2}).$$

These were found to be rather similar in Saxon and modern British teeth, and it is possible that they might be useful in group differentiation.

Finally two methods may be mentioned which have not yet been fully explored. The first is a new photographic development employing the so-called periphery camera (Fox, 1961). The object to be photographed moves through 360° at the same time as the camera's synchronized shutter moves across, the effect being to record a rounded object in a two-dimensional plane. This may prove useful for molar teeth where the shape would be reduced to a simpler pattern (Fig. 9). The second method is that of coordinate transformation (D'Arcy Thomson,

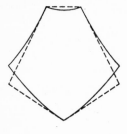 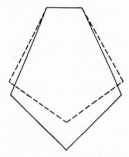

Fig. 10.   Transformations of canines. (Original outlines dotted.)

1942) and Fig. 10 shows this applied to a canine tooth. It may be clearly seen that by altering the values of the coordinates different shapes can be produced.

EXAMPLES OF PREVIOUS ANALYSES

In *Australopithecus africanus* (Taungs skull) the lower milk canine was stated by Ashton and Zuckerman (1950) not to differ significantly from that of a chimpanzee. The probabilities were for maximum AP diameter 0·9–0·8, and for labiolingual breadth 0·1–0·05.

Bronowski and Long (1951) calculated a discriminant function for chimpanzees and man for this tooth which had a value of +17·6 and −5·0 respectively. The measurements they based this on were the height, maximum anteroposterior length of upper half, maximum breadth of upper half, and the maximum anteroposterior length at the level of the basal cingulum. As the standard deviation of the function was 2·45 the range at 2½ times was 6·1 on either side, i.e. if the result lies between +23·7 and +11·5 the tooth is chimpanzee, and if between +1·1 and −11·1 it is human. In the case of the Taungs milk canine it was −7·9 and thus it did not belong to the chimpanzee group, but fell within the range of human teeth.

Later, Yates and Healy (1951) calculated discriminant functions from Ashton and Zuckerman's original data and found that the Taungs canine did show a resemblance to man. However, when the comparison was based on the antero-posterior diameter alone there was an almost significant divergence suggesting in conjunction with the labiolingual measurement that the specimen may belong to neither group. The authors point out that this is the weakness of the dis-criminant function as it is really designed only to classify objects which must belong to one group or the other. The better discrimination obtained in this study by Bronowski and Long (1951) was thus found to be in the initial measurements used, that is, the combination of the two anteroposterior diameters which emphasized the difference in form between the two groups compared. However, it was later discovered that the measurements given by Broom and Sheper (1946) and used by Ashton and Zuckerman (1950) were incorrect, thereby invalidating the previous comparisons.

Finally, Ashton, Healy and Lipton (1957) using eight revised measurements in their "distance" method show that for the same tooth man and chimpanzees are well separated, and that *Australopithecus africanus* is reasonably close to man (Fig. 7). These studies seem to emphasize two points: firstly that advanced statistics are no help if the basic data is at fault, and

K

secondly, that it is wise to choose measurements which are likely to bring out the difference in the form of objects rather than those which emphasize their similarity.

It is a common observation that teeth of different racial groups differ in both size and shape, and that the maxillary first incisor is one in which changes are easily seen. In order to demonstrate this fact English, African and Chinese teeth were measured according to the method already described, and

TABLE II

SHAPE OF MAXILLARY FIRST INCISORS

Type	Surface Area (mm2) M± SE$_m$ N	Tooth width Index M± SE$_m$ N	Taper degrees M± SE$_m$ N
English	86·83±1·26 50	73·21±0·83 50	7·90±0·32 50
Chinese	87·65±1·25 21	72·07±0·93 21	9·48±0·47 21
W. African	88·38±1·86 21	82·33±0·98 21	12·43±0·54 21

Table 2 shows the findings. Differences may readily be seen and, for example, African teeth are distinctly wider than Chinese or English, and all differ significantly from each other as regards taper.

There have been a number of excellent studies of the dentition of various ethnic groups which give among other things measurements (for example, Campbell, 1925; Middleton-Shaw, 1931; Moorrees, 1957; Nelson, 1938; Pederson, 1949; and Selmer-Olsen, 1949). However, oddly enough, there is a notable omission in these studies, and as Boyd (1950) remarks in connection with bones there is a scarcity of information about modern European material, and a real gap between what we know of living and fossil man. As regards teeth this may not be entirely true as there have been some measurements (Black, 1902; De Terra, 1905; and Keith, 1924), but in the main these do not seem to be accurate enough, nor are they suitably presented for further analysis. In view of this the author measured some seventeenth–nineteenth-century English skulls from the British Museum of Natural History and the Duckworth

Laboratory at Cambridge, recording the mesiodistal and buccolingual dimensions of the upper teeth in 67 males and 32 females. Unfortunately, the numbers of anterior teeth are small and standard errors have not been calculated for all of them. The figures are shown in the four following tables (3–6).

Table III
Modern English Teeth

Mesiodistal diameter. Male

Tooth	$M \pm SE_m$	N
I^2	6·35	10
C	7·70 ± 0·12	17
Pm^1	6·54 ± 0·07	38
Pm^2	6·49 ± 0·06	43
M^1†	10·49 ± 0·07	65
M^2	9·51 ± 0·07	57
M_3	8·82 ± 0·13	35

†Including St. Brides ossuary material.

Table IV
MODERN ENGLISH TEETH

Mesiodistal diameter. Female

Tooth	$M \pm SE_m$	N
I^2	6·12	4
C	7·42	8
Pm^1	6·40 ± 0·03	16
Pm^2	6·30 ± 0·09	15
M^1†	10·22 ± 0·10	31
M^2	9·23 ± 0·11	26
M^3	8·45 ± 0·18	14

†Including St. Brides ossuary material.

TABLE V

MODERN ENGLISH TEETH

Buccolingual diameter. Male

Tooth	$M \pm SE_m$	N
I^2	6·38	10
C	8·46 ± 0·14	17
Pm^1	8·82 ± 0·10	38
Pm^2	9·26 ± 0·09	42
M^1†	11·46 ± 0·07	65
M^2	11·48 ± 0·10	61
M^3	11·04 ± 0·15	27

†Including St. Brides ossuary material.

TABLE VI

MODERN ENGLISH TEETH

Buccolingual diameter. Female

Tooth	$M \pm SE_m$	N
I^2	5·97	3
C	7·97	7
Pm^1	8·62 ± 0·15	14
Pm^2	8·91 ± 0·14	14
M^1†	11·02 ± 0·10	32
M^2	10·90 ± 0·15	24
M^3	10·80	7

†Including St. Brides ossuary material.

In considering differences between modern populations, unlike fossil groups one is not concerned with establishing the distance of an unknown specimen from a given type, but rather with finding differences which might be of value in understanding genetic changes and variability in different groups. It might be noted here that the shape and size of teeth are probably little affected by environmental factors (Goose, 1956; Kraus and Furr, 1953; Montagu, 1933), and so genetic ones must play a major role in these differences.

The English male results have been graphed together with some examples from the liaerature, namely, Eskimos (Pedersen, 1949), Javanese (Mijsberg, 1931), and Lapps (Selmer-Olsen, 1949), both for mesiodistal and buccolingual diameters in Figs. 11 and 12.

Apart from considerations of overall size there are two immediate points of interest. The third molars appear to vary considerably between the groups, for example, as regards the mesiodistal diameters the Eskimo M_3 is 9·83 mm, Javanese M_3 is 9·20 mm, English M_3 is 8·82 mm, and the Lapp M_3 is 8·03 mm. A t-test between English and Eskimos gave a value of $t=3·792$ for 45 degrees of freedom, giving $P<0·001$, and it might be worth following up such a result by using the index $\dfrac{M_3}{M_1} \times 100$ already described.

The relation of the buccolingual diameters of Pm^2 to Pm^1 appears to vary and on calculating an index $\dfrac{Pm^2}{Pm^1} \times 100$ it is found that the English value is 104·98, Javanese 98·98, Lapp 97·86, and Eskimo 96·62.

A further feature not revealed by the graphs but present between the sexes is the difference between the buccolingual diameters. In the case of the maxillary canine, for example, the difference between sexes divided by the male diameter as a percentage will provide a means of comparing the groups. It is highest for Javanese 8·23, Eskimos being 7·53, Lapps 6·23, and English 5·79.

It may be seen, then, that measurement of teeth may reveal

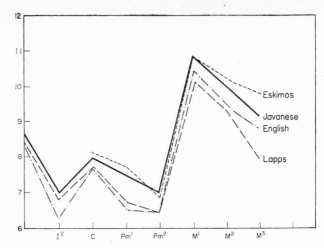

Fig. 11. Graph showing relation between mesiodistal diameters of maxillary teeth in Eskimos, Javanese, English, and Lapps (First incisor to third molar).

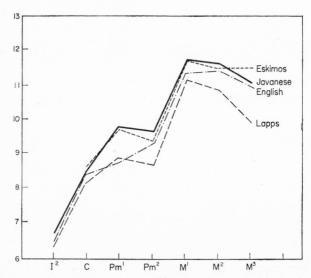

Fig. 12. Graph showing relation between buccolingual diameters of maxillary teeth in Eskimos, Javanese, English, and Lapps (First incisor to third molar).

differences between ethnic groups of various sorts some of which may repay further study, particularly with a view to establishing possible causes.

One might expect to find a close correlation between jaws and teeth since they are related functionally and presumably have some common genetic control. However, in recent times changes appear to be affecting jaws more than teeth, and consequently disharmony of size is occurring (Goose, 1961b; Hooton, 1946; Keith, 1924). In fact Hooton (1946) states that there is a trend for reduction in facial and dental growth, longstanding in evolution, but which has been suddenly accelerated under conditions of city life and cereal diets. This may be demonstrated by the examination of skulls from different historical periods in Britain; thus in Romano-British, Saxon or Medieval skulls there is in general a harmony between jaw and tooth, so that no undue crowding or spacing of the teeth occurs, but in modern jaws crowding is often present.

Lysell (1958b) compared 97 Medieval Swedish skulls with present-day material, and found the modern upper dental arches to be narrower, and in men, for instance, there was a significant decrease of $2·50 \pm 0·64$ mm at the first molars, and in women a decrease of $1·30 \pm 0·57$ mm. However, he advised caution in interpretation since the Medieval material may not have been entirely representative, and extractions in modern material may have upset the position of measuring points.

Lundstrom and Lysell (1953) in comparing Medieval Danish crania with modern Swedish 13-year-old children found decreases in widths of about $2·0$ mm in the premolar area, and 4 mm in the molar area. However, again there was the same doubt since the modern material was not strictly comparable, as the molars may have migrated forward due to early extraction of the deciduous molars.

To try to obtain a more definite answer I measured the palate widths of 403 Romano-British, Saxon, Medieval and modern English skulls in three places; between the first premolars, first molars, and second molars (Goose, 1961b). The modern dimensions were smaller than the other three groups, which were apparently similar, and on testing the modern results against the combined results of the other groups it was established that the differences were significant, with the exception of one result in which the numbers were too small to test (Table 7).

TABLE VII

COMPARISONS BETWEEN MODERN PALATE WIDTHS AND MEDIEVAL, SAXON AND ROMANO-BRITISH COMBINED

Width	Sex	Difference (mms)	Degrees of freedom	t	P
P^1–P^1	M	1·50	165	3·320	<0·01
	F	—	—	—	—
M^1–M^1	M	1·10	126	2·017	<0·05
	F	1·55	78	1·992	<0·05†
M^2–M^2	M	2·56	240	6·243	<0·001
	F	2·31	130	4·848	<0·001

†On the borderline.

The decrease in width evidently took place about the seventeenth century, since the "modern" group were of seventeenth- to nineteenth-century skulls and it is interesting to speculate upon the possible cause. It seems unlikely to be a genetic one, that is, associated with racial changes or hybridization, since there is no evidence of any such change during the recent past of British history. It may be supposed then that it was the result of the change to a softer diet, which led to a consequent lack of function. If this is the case, and in view of the fact that not everyone is affected, one would have to postulate that some individuals possess a genetic background which is not so conducive to the proper development of their jaws, but under conditions of hard food and sufficient mastication this deficiency is not revealed. However, when softer foods became common the genetic make-up played a more dominant role, resulting in inadequate growth and narrow jaws. Some support is given to this suggestion by the experiments of Watt and Williams (1951) who fed a series of rats on a hard diet and their litter mates on a soft one. The latter had smaller jaws.

During this recent period teeth do not seem to have changed materially (Goose, 1961a), although it is difficult to be certain about this, owing to the effect of attrition on the teeth of earlier populations.

The lack of harmony between jaws and teeth seems to be one of the main factors determining the increased number of irregularities of teeth at the present time, and it may be supposed that as there is more and more miscegenation, so there will be more and more disharmonies occurring. The absence of attrition in modern teeth is also important since there is effectively more tooth material to be accommodated than in earlier populations.

Perhaps before progressing much further in the understanding of the complex mechanisms controlling tooth and jaw size, more family studies are needed as well as more experimental work (as, for example, along the lines of Stockard and Johnson, 1941).

ACKNOWLEDGEMENTS

I should like to express my gratitude to Dr. E. H. Ashton for permission to reproduce Fig. 7, taken from his paper with Drs. M. J. R. Healy and S. Lipton, "The descriptive use of discriminent functions in physical anthropology" published in *Proc. Roy. Soc. B.* **146**, 552 (1957).

Also to Professor F. Twiesselmann for his permission to publish Fig. 6 taken from his monograph with Dr. H. Brabant, "Observations sur les dents et les maxillaires d'une population ancienne d'age Franc de Coxyde". Ext. du Bull. du Groupement International pour la Recherche Scientifique en Stomatologie, January 1960 No. 1 and October 1960 No. 3 and 4.

In addition I would like to thank Mr. F. Fox for his kindness in taking the photograph in Fig. 9 on the "Shell" Periphery Camera at Thornton Research Centre, "Shell" Research Limited.

Finally I am indebted to Messrs. Methuen and Company Ltd. for permission to quote from Dr. L. S. B. Leakey's book *Adam's Ancestors*, 4th ed. London, 1953.

REFERENCES

ASHTON, E. H., HEALY, M. J. R. and LIPTON, S. (1957) The descriptive use of discriminant functions in physical anthropology, *Proc. Roy. Soc. B.* **146**, 552.

ASHTON, E. H. and ZUCKERMAN, S. (1950a) Some quantitative dental characteristics of the Chimpanzee, Gorilla and Orang-Outang, *Phil. Trans. Roy. Soc. B.* **234**, 471.

ASHTON, E. H. and ZUCKERMAN, S. (1950b) Some quantitative dental characteristics of fossil anthropoids, *Phil. Trans. Roy. Soc. B.* **234**, 484.

AZOULEY, O. and REGNAULT, O. (1893) Variation in the form of teeth, *Bull. Mem. Soc. Anthrop. Paris* **4**, 266.

BEGG, P. R. (1954) Stone Age Man's dentition, *Amer. J. Ortho.* **40**, 298.

BLACK, G. V. (1902) *Descriptive Anatomy of the Human Teeth*, 4th ed. White, Philadelphia.

BOLTON, W. A. (1958) Disharmony in tooth size and its relation to the analysis and treatment of malocclusion, *Angle Ortho.* **28**, 113.

BOYD, W. C. (1950) *Genetics and the Races of Man.* Little and Brown, Boston.

BRONOWSKI, J. and LONG, W. M. (1951) Statistical methods in anthropology, *Nature* **168**, 794.

BRONOWSKI, J. and LONG, W. M. (1953) Milk canines and multivariate analysis, *Nature* **172**, 251.

BROOM, R and SCHEPER, S. G. W. H. (1946) *The South African Fossil Ape-men*, Transvaal Museum Mem. No. 2, Pretoria.

CAMPBELL, T. D. (1925) *Dentition and Palate of the Australian Aboriginal.* The Keith Sheridan Foundation Publications No. 1. University of Adelaide.

CARR, H. G. (1960) Some dental characteristics of the Middle Minoans, *Man* **60**, 157.

D'ARCY THOMPSON (1942) *Growth and Form*, 2nd ed. Cambridge Univ. Press.

DAVIES, T. G. H. and PEDERSEN, P. O. (1955) The attrition in deciduous teeth and first permanent molars in primitive and urbanised Greenland natives, *Brit. Dent. J.* **99**, 35.

DE TERRA, M. (1905). *Beitrage zu einer Odontographie der Menschenrassen.* Universitat. Zurich. Parchim. i.M. Druck van H. Freise.

FOX, F. (1961) All-round eye, *"Shell" Magazine* **41**, 219.

GABRIEL, A. (1955) The correlation of the size of human teeth with one another and with certain jaw measurements, *Dent. J. Austral.* **27**, 174.

GEORGE, V. H. (1928) Report to Dental Investigating Committee of the Med. Res. Council, London.

GOOSE, D. H. (1956) Variability of the form of maxillary permanent incisors, *J. Dent. Res.* **35**, 902.

GOOSE, D. H. (1961a) A metrical study of jaws and teeth of skulls from different historical periods in Britain. M.D.S. Thesis, Univ. of Liverpool.

GOOSE, D. H. (1961b) In press.

HOOTON, E. A. (1946) The evolution and devolution of the human face, *Amer. J. Ortho. Oral Surg.* **32**, 657.

HRDLICKA, A. (1952) *Practical Anthropometry*, 4th ed., ed. Stewart T.D. Wistar Inst. Philadelphia.

HUNTER, W. S. and PRIEST, W. R. (1960) Errors and discrepancies in measurement of tooth size, *J. Dent. Res.* **39**, 405.

KEITH, A. (1924) *Concerning Certain Structural Changes which are Taking Place in Our Jaws and Teeth.* London, Dental Board of U.K.

KRAUS, B. S. and FURR, M. L. (1953) Lower first premolars. Part 1, *J. Dent. Res.* **32**, 554.

LEAKEY, L. S. B. (1953) *Adams Ancestors*, 4th ed. Methuen, London.

LE GROS CLARK, W. (1950) Hominid characters of the Australopithecine dentition, *J. Roy. Anthrop. Inst.* **80**, 37.

LUNDSTROM, A. (1943) *Svensk Tandl Tidskr.* **36**, 574.

LUNDSTROM, A. and LYSELL, L. (1953) An anthropological examination of a group of Medieval Danish skulls, *Acta Odont. Scand.* **11**, 111.

LYSELL, L. (1958a) Quantitative and qualitative determination of attrition and the ensuing tooth migration, *Acta Odont. Scand.* **16**, 267.

LYSELL, L. (1958b) A biometric study of occlusion and dental arches in a series of medieval skulls from Northern Sweden, *Acta Odont. Scand.* **16**, 177.

MARTIN, R. (1928) *Lehrbuch der Anthropologie*, vol. **2**, 2nd ed. Fischer, Jena.

MIDDLETON-SHAW, J. C. (1931) *The Teeth, the Bony Palate and the Mandible in Bantu Races of South Africa.* Bale, London.

MIJSBERG, W. A. (1931) On sexual differences in the teeth of Javanese, *Proc. Sect. Sciences. Kon. Akad. v. Wetenschappen te, Amsterdam* **34**, 1111.

MONTAGU, M. F. A. (1933) The dentition of identical twins, *Hum. Biol.* **5**, 629.

MOORREES, C. F. A. (1957) *The Aleut Dentition.* Harvard Univ. Press, Cambridge.

MOSES, C. H. (1959) Human tooth form and arrangement from the anthropological approach, *J. Prosth. Dent.* **9**, 197.

MURPHY, T. (1959) The changing pattern of dentine exposure in human tooth attrition, *Amer. J. Phys. Anthrop.* **17**, 167.

NELSON, C. T. (1938) The teeth of the Indians of Pecos Pueblo, *Amer. J. Phys. Anthrop.* **23**, 261.

PEDERSEN, P. O. (1949) *The East Greenland Eskimo Dentition. Meddelelser om Gronland* **142**, Copenhagen.

PENROSE, L. S. (1954) Distance, size and shape, *Ann. Eugen. Lond.* **18**, 337.

PONT, A. (1909) Der Zahn Index in der Orthodontie, *Z. Zahnärzt Orthopodie* **3**, 306.

RIESENFELD, A. (1956) Shovel-shaped incisors and a few of the dental features among the native peoples of the Pacific, *Amer. J. Phys. Anthrop.* **14**, 505.

REMANE, A. (1927) *Zur Mesotechnik der Primatenzähne*. Handb. d. biol Arbeitsmethoden. Abderhalden.

ROBINSON, J. T. (1956) *The Dentition of the Australopithecinae*. Transvaal Museum Mem. No. 9. Pretoria.

SEIPEL, C. M. (1946) Variations of tooth position. (Suppl.) Lund. *Svensk Tandlakare. Tidskrift.* **39**.

SELMER-OLSEN, R. (1949) *An Odontometrical Study on the Norwegian Lapps*. Oslo.

SENYÜREK, M. (1959) *A Study of the Deciduous Teeth of the Fossil Shanider Infant*. Publications of the Faculty of Languages, History and Geography. Univ. Ankara, No. 128.

SMYTH, K. C. and YOUNG, M. (1932) Facial growth in children, *Med. Res. Counc. Sp. Rep. Ser.* **171**. H.M.S.O., London.

STOCKARD, C. R. and JOHNSON, A. L. (1941) *The Genetic and Endocrine Basis for Differences in Form and Behaviour*. (Amer.Anat.Mem.19) Wistar Inst. Philadelphia.

TWIESSELMANN, F. and BRABANT, H. (1960) Observations sur les dents et les maxillaires d'une population ancienne d'age Franc de Coxyde, *Bull. du. G.I.R.S.* **1**, **3**, **4**.

WATT, D. G. and WILLIAMS, C. H. M. (1951) The effects of the physical consistency of food on the growth and development of the mandible and maxilla of the rat, *Amer. J. Ortho.* **37**, 895.

WEIDENREICH, F. (1937) The dentition of Sinanthropus Pekinensis. A comparative odontography of the Hominids, *Palaeontologia Sinica*, New Series D, No. 1. Peiping.

WILLIAMS, J. L. (1928) New evidence of Man's relationships to the Anthropoid Apes, *J. Dent. Res.* **8**, 289.

YATES, F. and HEALY, M. J. R. (1951) Statistical methods in Anthropology. *Nature* **168**, 1116.

ANALYSIS OF THE AMERICAN INDIAN DENTITION

by **ALBERT A. DAHLBERG**
Department of Anthropology and Zoller Memorial Dental Clinic,
University of Chicago

MANY reports have appeared in the past regarding the morphology and metric characteristics of the dentition of the American Indian. None of these have gone very far beyond simple description for comparative studies and general anatomical reports. This presentation will attempt to give an analysis of the American Indian dentition on the evolutionary and functional basis, following the consideration of its morphology and comparative aspects. In pursuing such a course, ecological factors will be drawn into focus along with genetic and evolutionary theory.

Many elements of form and size in the American Indian dentition suggest the existence of some selective evolutionary advantage. It also appears that certain attributes have not necessarily been incidental acquisitions in the process of drift peculiar to the individuals of a particular geographic area. Pursuit of this problem includes inquiry into the environmental complex, the evidences of function in the teeth, the structural potentials of the teeth and ideas relating to survival of an organism.

The dentition of the American Indian is not a homogeneous representation of a homogeneous people. Actually the Amerind is represented by as much diversity of physical form and size as is to be found in other geographic areas, Europe for example. There are large, small, dark skinned, light skinned, thin, fat, mongoloid featured, other featured, fine haired and coarse haired groups within the Amerind populations. Their origins, derived from different migrations in the last twenty thousand

149

years and from the different genetic pools of Asia, make them a rather variable group. In spite of this there are also certain features that they do have in common. Some of these features are seen in high frequency in modern Asiatics also. We can cite the protostylid of lower molars, the shovel-shaped feature of upper incisors, and other general mongoloid traits of other parts of the body. The epicanthic fold is not seen in all Amerinds, but the black hair and generally dark skin is quite universal.

Comparison of measurements and traits of the teeth between several Indian tribes and with other ethnic and geographic groups gives one some perspective of the Indian dentition.

SIZE OF TOOTH CROWNS

Size of the teeth is quite basic and gives a means of description of some importance. The means of the Indian groups vary widely, but none as much as two standard deviations. The standard errors of the means set them off quite firmly. Small teeth versus large teeth or reduction or enlargement of tooth groups within the particular dentitions imply a range of functional capacity. Hence, a series of related as well as independent measurements will be given consideration along with some of the morphological entities.

Only the Australian Aboriginal and the East Greenland Eskimo exceed the modern American Indian in tooth size. Figures 1 and 2 show the mean buccolingual and mesiodistal tooth measurements of posterior teeth for upper and lower jaws of the Pima, Hopi, Yuma, and two Navaho tribes, the Ramah and the Tuba City. In practically all instances the Pima measure was the largest and the competition for low position varied with different teeth. Figure 3 gives a new measure, that of occlusal surface buccolingual occlusal width, in which the Ramah Navaho competed more successfully. The differences between tribes were not significant for these measures, but they were somewhat consistent. The range was much greater in the mesiodistal dimension, less in the buccolingual and least in the occlusal surface width. This is as would be expected, especially in the lower second molar which reflects the variability of the hypoconulid or the distal-most cusp.

The measurements were matched in proportion to each other in order to obtain an understanding of the relationships in the tooth mass. Figure 4 pictures the proportion of the mesio-distal-buccolingual measurements and reflects the greater

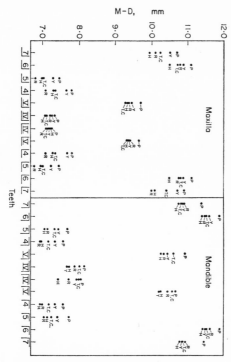

FIG. 1. The mesiodistal measurements for posterior deciduous and permanent teeth of five Amerind tribes are plotted to show the range and position according to size for males and females. M-D, mesiodistal; P, Pima; Y, Yuma; T.C., Tuba City Navaho; R, Ramah Navaho; H, Hopi.

mesiodistal length of the Pima teeth. Figure 5 compares the relative buccolingual measure to that of the width of the occlusal surface. The value 1·7, for example, indicates that the buccolingual mean dimension of the tooth was 1·7 times as large as the occlusal surface. The Pima M^1 has a buccolingual dimension that is 1·72 times that of the occlusal surface. This means that the Pima has a proportionately smaller occlusal surface on the unworn tooth than any of the other tribes.

One application of the buccolingual measurements is of particular interest; that is, in the comparison between the

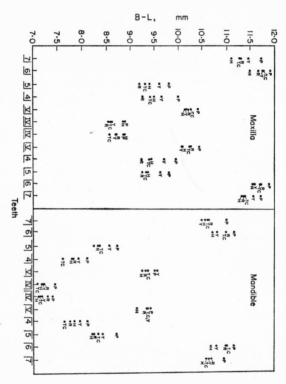

FIG. 2. The buccolingual measurements for posterior deciduous and permanent teeth of the five tribes are plotted.

upper second premolars and the first permanent molars. In general, modern populations have premolars with a bucco-lingual measure which averages about 80 per cent of that of the first upper molars. American Whites have an 81·0 per cent ratio and the Afalou, a mesolithic population of north-west Africa, had 85·4 per cent. Another mesolithic population

Taforalt, had a ratio of 89 per cent. Other African specimens commonly have large premolars. Many Europeans today have percentages that range from 80 to almost 90 individually, the

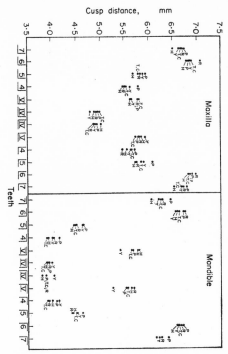

Fig. 3.   The distance between the tips of the buccal and the lingual cusps are plotted for the posterior teeth of the five tribes.

higher probably reflecting north-west African origins and the lower, eastern Mediterranean. In other early specimens the north-west Africans are represented by the larger premolars, contrasting with the middle-east and its very small ones. This proportion difference is highly important in thinking of efficiency of dentitions, drift and reductions in the dental pattern. It will be dealt with at length in the discussion at the end of the paper.

Before leaving the subject of the premolar–molar measure-

L

ment ratio it should be pointed out that in some of the instances
of premolar buccolingual reduction, the occlusal surface
measure has been found to be smaller in the molars, though the

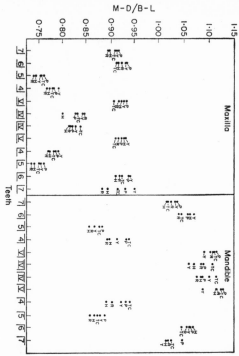

FIG. 4.   The ratios of mesiodistal to buccolingual measurements for the posterior teeth of the five tribes are plotted.

full buccolingual dimension of the molars has remained
relatively large.

Intrinsic to changes in size are some changes in form, especially
when the degree of change varies in different parts of a specific
tooth or in different parts of the dentition itself. When reductions of all but one of the teeth in a dentition occurs, for
example, the form of the unit changes and likewise its functional
capacities. This is seen in many dentitions where the first molar
maintains its size in the face of generally reduced dimension
of all the other teeth (Fig. 6A). Variations, of course, play on this

theme. The American Indian has in general a mixture of increase in size of the anterior teeth with reduced premolar size (Fig. 6B, C, D). Individual exceptions are always to be found as in any group.

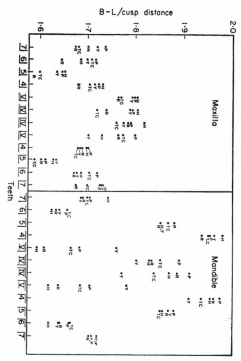

FIG. 5.   The ratio of the buccolingual to the intercusp measurements are plotted for the same five tribes.

In the American Indian the incisor teeth have a development of the lateral borders on the lingual surfaces which has caused them to be referred to as shovel-shaped. By many these conformations are called paracingular or palatine invaginations (Brabant, 1961). This does not satisfy some dentitions of Indians where it is much more than an invagination, actually a positive build up. Although this structural feature has been described as occurring in almost every population, in none has it been reported as pronounced as it is in the Amerind. The result of this additional ridging is a markedly stronger tooth and a larger unit of functional capacity. It occurs in almost 100 per cent of the American Indians in large form (Dahlberg, 1949). The paper on shovel-shaped incisors by Dr. Virginia Carbonell (p. 211) covers this subject in considerable detail and does not need expansion here.

MESIAL ROTATION OF INCISORS (WINGING)

Seemingly associated with this feature is an irregular alignment of the incisors (Enoki and Dahlberg, 1958). This condition has been variously referred to as "winging" or "bilateral mesial rotation". Figure 6c, D shows the axial rotation of the central incisors which brings the distal parts of the teeth into

A	B	C	D	E
Bilateral Winging	Unilateral Winging	Straight	Unilateral Counterwinging	Bilateral Counterwinging

FIG. 7. Classification of rotated central incisors. The labial side of the teeth depicted is up and the lingual down. These are the classes graphically illustrated in Fig. 8.

anterior prominence. Figure 7 shows the variations in this positioning from bilateral winging to bilateral counter winging. Figure 8 gives the class percentage distributions of these variation classes. The frequencies vary from 22 to 38 per cent among the Indian tribes, but drop to 10 per cent for Japanese and to 3 per cent for Chicago Whites. Although crowding is a factor in a few instances, this positioning of the teeth is frequently found where ample space is available for a straight alignment.

LATERAL INCISORS

The Amerind lateral incisors are large. There is a tendency for the cingular areas of the lingual surface (Fig. 6B) to bulge or exhibit excesses of structure, sometimes almost to the incisal edge, giving the tooth the appearance of a premolar. This has been called a barrel shape.

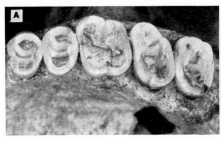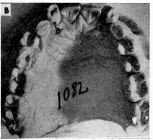

Fig. 6a. Photograph of left maxillary posterior teeth from Sialk, Iran. The metacone (distobuccal cusp) is normal and well developed in the first molar, somewhat smaller in the third, but markedly reduced in the second. The premolars are much smaller in the buccolingual dimension than the molar teeth (Musée de L'Homme, Paris).

Fig. 6b. The maxillary teeth of a cast of a young Pima Indian are shown in the photograph. The lateral incisors (B) exhibit the extreme of irregular overdevelopment of the cingular area on the lingual surface, making the two give the appearance of premolars. The canines and the left second molars are deciduous. The arch form is typically Amerind.

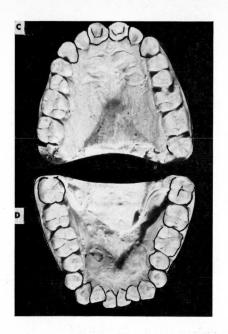

FIG. 6c. A photograph of a cast of the maxillary teeth of a Pima Indian. The central incisors are large, shovel-shaped and rotated mesially ("winged"). The laterals are normal in size and form and shovel-shaped. The premolars are small. The first molars are well formed (caries is seen on the mesial of the left one), and have well-developed hypocones and metacones. The hypocones are smaller on the second molars, and are absent on the left third molar. The metacone is somewhat reduced in size on the third molar also. This dentition does not have any of Carabelli's phenomena or extra cusps.

FIG. 6d. The lower dentition of the same individual seen in Fig. 6c. The incisors are large, show some slight degree of shovel character and are crowded. The molars are all well developed and show buccal pits. The protoconid and metaconid shifts change the Y5 occlusal pattern of the first molars to +5 in the seconds and thirds. Wear has obliterated the hypoconulids of the second molars. The entoconids are well developed in all six molars.

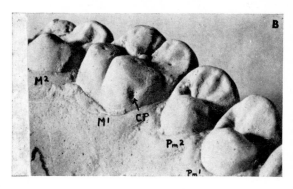

FIG. 9A. Linguo-occlusal view of maxillary teeth. A large
Carabelli cusp is located on the first molar. A bulge, not
sharply delineated is seen in the same location on the
second molar.

FIG. 9B. Linguo-occlusal view of maxillary teeth with a
Carabelli pit (CP) located on the first molar.

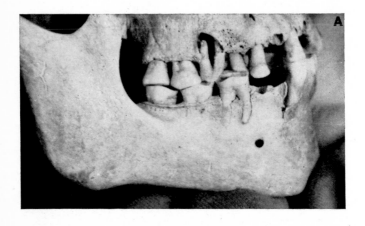

F<small>IG.</small> 10A. Lateral view of jaws of an early California Indian. Note the bone destruction around the roots of the upper first molar evidencing the alveolar abscess which resulted following exposure of the pulp chamber by the heavy wear on the occlusal plane. The character of the occlusion indicates a lateral movement with fairly heavy pressure in function. The occlusion is not suited for forward and back gliding with the obvious irregular occlusal plane. The first molar, particularly the upper one, shows much more wear than the other molars due to its six years of function before the second molars erupted. The upper second premolar also suffered from the heavy functional activity surrounding the first molar area.

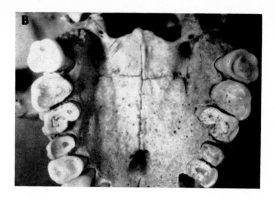

Fig. 10b.   Occlusal view of the maxillary teeth of the early California Indian seen in Fig. 10a. The first molar is the tooth which carries the greatest burden of function during the transition from the deciduous to the permanent dentition. In this individual the function was transferred from the first molar forward to the second premolar and then finally back to the second molar in the sequence of the wearing process.

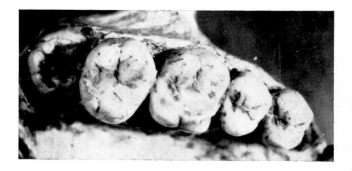

Fig. 10c.   Maxillary posterior teeth of a Natufian in whom the wear process has not effaced the topography. The substantial increase in size of the protocone due to the presence of a Carabelli cusp can be seen on the first molar. The premolars are small and the hypocone on the second molar is markedly reduced.

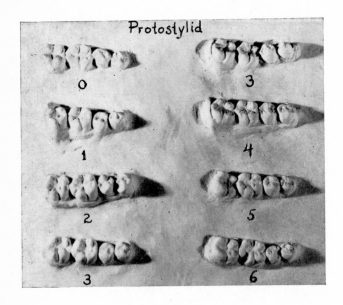

Fɪɢ. 11. A series of casts depicting the various gradations of the protostylid. It is one of a series of plaques issued in 1956 by the Zoller Memorial Dental Clinic laboratories for use in standardizing dental morphological units. Cast 6 shows a large protostylid. Casts 5, 4 and 3 show lesser degrees of expression of the cusp. Cast 2 has only a distal deviation gingivally of the buccal groove, cast 1 demonstrates a large pit at the base of the groove and cast 0 has no other structure than the straight buccal groove.

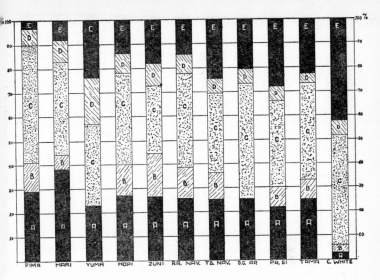

Fig. 8. Band ranges in percent for the various classes of rotated central incisors of ten Amerind tribes and of Chicago Whites.

PREMOLARS

The premolars have no morphological advantage in the Indian. In the lower premolars, the structures of the posterior portion of the occlusal surface are more positively portrayed than in the anterior portion. Even though in the maxilla they have only an 80 per cent buccolingual measure proportion to the molars, they are important in occlusal function.

CARABELLI'S CUSP

Carabelli's cusp plays little part in the American Indian dentition. It is generally of the small to moderate variety which does not serve to add much to the buccolingual measure in the Indian in the manner that it does in some populations, the Melanesians, for example (Fig. 9A). Many groups have found the presence of the cusp an important addition. In the pestle-mortar action of the protocone in the opposing posterior moiety of the lower molars, a larger pestle (protocone plus Carabelli's cusp) is of greater value. The need for this is

TABLE I

FREQUENCY OF OCCURRENCE OF CARABELLI'S CUSPS AND PHENOMENA IN THE PIMA INDIANS (ARIZONA)

Tooth	Stat	a	b	c	d	e	f	g	TOTAL
m^3	$N_{R\&L}$	2 / 3							2 / 3
	N_T	5							5
	%	100							
m^2	$N_{R\&L}$	34/35	9 / 6	2 / 2	4 / 4		1 / 3		50/50
	N_T	69	15	4	8		4		100
	%	69	15	4	8		4		
m^1	$N_{R\&L}$	9 /10	21/17	10/ 6	17/21	10/16	27/22	6 / 8	100/100
	N_T	19	38	16	38	26	49	14	200
	%	9.5	19	8	19	13	24.5	7	
dv	$N_{R\&L}$	/ 3	23/22	11/ 6	7 / 8	8 / 7		1 / 4	50/50
	N_T	3	45	17	15	15		5	100
	%	3	45	17	15	15		5	
m^3	$N_{R\&L}$	4 / 4							4 / 4
	N_T	8							8
	%	100							
m^2	$N_{R\&L}$	43/42	/ 1	3 / 3	2 / 2	1 / 1		1 / 1	50/50
	N_T	85	1	6	4	2		2	100
	%	85	1	6	4	2		2	
m^1	$N_{R\&L}$	22/25	26/18	6 / 6	19/21	10/13	12/12	5 / 5	100/100
	N_T	47	44	12	40	23	24	10	200
	%	23.5	22	6	20	11.5	12	5	
dv	$N_{R\&L}$	2 / 1	17/12	11/12	5 /12	9 / 8	1 / 1	5 / 4	50/50
	N_T	3	29	13	17	17	2	9	100
	%	3	29	13	17	17	2	9	

TABLE II
FREQUENCY OF OCCURRENCE OF CARABELLI'S CUSPS AND PHENOMENA IN A SAMPLE OF CHICAGO WHITE INDIVIDUALS

Sex	TOOTH	Measure	a	b	c	d	e	f	g	h	TOTAL
♂	m³	N R&L	9/4	1/							10/4
		N_T	13	1							14
		%	92.9	7.1							
	m2	N R&L	31/30	4/12		9/3	1/	/1	4/5		50/50
		N_T	61	16		12	1	1	9		100
		%	61	16		12	1	1	9		
	m1	N R&L	10/11	13/14	2/2	7/3	1/1	9/8	25/27	3/4	70/70
		N_T	21	27	4	10	2	17	52	7	140
		%	15	19.3	2.9	7.1	1.4	12.1	37.1	5	
	dv	N R&L		2/4	2/2	2/1	3/2	3/3	8/8		20/20
		N_T		6	4	3	5	6	16		40
		%		15	10	7.5	12.5	15	40		
♀	m3	N R&L	3/6	/1							3/7
		N_T	9	1							10
		%	90	10							
	m2	N R&L	24/28	4/5		11/8	1/	4/3	6/6		50/50
		N_T	52	9		19	1	7	12		100
		%	52	9		19	1	7	12		
	m1	N R&L	12/7	10/10	1/1	3/6	7/6	10/13	25/26	2/1	70/70
		N_T	19	20	2	9	13	23	51	3	140
		%	13.6	14.3	1.4	6.4	9.3	16.4	36.4	2.1	
	dv	N R&L	2/1	1/2	2/2		1/3	2/3	8/6	2/1	18/18
		N_T	3	3	4		4	5	14	3	36
		%	8.3	8.3	11.1		11.1	13.9	38.3	8.3	

attested to by a great many specimens in museum collections, typical of which is the early California Indian pictured in Fig. 10A. The high demands of function in the first molars is evident by excessive wear and by the alveolar abscess seen in the first permanent molar of the individual pictured. Many groups (Fig. 10 B and C) had compensation for reduced size of other teeth by the presence of a Carabelli's cusp.

TABLE III

PERCENTAGE DISTRIBUTION OF CARABELLI'S CUSP

♂

Population	dm²			M¹			M²			M³		
	a	bc	d to g	a	bc	d to g	a	bc	d to g	a	bc	d to g
Pima	3·0	62·0	35·0	9·5	27·0	63·5	69·0	19·0	12·0	100		
Old Harbor	0·0	28·5	71·4	25·0	16·6	58·3	83·8	5·4	10·8	100		
Kaguyak		(1 only)		20·0	6·7	73·3	92·9		7·1			
Sioux	5·0	51·3	43·7	16·4	40·8	42·8	76·8	23·5				
Am. White	0·0	25·0	75·0	15·0	22·2	62·7	61·0	16·0	23·0	92·9	7·1	

Classification of the Carabelli's cusp, as with other continuous variables, has always been a problem (Pedersen, 1949; Kraus, 1951; Carbonell, 1960; Kustaloglu, 1960; Shapiro, 1949; Dietz, 1944). In all the efforts on this subject, size has been used mainly to determine the categories. The complex has been confused to some extent by a variety of grooves, furrows and pits occurring in the same area. These are all variations related to the cingulum and probably the results of interplay of many genes. In order to allow wider use for comparison of the data presented here, seven classes for Carabelli's cusp are included ranging from a completely smooth, uninvolved surface to a single furrow, a pit, double furrow and on through three gradations of size of a cusp (as exemplified by Tables I and II). Table III gives a grouping of classes from the previous charts in order to give a general idea of the nature of the distribution of this structure. The "a" columns of the four teeth represent those having no pit, furrow or cusp. The "bc" columns combine the furrow and pits, distinguishing them from the third or "d to g" columns which include cusps of all sizes.

It should be pointed out that erroneous conclusions might be arrived at from data such as is given in these tables. For example in the Pima one might assume that the Carabelli's cusp is manifested in the first permanent molar more than in the second deciduous molar. Actually in any given individual the cusp is always present in the deciduous tooth if it is present in the permanent ones. The data on each tooth can represent a different age group of the population unless the figures are derived at by serial studies of a large number of individuals in which each of all four teeth is documented. This would eliminate certain aspects of cultural bias such as are known in some groups, viz. intrusions of new genes and time and place movements of populations, past and present. This is one problem not generally recognized and considered in dental metric studies. Such analyses of data are being pursued currently at the University of Chicago Zoller laboratories.

With this reservation it is seen that the reports of previous workers are generally confirmed, with a high frequency of Carabelli's cusp on M^1 of the caucasoids.

THE PROTOSTYLID

Extra cusps are found on teeth from time to time. These are of two varieties. One of these is anomalous and has no regularity of design or of seeming significance other than that of a supernumerary accidental occurrence. They are sometimes confused with other structures when they happen to occur at a site normally occupied by other known entities. This is exactly the circumstance involving the protostylid, which, like the Carabelli's cusp, is a genetically determined one and has an ancestral reputation dating back through dentitions to practically all of the fossil forms. Hence, some previous publications describing the lower molars have discussed facial cusps and paramolars which have included both supernumerary cusps and protostylids.

The protostylid is another continuous variable involving a pit, furrow, and varying degrees of expression of a cusp located in the anterior of the occlusal third of the buccal surface of lower molars (Fig. 11). It arises along with the gingival portion of the buccal groove from which it parts and courses antero-occlusally. The protostylid is a genetic structure of the primary architecture and hence is manifested with greatest size and character in the deciduous second lower molars and decreasingly from this tooth through the sequence of first, second and third molars (Dahlberg, 1950; Kustaloglu, 1962; Suzuki and Sakai, 1954, 1955).

Associated with the actual cusp is a pit which is frequently noted at the gingival end of the buccal groove and a distal deviation of the buccal groove itself. Similarly to the circumstances of the Carabelli's cusp the classes used in the five populations represented in the Tables IV, V and VI differentiate the smooth surface with no structure from that containing the pit, the distal deviation of the buccal groove and the various gradations of size.

Table VI groups the 2 to 5 categories and shows the higher frequency of the protostylid in the Pima Indian group. The Aleuts and Sioux exhibit less of this structure than the Pima, again a likely reflection of admixture. Pedersen (1949) paid particular attention to facial cusps in his work on the Greenland

TABLE IV

FREQUENCY OF OCCURRENCE OF PROTOSTYLIDS AND PHENOMENA IN THE PIMA INDIANS (ARIZONA)

TOOTH		PROTOSTYLID 0	P	1	2	3	4	5	TOTAL
m_3									
m_2	$N_{R\&L}$	16/11	27/26	3/8	1/3	1/1	17	1/1	50/50
	N_T	27	53	11	4	2	1	2	100
	%	27	53	11	4	2	1	2	
m_1	$N_{R\&L}$	7/7	65/66	7/5	11/10	5/4	3/5	2/3	100/100
	N_T	14	131	12	21	9	8	5	200
	%	7	65.5	6	10.5	8.5	4	2.5	
dv	$N_{R\&L}$	/1	18/21	1/1	23/21	4/3		4/3	50/50
	N_T	1	39	2	44	7		7	100
	%	1	39	2	44	7		7	
m_3									
m_2	$N_{R\&L}$	23/17	22/25	2/5	3/2			/1	50/50
	N_T	40	47	7	5			1	100
	%	40	47	7	5			1	
m_1	$N_{R\&L}$	32/28	39/44	12/17	14/9	2/1	1/1		100/100
	N_T	60	83	29	23	3	2		200
	%	30	41.5	14.5	11.5	1.5	1		
dv	$N_{R\&L}$	11/11	16/17	1/3	19/18	2/7		1/1	50/50
	NT	22	33	4	37	2		2	100
	%	22	33	4	37	2		2	

Eskimo and reported very large pits, having no enamel in the base. Moorrees (1957) reported no protostylids among the Aleuts from Nikolski and the Aleutian islands to the west. Those found in Kodiak Island (Old Harbor and Kaguyak) are not numerous, but could be associated with the differences

TABLE V

FREQUENCY OF OCCURRENCE OF PROTOSTYLIDS AND PHENOMENA IN A SAMPLE OF CHICAGO WHITE INDIVIDUALS

TOOTH		PROTOSTYLID 0	P	1	2	3	4	5	TOTAL
♂									
m3	N_R&L	3/2	1/1						4/3
	N_T	5	2						7
	%	71.4	28.6						
m2	N_R&L	17/25	17/7	4/4	2/2			/2	40/40
	N_T	42	24	8	4			2	80
	%	52.5	30	10	5			2.5	
m1	N_R&L	15/11	32/36	2/3	1/				50/50
	N_T	26	68	5	1				100
	%	26	68	5	1				
dv	N_R&L	4/6	12/12	4/	/2				20/20
	N_T	10	24	4	2				40
	%	25	60	10	5				
♀									
m3	N_R&L	1/4	2/		1/			/1	4/5
	N_T	5	2		1			1	9
	%	55.6	22.2		11.1			11.1	
m2	N_R&L	11/17	37/26	2/3	/2	/1	/1		50/50
	N_T	28	63	5	2	1	1		100
	%	28	63	5	2	1	1		
m1	N_R&L	5/5	40/39	2/2	1/3	1/	/1	1/	50/50
	N_T	10	79	4	4	1	1	1	100
	%	10	79	4	4	1	1	1	
dv	N_R&L	2/1	13/14		5/4				20/19
	N_T	3	27		9				39
	%	7.7	69.2		23.1				

between the eastern and western Aleuts described by Moorrees (1957) and Laughlin and Marsh (1951).

Variability of the hypocones and metacones of maxillary teeth and the entoconids and hypoconulids of the mandibular teeth is a very significant source of differential in occlusal

TABLE VI

PERCENTAGE DISTRIBUTION OF THE PROTOSTYLID

♂

Population	dm²				M₁				M₂				M₃			
	O	P	1	2–5	O	P	1	2–5	O	P	1	2–5	O	P	1	2–5
Pima	1·0	39·0	2·0	58·0	7·0	65·5	6·0	25·5	27·0	53·0	11·0	9·0	27·0	53·0	11·0	9·0
Old Harbor	17·6	35·3	0·0	47·1	42·1	42·1	2·6	13·2	64·5	29·0	3·2	3·2	100			
Kaguyak	9·7	59·7	0·0	1 indiv.	20·0	60·0	10·0	10·0	54·6	36·3	9·1	0·0	83·3	16·7		
Sioux	25·0	60·0	10·0	30·6	19·8	56·2	12·4	11·6	38·9	52·8	2·8	5·6	71·4	28·6		
Am. White				5·0	26·0	68·0	5·0	1·0	52·5	30·0	18·0	7·5				

TABLE VII

PERCENTAGE DISTRIBUTION OF HYPOCONE

♂

Population	dm²				M¹				M²				M³			
	4	4−	3+	3	4	4−	3+	3	4	4−	3+	3	4	4−	3+	3
Pima	56·0	44·0			77·0	23·0			6·0	68·0	18·0	8·0				
Old Harbor	7·1	92·9			60·0	36·0	4·0		2·1	60·9	19·6	17·4	8·3	33·3	58·3	
Kaguyak		2 indiv. 50·0	2 indiv. 50·0		66·7	16·7	16·7		8·3	16·7	50·0	25·0				100
Pine Ridge Sioux	17·4	82·6			58·5	41·5				57·1	4·8	38·1				
Am. White	40·0	48·9	11·1		80·7	18·2	1·1		25·8	42·2	19·5	12·5	15·8	36·8	47·4	

TABLE VIII

PERCENTAGE DISTRIBUTION OF METACONE

♂

Population	dm₂				M₁				M₂				M₃			
	4	3	2	1	4	3	2	1	4	3	2	1	4	3	2	1
Pima	98·0	2·0			94·0	6·0			75·0	25·0						
Old Harbor																
Aleut	84·2	15·8			94·3	5·7			45·8	50·0	2·1	2·1	20·0	60·0	20·0	
Kaguyak	100				84·6	15·4			26·7	73·3						
Pine Ridge																
Sioux	93·4	6·6			75·2	24·8			41·7	58·3						
White	84·4	15·2			91·6	7·8	0·6		41·8	51·5	6·7			75·0	25·0	

TABLE IX
PERCENTAGE DISTRIBUTION OF PATTERNS ON LOWER MOLARS†

Group‡	No. of Individuals	Y5	+5	Y4	+4
Mongol	36	100			
Alaska Eskimo	67	89·6	6·0	1·5	3·0
E. G. Eskimo	143	95·7	2·8	0	1·4
Texas Indian	160	68·7	30·6	0·6	0·0
Pecos Indian	332	88·6	10·8	0	0·6
Pima Indian	162	99·4	0·6		
M₁Ancient European White	54	83·0	0·0	11·0	6·0
European White Male	98	87·0	2·0	7·0	4·0
Chicago White	75	84·0	2·0	8·0	2·0
African Negro	97	99·0		1·0	
Kish (Mesopotamia)	53	7·5	43·5	7·5	34·0
Old Harbor Koniag	43	76·7	20·9		2·3
Mongol	39		31	5	64·0
Alaska Eskimo	132	12·8	63·8	3·0	20·5
E. G. Eskimo	115	19·0	42·0	4·0	35·0
Texas Indian	206	1·5	26·2	3·4	68·9
Pecos Indian	313	8·3	24·3	1·3	66·1
M₂Pima Indian	89	2·0	69·0	1·0	28·0
Ancient European White	54	2·0	11·0	9·0	77·0
European White	110		1·0	5·0	94·0
African Negro	96	17	8·0	12·0	63·0
Kish (Mesopotamia)	46		13·0	11·0	76·0
Old Harbor Koniag	34	8·8	32·4	8·8	50·0
Mongol	31		77·0		23·0
Alaska Eskimo	59	20·4	69·5	0·0	10·2
E. G. Eskimo	55	15·0	74·0	11·0	0·0
Texas Indian	91	12·1	47·3	6·6	34·1
Pecos Indian	249	8·4	51·0	4·8	35·8
Pima Indian	7		57·0		14·0
M₃Ancient European White	35	6·0	34·0	11·0	49·0
European White	74	4·0	34·0		62·0
African Negro	88	20·0	59·0	3·0	17·0
Kish (Mesopotamia)	33	3·0	18·2	3·0	72·8
Old Harbor Koniag	12		58·3		41·7

†The sources of the data given here are to be found in Dahlberg (1949), except in the case of the Kish (Carbonell, 1958) and Old Harbor Koniag (Dahlberg and Tomita, 1962) populations.

‡The percentage figures of a few of the groups do not add up to 100 because the authors in some instances included other categories of patterns. However, the figures are not too far off to be of comparative value.

problems and in morphological studies. These variations take the form of suppression of full expression or a trend in reduction of size (Fig. 6A, C and D).

HYPOCONE VARIABILITY

The last cusp to be added in the evolution of the maxillary molars was the hypocone (distolingual cusp). It is also the most variable of the cusps of the upper teeth. Table VII contains the frequencies of the various degrees of reduction of the hypocone. The strong portrayal of hypocone in the deciduous second molar and permanent first molar is evident with a trend towards reduction in the second and third molars. Figure 6C shows a slight reduction of hypocone in the maxillary first molars, rather marked in the second, and absence of the hypocone on the left third molar.

METACONE VARIABILITY

The metacone (distobuccal cusp of maxillary molars) frequently is found to be reduced in size in some modern and to a lesser extent in certain fossil groups (Le Moustier, Krapina and Grimaldi). The major reductions are generally in the second and third molars and in some individuals very strikingly, as seen in Fig. 6A, in the second molar but not in the others. This latter trend seems to have developed in some of the dentitions of the Mediterranean regions, particularly to the east. Many modern Middle East and some European dentitions exhibit this peculiar trait.

Finding the second permanent molar more involved with the reduction of metacone and hypocone than the third is one of the several exceptions to the expected pattern stemming from the field concept. It shows the ability of an organism to modify the pattern genetically, presumably at any point. This concept needs more study and exploitation in tissue techniques.

Indians do not show this reduction as much or as frequently as do other populations (Table VIII).

ENTOCONID VARIABILITY

What seems to be a matching though not correlated occur-

M

rence to the metacone reduction in the upper teeth is the tendency for reduction of the entoconid of the lower molars in some individuals. No attempt has been made to measure this phenomenon. It is interesting to note that this cusp is part of the talonid or heel, the late arrival to the original trigonid. It does not seem to be associated with reductions of the hypoconulid which is reflected in the occlusal surface patterns.

MOLAR OCCLUSAL SURFACE PATTERNS

Topographical patterns of the occlusal surfaces of mandibular molars have long been a subject of interest to dental anthropologists. These patterns reflect not only the numbers of cusps, but also differences in their size and positions. The basic classifications of Hellman (1928) have been carried forward by workers such as Nakamura (1957) and Jorgensen (1955), who added another groove category, the "X", to supplement the original "+" and "Y". The designation of one or the other of these is dependent on the varying relationships of the cusps as a consequence of their sizes. If the metaconid is larger and the entoconid smaller, the intervening groove is located more distally on the surface and attains a different relationship with the grooves and cusps on the buccal half of the surface. Likewise other size changes, particularly of the buccal cusps, are responsible for differing patterns. The hypoconulid is missing completely in some teeth and changes the cusp number designation from 5 to 4. In all the Amerind groups reported in the literature the first molar is with very few exceptions a five-cusped tooth (Table IX). A decided shift to the four-cusped variety is seen in the second molars and then back to the five cusps in the third (Table IX). This is the trend for most populations other than the European and the inhabitants of India.

The absence of the hypoconulid in the second molar while being present in the first and third is another exception to the pattern expected in the field concept. It demonstrates the possibilities of morphologic alterations during ontogeny. The regularity of this patterning rules out the improbable suggestion that it might be accidental.

The five-cusped tooth is always a larger tooth than the four-cusped one (Dahlberg, 1961). This makes a difference in occlusal surface area, if not necessarily in efficiency.

THIRD MOLARS

Data available at present suggests that Mongoloid peoples have rather higher percentages of agenesis of third molars than do other groups. Melanesians, whose teeth are very large and who have generally large Carabelli's cusps, both qualities desirable in difficult dietary environments, have a very low percentage (4 per cent) of missing third molars. Third molars are very useful in primitive societies where the teeth located more anteriorly in the mouth have had severe wear for many years prior to the eruption of this late arriver. Conceivably, this tooth could play an important part in the dental life and efficiency of some circumstances. The Amerind has certainly found it useful.

DISCUSSION

Preliminary to the discussion of dentitions in their environment, two thoughts on interpretation and caution should be introduced.

First, the cusps and anatomical structure of the teeth are the end points of the developmental process. The potentials of structure can be seen in the early stages by microscopic techniques involving tissue culture, transplants and simple observation of embryonic materials (Glasstone, 1939, 1961; Kraus, 1959, 1960; Gaunt, 1956, 1959, 1960, 1961; Butler, 1961; Lewis and Garn, 1957, 1960). Whatever relationships different classes of structures have to each other in the range of phenotypes can be observed and determined to some extent on this level. On the other hand, added factors of a gradient nature are in operation and regulate and modify the succeeding processes that lead to the finished tooth. What the organism does with these finished products is another matter and their future is subject to selective processes.

Secondly, the cautionary remarks made in the discussion of the statistics of Carabelli's cusp earlier in this paper might be expanded here. It is so easy to assume on the surface of thing that a given sample is biased, reasonably unbiased, or for al practical purposes unbiased. There are, however, many pitfall in these determinations. It has been disconcerting to workers to see such large differences in reports of different samples of the same (or seemingly the same) ethnic or geographical populations This is seen in the tables in this paper also. The true picture would include consideration of consanguinity (Slatis, *et al.* 1958, 1961), cultural backgrounds, and events of genetic population constitution of different age segments of the groups as well as the care ordinarily taken to assure the unbiased nature of the sample.

Many workers and observers feel that since the time of the reduction of the canines and the transference from the mouth to the hand of man of many of the tool and defense devices the teeth have not been of any apparent consequence in the evolutionary picture. It would be well to reconsider this question, taking into account the performance of dentitions in certain stress circumstances of the past. Today's societies, with the varieties of available food, the ready replacement of teeth lost for one or another reason and the absence in many quarter of a feeling of necessity for maintenance of the dentition, are not very good vantage points from which to view dentition of the past and their importance in given situations. More to the point would be a full study and appreciation of groups experiencing marginal circumstances of food availability. Evidence of ancient and primitive populations in these situations is not entirely rare. The Indians offer many. The clam eaters of Kentucky (Snow, 1948, and Johnston and Snow, 1961) and the Texas Indians (Goldstein, 1948) are two that are well documented.

Many skeletal collections exhibit teeth that during life had been called on to do unusual things. It is quite common to see extreme imbalance of occlusal planes, patchy excessive wear displaced teeth and changes resulting from acute alveolar abscesses in the dentitions of ancient groups. In the harshness of the environment the teeth were milled into highly efficient machines at early ages. This virtue, though, had a relatively short life. Exposure of pulps and nerve tissues in instances of rapid wear required shifts to different chewing or functioning areas. This in turn resulted in a change in the occlusal plane as new wear and function patterns developed. The major events in the lives of these peoples not only included birth, puberty, marriage and death, but also, no doubt, long periods of distress and disability during the time that it took for an alveolar abscess to resolve.

In circumstances where teeth are worn down severely soon after eruption it is difficult to relate selective pressures to tooth form. Whether or not new and enlarged cusps or characteristics contributed to greater wearability and thus gave a subtle selective advantage is conjectural. Most certainly drift has played a part in dental morphological shifts. Also, no doubt, non-adaptive traits developing as side products of genes selectively important because of other effects set the stage for dealing with eventual crisis events. In any case, it appears that there could have been major selective pressures in some instances, and minor ones in others, depending upon the crises encountered.

Considerable variations exist in the environments in which man is found. These include the nature of his food as well as his physical surroundings. The absence or presence of certain types of food was critical in times past. The availability of nutritional and caloric elements and the relative ease or difficulty of deriving them were of high importance. It is quite a different matter to obtain 1500 to 3000 cal from tough sandy roots, than from bananas or juicy fruits, rainwashed and clean, hanging within reach on trees. If a man had worn his teeth down severely with heavy abrasive materials in tough difficult foods, he is unlikely to have had very good prospects for a long-continued useful dental life. It is also important to point out here that it is not necessarily coarse abrasives that do the greatest damage to the teeth. Constant stropping action with fine abrasives and silts has been found in our laboratories to do as much damage as, or more than, the coarser particles.

At some point in the late Pleistocene the dentitions reduced markedly in size and to some extent in form. Whatever the causes, the dentitions that evolved in the eastern Mediterranean areas resulted in further reduction than did those of certain other areas. The premolars are very small compared to the molars in buccolingual dimension, the metacone is greatly reduced and lingually positioned and the teeth are generally smaller. Other dentitions took varied courses, but mainly towards reduction. The European has survived without the hypoconulid and the attendant greater tooth mass. Populations in less favoured environments have larger teeth and, as in the Amerind, the advantage of additional dental potential in the structure of the incisors.

It is not intended to over-emphasize the significance of teeth in survival, but they were certainly positive contributors and at times no doubt must have been decisive even before Palaeolithic times.

We may well speculate whether the form and size of dentition in the early Asiatic immigrants was particularly well adapted to the rigours of conquering the New World. It seems unlikely that the teeth of, say, the peoples of the Eastern Mediterranean would have been so successful in the variety of new environments experienced by the "first" Amerinds.

ACKNOWLEDGEMENTS

Many individuals have contributed to the American Indian data discussed in this presentation, both in the field and in the laboratory. Special appreciation must be expressed for the early work of Drs. Virginia Carbonell, Omur Kustaloglu, Renée Menagaz Bock, Fujio Miura, Jud Epling and James Brown. During the past year Dr. Kinai Tomita of the Tokyo Medical and Dental University has been a visiting professor in the Zoller laboratories of the University of Chicago, and is responsible for a major share of the statistical analysis of the Indian material as well as participating actively in the study generally.

REFERENCES

BRABANT, H., SAHLY, A. and BOUYSSOU, M. (1961) Etude des dents prehistoriques de la station archeologique des Matelles, *Bull. du G.I.R.S.* **4**, 382.

BUTLER, P. M. (1939) Studies of the mammalian dentition. Differentiation of the post-canine dentition *Proc. Zool. Soc. Lond.* **B 109**, 1.

BUTLER, P. M. (1961) Personal communications regarding microscopic studies of early tooth germs by him and workers in the Zoology Department of the Royal Holloway College, London.

CARBONELL, VIRGINIA (1958) *The Dentition of the Kish Population,* 3000 B.C. Thesis submitted for the M.A. degree, University of Chicago.

CARBONELL, VIRGINIA (1960) The tubercle of Carabelli in the Kish dentition, Mesopotamia, 3000 B.C., *J. Dent. Res.* **39**, 124.

DAHLBERG, ALBERT A. (1945) The changing dentition of man, *J. Amer. Dent. Ass.* **32**, 676.

DAHLBERG, ALBERT A. (1949) The dentition of the American Indian. In LAUGHLIN, W. S. (ed.). *The Physical Anthropology of the American Indian,* pp. 138-76. Viking Fund, New York.

DAHLBERG, ALBERT A. (1950) The evolutionary significance of the protostylid, *Amer. J. Phys. Anthrop.* **8**, 15.

DAHLBERG, ALBERT A. (1961) Relationship of tooth size to cusp number and groove conformation of occlusal surface patterns of lower molar teeth, *J. Dent. Res.* **40**, 34.

DAHLBERG, ALBERT A. (1962) On the teeth of early Sapiens. In KURTH, G. (ed.). *Evolution and Hominisation,* pp. 205-11. Fischer Verlag, Stuttgart.

DIETZ, VICTOR H. (1944) A common dental morphotropic factor, the Carabelli cusp *J. Amer. Dent. Ass.* **31**, 784.

ENOKI, KEI and DAHLBERG, ALBERT A. (1958) Rotated maxillary central incisors. *Orthodontic J. Japan* **17**, 157. (Abstract in *J. Dent. Res.* **38**, 203.)

GARN, S. M. and LEWIS, A. B. (1957) Relationship between the sequence of calcification and the sequence of eruption of the mandibular molar and premolar teeth, *J. Dent. Res.* **36**, 992.

GAUNT, W. A. (1956) The development of enamel and dentine on the molars of the mouse, with an account of the enamel-free areas, *Acta Anatomica* **28**, 111.

GAUNT, W. A. (1959) The vascular supply to the dental lamina during early development, *Acta Anatomica* **37**, 232.

GAUNT, W. A. (1959) The development of the deciduous cheek teeth of the cat, *Acta Anatomica* **38**, 187.

GAUNT, W. A. (1960) The vascular supply in relation to the formation of roots on the cheek teeth of the mouse, *Acta Anatomica* **43**, 116.

GAUNT, W. A. (1961) The presence of apical pits on the lower cheek teeth of the mouse, *Acta Anatomica* **44**, 146.

GAUNT, W. A. (1961) The development of the molar pattern of the golden hamster (*Mesocricetus duratus W.*), together with a reassessment of the molar pattern of the mouse (*Mus musculus*), *Acta Anatomica* **45**, 219.

GLASSTONE, SHIRLEY (1939) A comparative study of the development *in vivo* and *in vitro* of rat and rabbit molars, *Brit. Dent. J.* **66**, 460, 523.

GLASSTONE, SHIRLEY (1961) The regulative changes in tooth germs grown in tissue culture. American Association for the Advancement of Science Symposium on *Oral Aspects of Genetics*. Denver. In press.

GOLDSTEIN, M. S. (1948) Dentition of Indian crania from Texas, *Amer. J. Phys. Anthrop.* **6**, 63.

GRAINGER, R. M., PAYNTER, K. J. and SHAW, J. H. (1959) Differences in the morphology and size of the teeth, *J. Dent. Res.* **38**, 105.

HELLMAN, MILO (1928) Racial characters in human dentition, *Proc. Amer. Phil. Soc.* **67**, 157.

JOHNSTON, F. E. and SNOW, C. E. (1961) The reassessment of the age and sex of the Indian Knoll skeletal population, *Amer. J. Phys. Anthrop.* **19**, 237.

JORGENSEN, K. D. (1955) The Dryopithecus pattern in recent Danes and Dutchmen, *J. Dent. Res.* **34**, 195.

KRAUS, BERTRAM S. (1951) Carabelli's anomaly of the maxillary molar teeth, *Amer. J. Hum. Genet.* **3**, 348.

KRAUS, BERTRAM S. (1959) Calcification of human deciduous teeth, *J. Amer. Dent. Ass.* **59**, 1137.

KRAUS, BERTRAM S. (1960) The growth and morphology of the bony palate, *J. Dent. Res.* **39**, 1177.

KUSTALOGLU, OMUR A. (1960) The Evolution and Significance of the Carabelli Cusp. Master's thesis. University of Chicago.

KUSTALOGLU, OMUR A. (1962) Paramolar structures of the upper dentition, *J. Dent. Res.* **41**, 75.

LAUGHLIN, W. S. and MARSH, G. H. (1951) A new view of the history of the Aleutians, *Arctic* **4**, 76.

LEWIS, A. B. and GARN, S. M. (1960) The relationship between tooth formation and other maturational factors, *Angle Orthodontist*, **30**, 70.

MOORREES, COENRAAD, F. A. (1957) *The Aleut Dentition. A Correlative Study of Dental Characteristics in an Eskimo People.* Harvard University Press, Cambridge.

NAKAMURA, MITUO (1957) Occlusal surface pattern of the lower molars in recent Japanese, *Acta Anatomica Nipponica* **32**, 510.

PEDERSEN, P. O. (1949) The East Greenland Dentition, *Meddelelser om Gronland* **142**. Copenhagen.

SAKAI, TAKURO (1955) Anthroposcopic observations of the proto-stylid in the Japanese, *Shinshu Igaku Zassi* **4**, 329.

SHAPIRO, M. M. J. (1949) The anatomy and morphology of the tubercle of Carabelli, *J. Dent. Ass. S. Afr.* **4**, 355.

SLATIS, H. M., REIS, R. H. and HOENE, R. E. (1958) Consanguineous marriages in the Chicago region, *Amer. J. Hum. Genet.* **10**, 446.

SLATIS, H. M. and HOENE, R. E. (1961) The effect of consanguinity on the distribution of continuously variable characteristics, *Amer. J. Hum. Genet.* **15**, 28.

SNOW, C. P. (1948) Indian Knoll Skeletons, *University of Kentucky Report in Anthropology* **4**, 00.

SNYDER, RICHARD G. (1960) Mesial margin ridging of incisor labial surfaces, *J. Dent. Res.* **39**, 361.

SUZUKI, MOKOTO and SAKAI, TAKURO (1954) On the protostylid of the Japanese, *Zinruigaku Zassi* **63**, 81.

SUZUKI, MAKOTO and SAKAI, TAKURO (1956) On the occlusal surface patterns of cusps of maxillary molars in recent Japanese, *Zinruigaku Zassi* **65**, 54.

CONGENITAL ABSENCE OF TEETH IN HUMAN POPULATIONS

by **DON R. BROTHWELL**
Sub-Department of Anthropology, British Museum
(Natural History)
VIRGINIA M. CARBONELL
Department of Dental Histology and Pathology, London Hospital
Medical College
and DENYS H. GOOSE
Department of Preventive Dentistry, University of Liverpool

Both the permanent and the deciduous dentitions of man may display a deficiency in the number of teeth.

The complete or nearly complete absence of tooth structures is rare and less than 150 cases have been described. Both dentitions or only one may be affected in the same individual.

Congenital absence of one or a number of teeth, which we shall refer to as hypodontia for brevity, is not so uncommon. This may affect both the anterior and posterior teeth (as in Fig. 1) or just one type of tooth (as in Fig. 2b). Salzmann (1957) gives the order of frequency of missing teeth as third molars, maxillary lateral incisors, maxillary or mandibular second premolars, mandibular central incisors, and maxillary first premolars—absence of other teeth being too infrequent to classify.

In the majority of cases only one or two teeth are missing, as shown for example by the most commonly affected teeth, the third molars (Fig. 3). Because of the infrequency of some forms of hypodontia, only the lateral incisors and third molars have so far received anthropological attention, although the eventual collection of large dental samples might demonstrate population variability for certain other teeth. Grahnen (1956), for example, found in a sample of 1006 Swedish children that mandibular

179

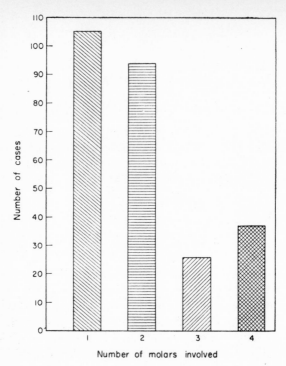

Fig. 3. Distribution of 262 Swedish Individuals according to the number of congenitally missing third molars. (Original data given by Grahnen, 1956.)

second premolars showed in fact a higher frequency of hypodontia (2·8 per cent) than maxillary lateral incisors (1·6 per cent).

As no significant differences between the frequencies of hypodontia in the two sexes have yet been established (Grahnen, 1956), this aspect is not considered further. Owing to the unsatisfactory nature of a number of the sample sizes, data for the upper and lower jaws are combined when possible, although there is some evidence of a frequency difference between them (Dolder, 1936; Werther and Rothenberg, 1939; Grahnen, 1956).

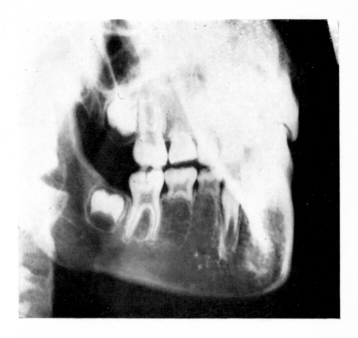

Fig. 1.   Congenital absence of permanent teeth in a girl of
11 years. All her premolars but one are missing, and also
one maxillary second incisor, and her third molars.

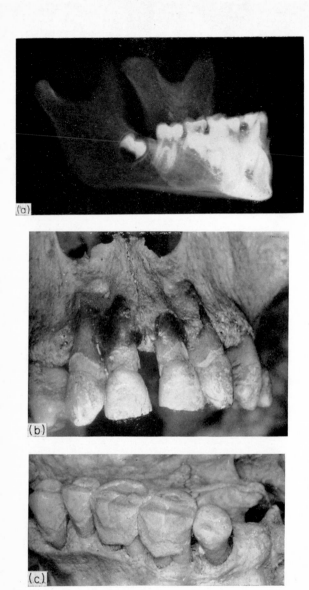

Fig. 2. Examples of hypodontia from earlier populations.
(a) Kish, Mesopotamia (3000 B.C.) Mandible with absence
of second premolars and third molars (Chicago Nat. Hist.
Mus. 192692). (b) and (c) Romano-British dentition with
missing upper lateral incisors associated with diminutive
third molars (B.M.N.H. 11–8–426).

AETIOLOGY

Werther and Rothenberg (1939) group the causal factors into four major categories. *Local influences* to the tooth germs in the jaws, such as sequestrating osteomyelitis, tumours, various types of trauma, and exposure to radiation, do not have sufficient influence to warrant consideration as factors of anthropological interest. *Constitutional diseases* such as tuberculosis, rickets, congenital syphilis, and exanthematous fevers have been enumerated as possible aetiologic factors. There is, however, no satisfactory association as yet between such disorders and hypodontia of the permanent dentition (Grahnen, 1956). *Endocrine and nutritional disturbances* have been associated with hypodontia by some (Wheelon, 1925; Howard, 1926; Thoma, 1944), but again fully satisfactory evidence as regards this relationship has not yet been published. *Heredity* is certainly the most important determinant of hypodontia, whether many teeth are affected or only one or two. Considering all forms of hypodontia together, there is clearly a wide range of genetic factors with which it may be associated. Severe deficiency in number is common for example in the sex-linked recessive type of anidrotic ectodermal dysplasia. Some degree of absence is also sometimes associated with mongolism, the result of a chromosomal anomaly (Downs, 1927; Spitzer and Robinson, 1955). On the other hand, absence of maxillary lateral incisors has been attributed to a recessive gene (Iltis, 1948) but more commonly to a dominant gene (Montagu, 1940; Mandeville, 1950; and others). A detailed review of the hereditary aspects of numerical variation is given by Grahnen (1956). The result of the various studies would seem to show beyond doubt that hypodontia in the permanent dentition of man, including the numerical variations of anthropological interest, are "primarily determined by genetic factors with a fairly marked degree of penetrance" (Grahnen, 1956).

ABSENCE OF MAXILLARY LATERAL INCISORS

Various reviews of the absence and "reduction" of these teeth have been undertaken including those of Montagu (1940), Dahlberg (1951) and Lysell (1953). Of the Anthropoidea, man is not the only genus to display absence in the incisor region, and in a sample of 1633 apes 0·4 per cent were affected (Table 1).

In general, the frequency is not higher than 2·5 per cent in modern human populations (Table II) although small isolated communities can show higher incidences, as for example the mountain village dwellers of Illgan, Switzerland, where 21·5 per cent absence was recorded by Jöhr (1934). Unlike the data which follows for third molar absence, no clear pattern of variability in human populations can be seen from the frequencies available, there being relatively low and high figures among the European, Mongoloid and Negro samples studied.

ABSENCE OF THIRD MOLARS

By far the commonest form of hypodontia is that in the third molar region. Considering large samples only, the frequencies range from 0·2 per cent to over 25·0 per cent in man, and contrary to general belief, the incidence among anthropoid apes falls within this range (1·2 per cent of 1633 specimens).

In earlier human populations, there would appear to be no case so far described of third molar absence in the *Pithecanthropus* group, or in the dentitions of *Atlanthropus* or Heidelberg Man. Also, in the dentition of the Neanderthal variety of man there is no absence (Table III). By Upper Palaeolithic times, however, it was certainly in evidence to a noticeable degree, at least in the European area. By the Neolithic period various samples suggest that hypodontia had become relatively common. Although much speculation seems unwarranted, it does appear likely that the period between about 30000 B.C. and 5000 B.C. was particularly significant from the point of view of the increasing tendency to third molar hypodontia.

In the recent and modern populations so far studied (Table IV), the greatest variability is to be seen in South-East Asia and Oceania. The Mongoloid populations in the northern part of this area all have quite high frequencies, but there is a cline to smaller figures in the Southern Australoid groups. This frequency range of over 30 per cent is greater than known for any other region of the world. In the other Mongoloid peoples

TABLE I

CONGENITAL ABSENCE OF TEETH IN THE PONGIDAE†

Genus	Number of specimens	Absence			Number of specimens
		Class of tooth			
		I	Pm	M‡	
Gorilla	546	2	1	1	4
Pan	467	–	2	8	9
Pongo	229	1	1	5	7
Hylobates	306	3	1	7	11
Symphalangus	85	1	–	–	1

†Data from Colyer, 1936.
‡All the cases were third molars.

TABLE II

FREQUENCY OF LATERAL INCISOR HYPODONTIA IN VARIOUS MODERN HUMAN POPULATIONS

Author	Population	Number investigated	% frequency of hypodontia
Rose (1906)	Swedish males	1484	2·1
Hrdlicka (1921)	American white males	500	1·4
Hrdlicka (1921)	American negro males	307	1·6
Hrdlicka (1921)	Chinese males	547	0·2
Dolder (1936)	Swiss children (Bern)	10,000	0·5
Pedersen (1949)	East Greenland Eskimos	603	1·2
Mandeville (1950)	English children	2314	1·0
Rantanen (1955)	Finnish undergraduates	2200	1·0
Almeida (1949)	Angolan	1000	0·5
Sinclair et al. (1950)	Papuans	332	2·1

Table III

Frequency of Third Molar Hypodontia in Some Earlier Populations

Author	Population	No. of specimens†	% M3 hypodontia	Total thirds possible	% M3 absent
Brothwell	Neanderthal Man	28	0	58	0
Brothwell	Upper Palaeolithic Man	34	11·8	102	3·9
Brothwell	Mesolithic Man (Europe and N. Africa)	53	1·9	154	0·6
Ruffer (1920)	Egyptian Predynastic	156	12·2		
Holmer and Maunsbach (1956)	Swedish Neolithic	134m	14·2m	464‡	8·8
Brothwell	French, Belgium and British Neolithic	156	16·7	334	10·8
Angel (1944)	Neolithic to Medieval Greece	278	20·5		
Goose (1961)	Anglo-Saxons	100ma	8·0ma	200ma	7·0ma
Goldstein (1948)	Texas Indians (Pre- and Pro-historic)	173	19·5		
Twisselmann and Brabant (1960)	Belgium Medieval (Coxyde)	427	7·4		
Carbonell (1958)	Kish, Mesopotamia, 3000 b.c.	36m	2·6m		

†Unfortunately in early specimens the jaws are often incomplete, but nevertheless give an approximate frequency.

‡This figure is for maxillae and mandibles.

m = mandibles only. ma = maxillae only.

—the Eskimo and American Indians—frequencies are still high. Among the Eskimo, there is some indication of variability resulting from group isolation, a fact compatible with certain other traits which have been studied in this group, although size of sample is still far from that desirable.

The data for Europeans from Sweden, America, and Germany provide more reliable evidence of group variability, although the range is not so great. Generally low figures are present in Negroes, the highest frequency being in a small sample of American Negroes (which could include hybrids). Relatively small percentages of third molar absence need not be associated with a proportionately small frequency of maxillary

lateral hypodontia, and among the Angolan series examined by
Almeida (1949) the frequency of maxillary lateral hypodontia
was greater than that for third molar absence.

REDUCTION IN TOOTH NUMBER AND HUMAN EVOLUTION

A very early hypothesis advanced concerning the evolution of
human jaws and teeth is that in the trend for smaller jaws there
is a correlated need to reduce or eliminate some of the teeth.
This idea was advanced as early as 1865 by Darwin, and has
been reiterated by Keith (1924), Bolk (1916), Hellman (1936),
and others. On the other hand McQuillan (1870) and Goddard
(1894) regarded the trend towards a reduction in number of
teeth as evidence of a "reversion" or an "atavistic" process
simulating earlier phases of primate evolution. It seems
important to remember, however, that hypodontia—like
hyperdontia—can also be regarded as evidence of numerical
variability that has no close connection with the phylogenetic
development of the dentition (Hellgren, 1960). Indeed it was
realized by Ruffer (1920) and others that absence of third
molars for example could be associated with very ample dental
arch size and spacing, a situation which is contrary to the
idea of hypodontia related to inadequate space.

As in so many instances of biological variability, probably a
number of factors, perhaps varying through time and from
group to group, have been involved in determining the present
frequency differences for hypodontia. Possibly the following
should be considered as contributory factors.

(a) That hypodontia is to some extent associated with
general evolutionary changes in jaw form and size, and
especially to the area taken up in other anthropoids by
the premaxilla and to the most posterior part of the arch.

(b) That genetic drift acting on normal variability—perhaps
in the very early racial isolates—produced differences at
least in the third molar region.

(c) In the case of the third molar, absence may in some
instances confer slight selective advantage. Insufficiently
erupted, or impacted, teeth may give rise to chronic

N

Table IV

Congenital Absence of Third Molars in Some Recent Populations
(Samples of less than 100 are not included)

Group	Number of cases	% lacking one or more M3	Author
Europeans			
Swedish	1064	25·0	Grahnen, 1956
German[1]	1600	5·8	Friedrich, 1951
American "White"	2112	9·0	Goblirsch, 1930
English[1]	185	24·3	Carr, Brothwell and Glasstone[2]
Negroes			
West African	163	2·5	Hellman, 1928 Brothwell and Carbonell[2]
East African	188	1·6	Chagula, 1960
Angolan	1000	0·2	Almeida, 1949
South African Bantu[3]	136	4·4	Shaw, 1931
American Negro	119	11·0	Hellman, 1928
E. Asia and Oceania			
Chinese	118	32·2	Knap, 1937 Brothwell and Carbonell[2]
Japanese	1300	18·4	Hamano, 1926
Burmese[4]	100	11·0	Hughes
Hawaiians[5]	138	15·7	Chappel, 1927
Australians[6]	600	1·5	Campbell, 1925
New Guinea	332	2·7	
Arctic and American Mongoloids			
American Indians	119	12·6	Hellman, 1928 Brothwell and Carbonell[2]
E. Greenland Eskimo	257	36·6	Pedersen, 1949
S.W. Greenland Eskimo	210	29·5	Pedersen, 1949
Alaskan Eskimo[1]	759	26·6	Goldstein, 1932

[1]Mandibles only.   [2]Unpublished data.   [3]Maxillae only.
[4]Unpublished data of Mr. D. Hughes. [5]Average of ♂ and ♀ means.
[6]Percentage estimated by us from the number with hypodontia and the total sample number which Campbell examined.

sepsis; and although still a debatable concept, it seems likely that such a focus of infection could influence the general "fitness" of the individual. Such third molar upsets are by no means purely phenomena of "civilized" communities, and Goldstein (1932) for instance found in a sample of 759 adult Eskimo that impacted lower third molars occurred in 15·3 per cent. Considering this and other anomalous conditions which may occur in the posterior region of the mouth, the effect as a selective factor could be far from negligible.

(d) In a certain strain of mice, Gruneberg (1951) noted hypodontia of the third molars in 17·9 per cent; considered by him to be determined by multiple genes and "the condition of the mother during pregnancy". Grahnen (1956) suggests that this nature–nurture relationship might in some instance be also applicable to man, although there is no satisfactory evidence as yet.

(e) As regards third molar absence, a final tentative possibility is that in the course of man's paedomorphic evolution, the continued prolongation of eruptive time has reached a "critical age level" as regards the formation of the last erupting tooth. This form of evolutionary "retardation" has already been suggested by De Beer (1951).

Although some of the factors thus outlined are very speculative they nevertheless all seem worthy of further consideration. There are certainly no good grounds for believing that an increase of hypodontia in *Homo sapiens* is purely associated with the trend towards smaller jaws.

REFERENCES

Almeida, R. de (1949) *Contribuicào para o estudo de alguns Caracteres Dentários dos Indigenas da Lunda*. Publicacóes Culturais No. 3, Lisbon.

Angel, J. L. (1944) Greek teeth: ancient and modern, *Hum. Biol.* **16**, 283.

Bolk, L. (1916) Problems of the human dentition, *Amer. J. Anat.* **19**, 91.

Campbell, T. D. (1925) *Dentition and Palate of the Australian Aboriginal*. Sheridan Foundation Publications, No. 1, University of Adelaide.

Carbonell, V. M. (1958) *The Dentition of the Kish Population*. Dissertation for the Masters Degree, University of Chicago.

Chagula, W. K. (1960) The age at eruption of third permanent molars in male East Africans, *Amer. J. Phys. Anthrop.* **18**, 77.

Chappel, H. G. (1927) Jaws and teeth of ancient Hawaiians, *Mem. Bishop. Mus. Honolulu* **9**, 251.

Colyer, F. (1936) *Variations and Diseases of the Teeth of Animals*. Bale and Danielsson, London.

Dahlberg, A. A. (1951) The dentition of the American Indian. In W. S. Laughlin (ed.) *The Physical Anthropology of the American Indian*, pp. 138–76. Viking Fund, New York.

Darwin, C. (1883) *The Descent of Man and Selection in Relation to Sex*. Murray, London.

De Beer, G. R. (1951) *Embryos and Ancestors*. Clarendon Press, Oxford.

Dolder, E. (1936) Zahn-Unterzahl, *Schweiz. Mschr. Zahnhk.* **46**, 663.

Downs, W. G. (1927) Studies in the causes of dental anomalies, *Genetics* **12**, 570.

Friedrich, E. (1951) Die Weisheitszähne im Unterkiefer in der Unterzahlstatistik mit Berücksichtigung der Vererbungsfrage, *Stoma.* **4**, 41.

Goblirsch, A. W. (1930) A study of the third molar teeth, *J. Amer. Dent. Ass.* **17**, 1849.

Goldstein, M. S. (1932) Congenital absence and impaction of the third molar in the Eskimo mandible, *Amer. J. Phys. Anthrop.* **16**, 381.

Goldstein, M. S. (1948) Dentition of Indian crania from Texas, *Amer. J. Phys. Anthrop.* **6**, 63.

Goose, D. H. (1961) *A Metrical Study of Jaws and Teeth of Skulls from Different Historical Periods in Britain*. M.D.S. Thesis. University of Liverpool.

Grahnen, H. (1956) Hypodontia in the permanent dentition. A clinical and genetical investigation, *Odont. Revy.* **7**, Suppl. 3.

Gruneberg, H. (1951) The genetics of a tooth defect in the mouse, *Proc. Roy. Soc.* **138**, 437.

Hamano, N. S. I. K. (1926) Communication cited by Pedersen, 1949.

Hellgren, A. (1960) Variation in the dentition. In A. Lundstrom (ed.), *Introduction to Orthodontics*, pp. 77–103. McGraw-Hill, New York.

HELLMAN, M. (1928) Racial characters in human dentition. *Proc. Amer. Philos. Soc.* **67**, 157.

HELLMAN, M. (1936) Our third molar teeth, their eruption, presence and absence, *Dent. Cosmos.* **78**, 750.

HOLMER, U. and MAUNSBACH, A. B. (1956) Odontologische Untersuchung von Zähnen und Kiefern des Menschen aus der Steinzeit in Schweden, *Odont. Tidskr.* **64**, 437.

HOWARD, C. (1926) A study of jaw and arch development considered with the normal and abnormal skeleton, *Internat. J. Orthodont.* **12**, 1.

HRDLICKA, A. (1921) Further studies on tooth morphology, *Amer. J. Phys. Anthrop.* **4**, 141.

ILTIS, H. (1948) Inheritance of missing incisors, *J. Hered.* **39**, 363.

JÖHR, A. C. (1934) Reduktionserscheinungen an den oberen seitlichen Schneidezähnen, dominant gehäuft in einen Schwyzer Bergdorf, *Arch. Julius Klaus-Stift.* **9**, 73.

KEITH, A. (1924) *The Antiquity of Man.* Williams and Norgate, London.

KNAP, M. (1937) Een onderzoek naar de anwezigheid en ligging van den verstandskies bij verschillende bevolkingsgroepen in Nederl-Indie, *Tandheelk. Correspbl. vor Nederl.-Indie.* **5**, 87. (Quoted by Pedersen, 1949.)

LYSELL, L. (1953) Anodonti och hypodonti, *Svensk Tandlak.-tskr.* **46**, 79.

MANDEVILLE, L. C. (1950) Congenital absence of permanent maxillary lateral incisor teeth: a preliminary investigation, *Ann. Eugen., London.* **15**, 1.

McQUILLAN, J. H. (1870) Hereditary transmission of dental irregularities, *Dent. Cosmos.* **12**, 27, 73, 193.

MONTAGU, M. F. A. (1940) The significance of the variability of the upper lateral incisor in man, *Hum. Biol.* **12**, 323.

PEDERSEN, P. O. (1949) The East Greenland Eskimo dentition, *Meddelelser om Gronland* **142**. Copenhagen.

RANTANEN, A. (1955) Ylälenan toisen inkisiivin reduktioilmiöistä, *Finska Tandlak. Sallsk. Forhandl.* **51**, 155.

ROSE, C. (1906) Über die Rückbildung der seitlichen Schneidezähne des Oberkiefers und der Weisheitzähne im menschlichen Gebisse, *Dtsch. Mschr. Zahnhk.* **24**, 225.

RUFFER, A. (1920) Study of abnormalities and pathology of ancient Egyptian teeth, *Amer. J. Phys. Anthrop.* **3**, 335.

RUSHTON, M. A. (1953) Teeth. In A. Sorsby (ed.) *Clinical Genetics.* Butterworth, London.

SALZMANN, J. A. (1957) *Orthodontics. Principles and Prevention.* Lippincott, Philadelphia.

SHAW, J. C. M. (1931) *The Teeth, the Bony Palate, and the Mandible in Bantu Races of South Africa.* Bale and Danielsson, London.

Sinclair, B. Y., Cameron, D. A. and Goldsworthy, N. E. (1950) Observations on dental conditions among native peoples in Papua-New Guinea. In *Report of the New Guinea Nutrition Survey Expedition*, 1947, pp. 217–62. Pettifer, Sydney.

Spitzer, R. and Robinson, M. I. (1955) Radiological changes in teeth and skull in mental defectives, *Brit. J. Radiol.* **28**, 117.

Thoma, K. H. (1944) *Oral Pathology*. Mosby, St. Louis.

Twiesselmann, F. and Brabant, H. (1960) *Observations sur les dents et les maxillaires d'une population ancienne d'age Franc de Coxyde (Belgique)*. *Bull. G.I.R.S.*, No. 1, 3 and 4. Liège.

Werther, R. and Rothenberg, F. (1939) Anodontia, *Amer. J. Orthodont.* **25**, 61.

Wheelon, H. (1925) Clinical significance of the congenital absence of the upper lateral incisor teeth, *Endocrinology* **9**, 35.

THE DENTITION IN THE ASSESSMENT OF INDIVIDUAL AGE IN SKELETAL MATERIAL

by A. E. W. MILES

Department of Dental Histology and Pathology,
The London Hospital Medical College

It is not uncommonly desirable to estimate the age of subjects from skeletal material; for example, of contemporary subjects for forensic purposes as a step towards the ultimate establishment of the identity of the individual, and sometimes of ancient human remains for archeological purposes. Evidence of age may be deduced from the bones; for instance, from the study of the pubic symphysis or of the state of closure of cranial sutures (Brooks, 1955). Alternatively age may be deduced from the teeth. Indeed it is not uncommon for the bony parts to be so fragmentary that the teeth, which tend to survive much longer than other parts of the skeleton, provide the sole basis for an age estimation. It is generally acknowledged that none of the criteria used is very reliable, except in young subjects while the epiphyses remain ununited or while the dentition is immature.

Most of the published work refers to the forensic aspects of this subject and shows that age can be assessed from the teeth during the period of tooth development, that is up to about 18 years of age, with a fairly high degree of accuracy. In infants it may be possible to determine the age to within a few months or even weeks. I have elsewhere (Miles, 1958) reported a case where, making use of the fact that Massler and Schour (1946) have shown that deciduous dentine is laid down at about 4 μ per day, the age of the mummified remains of an infant was estimated to be a little over 3 months by measuring the thickness of dentine on the pulp or post-natal side of the neonatal

191

line in a longitudinal ground section of one of the deciduous molars.

A similar example which I have permission to quote (A. Boyde, unpublished) makes use of the fact that there is good evidence that the intervals between cross-striations of enamel prisms represent the amount of prism formed every 24 hr (Massler and Schour, 1946). The number of cross-striations between the neonatal line and enamel being formed at the time of death was counted in longitudinal sections of the teeth of a child from an Anglo-Saxon grave. From the state of development of the dentition as a whole, in comparison with that of contemporary children, the Anglo-Saxon child was estimated to be about 5 years of age. As a first stage the number of cross-striations between the neonatal line in the enamel of a first permanent molar and another easily identified incremental

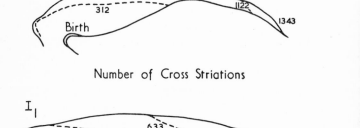

FIG. 1. *Above.* Drawing made from the longitudinal section of the first permanent molar showing the position of the principal incremental lines and their distances, in terms of of number of cross-striations, from the birth line. *Below.* Drawing made from the longitudinal section of the maxillary central incisor showing the corresponding 312, 633 and 1122 lines and counting continued as far as the last-formed enamel at the cervix.

line was found to be 312 (Fig. 1). The cervical enamel had suffered post-mortem damage so that in order to reach enamel still being formed it was necessary to transfer the counting to other teeth. A permanent central incisor was chosen and sectioned. The pattern of incremental lines corresponding to that in the molar was identified and counting was continued from the "312" line. The total number of cross-striations as far as the cervix of the tooth was 1692. Taking these to to be days in the life of the child an estimate of a little over $4\frac{1}{2}$ years is arrived at. This is a slight underestimate because the cervical enamel of this tooth had been completed and root formation had proceeded, probably for a month or two. Strictly speaking, in order to reach an enamel surface certainly being actively added to at the time of death counting should be continued on a section of a canine tooth. Apart from its interest as an example of age estimation this case suggests that the chronology of tooth development in Anglo-Saxon children was not far removed from that pertaining at the present time and is thus relevant to a matter to be discussed later.

In assessing age from dentitions that are immature, use is commonly made of a chart prepared by Schour and Massler (1941), published in slightly modified form by the American Dental Association and reproduced in many textbooks. Part of the chart is reproduced as Fig. 2. According to Kraus (1959) this chart, like many charts and tables of its kind, is based to a large extent upon observations made by Logan and Kronfeld (1933) and Kronfeld (1935) on sections of the jaws of 30 infants and children aged up to 15 years. Apart from the fact that no idea of the range of variation or of sex differences could be obtained from such a small number of subjects, many of the subjects studied died from prolonged debilitating illnesses which could have affected the chronology of tooth development (Garn, Lewis and Polacheck, 1959). Nevertheless, in practice the Schour and Massler chart appears to give useful and reasonably reliable results (Brauer and Bahador, 1942; Miles, 1958; Gray and Lamons, 1959). Its use is, however, virtually limited to ages below 15 years because no stages of growth of the third molars are recorded for the ages between 15 and 21 years.

In recent years there has been an accumulation of information about the progression of tooth growth by means of which revision of the chart could be undertaken. Kraus (1959) has, for instance, published data on the chronology of the early stages of formation of the deciduous teeth in 95 foetuses and Stack (1960) has recorded the growth status of foetal and infant dentitions, expressed in terms of dry weight of tooth substance. These contributions should provide assistance in the assessment of foetal and infant age.

Gleiser and Hunt (1955) have described in detail the stages of growth of the mandibular first permanent molar in radiographs of 25 girls and 25 boys taken at 6 monthly intervals from birth onwards. A similar, but larger and more extensive, longitudinal study by Garn *et al.* (1959) has provided data relating to all the permanent mandibular molars and premolars. Being based on a study of 225 children and presented with particularly good statistical treatment, this study shows, virtually for the first time, the range of variation that exists; for instance, the 50th percentile value for the age of apical closure of the first permanent molar in girls was 10·4 years and the 5th and 95th percentiles were 9·0 and 11·4 years respectively. These workers modestly issue the warning, however, that the size of their population sample falls short, though not grossly, of the number necessary for the establishment of a system of reliable "norms" (See Nolla, 1960).

It is worthy of note that Garn *et al.* found that the chronology of tooth development was slightly less variable than that of osseous development among the same group of subjects.

A smaller but similar longitudinal study by Fanning (1961), as well as providing data comparable, but by no means in complete agreement, with those of Garn *et al.*, has added information about the chronology of resorption of the roots of the deciduous teeth.

The mean values given by Gleiser and Hunt for the early stages of formation of the first permanent molar are several months later than those depicted on the Schour and Massler chart and the data of Garn *et al.* (1959) put these stages slightly later still. These discrepancies are not gross, however, especially when the whole dentition is being assessed.

Demisch and Wartmann (1956), in a paper devoted solely to the third molar, and Garn *et al.* (1959), give data for the growth of this tooth only as far as the beginning of root formation, namely about 15 years. The chronology of the completion of the root does not appear to have been the subject of special study.

Although it can be of any importance only where age assessments of extreme exactitude are being attempted, it should perhaps be borne in mind in interpolating from observed stages of tooth growth that there is evidence that growth of teeth as seen radiographically does not proceed at an entirely steady pace; the data of Gleiser and Hunt (1955) and of Fanning (1961) suggest that there is a pause or period of deceleration between the stages of completion of the crown and commencement of root formation.

When material can be sexed, allowance can be made for the fact that tooth development is very slightly but significantly more advanced in girls than in boys at all stages, even before puberty (Gleiser and Hunt, 1955; Garn, Lewis, Koski and Polacheck, 1958). The differences are of the order of 1 month in infancy and 4 months at 9 years and are slightly greater in respect of eruption than of tooth formation. These sex differences are, however, about three times less than those for osseous development over the same period so that, where material of unknown sex is concerned, estimates of age based upon the dentition are more likely to be correct than ones based upon osseous development.

Little appears to be known about possible racial differences in the chronology of tooth development and tooth growth. Racial differences could, however, reasonably be expected to be of small degree because the times of tooth eruption, which are more affected than tooth growth by sex differences, hormonal disturbances and dietary deficiencies, show only relatively slight racial differences (Steggerda and Hill, 1942; Hunt and Gleiser, 1955).

To assess age from the mature dentition, account must be taken of various dental minutiae which tend to change with age, such as the thickness of cementum, size of pulp cavities,

degree of wear of the teeth and the state of supporting tissue
The Gustafson method (Gustafson, 1950) awards 0–3 poin
for each of six such criteria and, from the total number of poin
scored, age is assessed by reference to a regression line prepare
from teeth of known age. Gustafson's work is widely and proper
acknowledged to be an extremely valuable attempt to introdu
a method which is not entirely subjective or intuitive.

Although there is no doubt that the Gustafson method ha
introduced a highly important principle, I am bound to sa
that I have not found the method quite as helpful as expecte
In 1959, thanks to the courtesy of, and in collaboration wit
Dr. D. B. Scott of the National Institute of Dental Researc
Bethesda, Washington, D.C., I assessed the age of about 2(
teeth of known age by the intuitive method or what we calle
the "visual guess", that is by inspecting them carefully an
evaluating subjectively various factors by a process in whic
previous experience was brought to bear intuitively rather tha
deliberately or systematically. We then estimated the age of t
same teeth by the Gustafson method. The results by th
Gustafson method were better but not by very much. Thirty
eight per cent were good estimates by the Gustafson metho
that is within 3 years of the real age, and 34 per cent were goo
estimates by the intuitive method.

Of the six criteria used by Gustafson, translucency of the ro
is the one which most lends itself to measurement. If a long
tudinal section of a tooth is held up to the light, provided it
not a young one, the apex is seen to be quite translucent (Fi
3). This translucency is the result of a process which tends
start at the apex of the root and with advancing age graduall
to extend along the root.

Figure 4 shows graphically the results of measuring with a
eyepiece graticule on sections of incisors of known age th
length of root that was translucent. Although it is evident fro
the amount of scatter that the relationship between ro
translucency and age is not an extremely close one, the calculate
regression line fits reasonably well. Using these data to asse
the age of another group of teeth gave 32 per cent goo

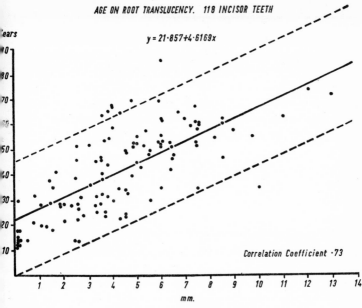

FIG. 4.   The relation of age to length of translucent root in longitudinal sections of 118 incisor teeth.
—————————(solid line) calculated regression line.
— — — —(broken line) 95 per cent confidence limits.

timates (±3 years) compared with 38 per cent of good timates using the Gustafson method. The value of this kind of objective data lies in the fact that use could presumably be made of it for age assessment by those with virtually no previous experience of either root translucency or age determination.

Zander and Hürzeler (1958) have described a method of calculating the mean thickness of cementum over the root surface from optical projections of transverse sections of the root and have shown that there is a straight line relationship between age and thickness of cementum.

If further steps could be taken to substitute objective measurement for the points system in the Gustafson method it might become possible to apply the sound basic principle of the method much more effectively.

It is very doubtful how much of the data and experience gained from a study of contemporary dentitions is applicable to archeological material because, in general, in earlier times dentitions were used with much greater vigour and in consequence wear of the teeth was much greater. Estimations of age of archeological material based upon the dentitions, even when made by experienced people, usually amount to little more than guesswork.

Consideration of the problem of assessing the ages of about 190 individuals excavated from an Anglo-Saxon burial site at Breedon-on-the-Hill in Leicestershire, and kindly placed at my disposal by Mr. D. Brothwell, has suggested the possibility of using wear of the teeth for assessing the age of individuals in such groups of skulls in a more systematic way than has hitherto been the case.

About one half of the skulls have reasonably complete dentitions and of these 38 are of young subjects with immature dentitions. An example of one of the older and more intact skulls is shown in Figs. 5 and 6. The dentition is very much worn with ante-mortem loss of a few teeth. It would be hard to say, even taking into account the state of the cranial sutures, whether the age of this person was nearer 40 or 60 years.

The plan of approach was to try to establish the rate of wear of the teeth from a study of the young skulls of which the age could reasonably be established from the state of development of the dentition, and so to acquire data which could be extrapolated or, as it were, projected forward to form a basis for the estimation of the ages of the older subjects.

The ages of the 38 dentally immature specimens were carefully estimated making use solely of the state of development of the dentitions in relation to the Schour and Massler chart modified slightly to take account of the works of Gleiser and Hunt and Garn et al. to which reference has already been made. Radiographs were available but a large proportion of the teeth could be removed from the skulls so that the stage of formation of the roots could be studied directly. For the assessment of the ages of those dentitions which had advanced beyond the state of commencement of the formation of the roots of the third molars (M_3) age was based on the assumption that M_3 erupted at about 18 years and that it took about 1 year for the tooth to pass through the stage of initial emergence from its crypt and reaching occlusion. Account was taken in particular of unpublished data collected in my department from a study of extracted third molars and radiographs of contemporary people. These data suggest that by 18 years the roots of M_3 are usually nearly complete in length and the apical canals are beginning to close; by 20 years the apical canals are usually closed although apical canals large enough to be seen with the naked eye are not uncommon; by 22 years the apical canals are not only closed but, in radiographs, are distinctly more constricted than at earlier periods.

Providing the assumption is made that the chronology of tooth development in these Anglo-Saxon people was similar to that which pertains at the present time, which seems not unreasonable, this group of 38 skulls can be regarded as a group of subjects of known ages.

Of the 38 skulls of "known age", 32 which had at least the first permanent molars erupted were suitable for the next stage which was to study the rate of wear of the permanent dentition. Attention was concentrated on the molar part of the dentition and observations on wear on other parts have been confined to noting that premolar wear proceeds in fairly close parallel with molar wear but incisor wear is much more erratic and variable.

When the 32 skulls, which ranged in fairly evenly distributed age order from 6 to 19 years, were arranged in that order a number of things became evident. First, wear of the occlusal surfaces of the teeth in general progressed in an orderly fashion through the range. Stages of polishing of the cusps were followed by the appearance of facets which increased in number and size according to a fairly regular pattern. Then small islands of dentine appeared at the tops of cusps and gradually increased in size. In several instances more than one skull was assigned the same age; for example, as many as 6 were estimated to be 18–19 years of age and such skulls showed quite closely similar degrees of wear so that there did not seem to be any wide individual variation in the material.

An observation made at this stage, which was utilized later, was that facets of wear appeared on the mesial aspects of the first and second molars, where they had contact with their neighbours, within a year or two of erupting and becoming functional.

It is now necessary to introduce the concept of the functional age of the teeth as opposed to the age of the subject. By functional age of a tooth is meant the length of time it has been a functional unit in the mouth. The first permanent molar erupts and starts its life of function at 6 years, the second molar at 12 years and the third molar at 18 years, so that in a subject aged 30 the first molar will have a functional age of 24 years, the second molar a functional age of 18 years and the third molar will have a functional age of 12 years. Similarly by a reverse process, if we say that a first permanent molar has a functional age of 19 years, it implies that the subject is 25 years of age.

From the group of skulls of known age we were able to see the condition of the first molar at its various functional ages up to 12 years and the second molar at various functional ages up to 6. It was found that at 18 years of age the second molar, with a functional age of 6 years, showed slightly less wear than the first molar at the same functional age, namely the first molar of a 12-year-old subject; that is second molars appeared to have worn at a slightly slower rate than first molars.

This was an important stage to have reached because, especially during the period of growth in adolescence, several factors are at work which might be supposed to affect the rate of wear of the dentition. As the dentition increases in size by the addition of more molars at the back, the rate of wear might diminish because the work done by the dentition would be more widely shared. Particularly at puberty, the muscular power of the jaws is increasing and this, together with the increased food intake associated with active somatic growth, would tend to increase the rate of wear. The position of the tooth in the dental arch might well affect the work done and hence the rate of wear; e.g. it must not be taken for granted that the rate of wear in the first molar region would be the same

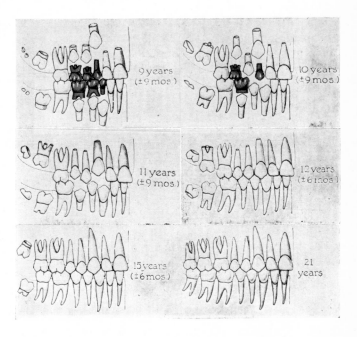

FIG. 2. A part of the Schour and Massler Chart. (*Reproduced by permission of the publishers, American Dental Association.*)

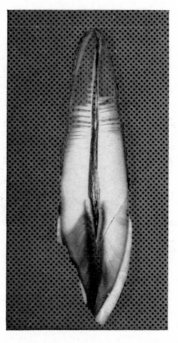

Fig. 3.   Longitudinal ground section of an incisor of a man
aged 52 years.   × 4.

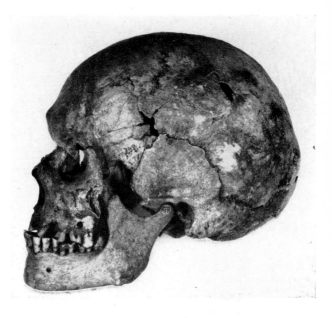

FIG. 5.   Lateral view of one of the better preserved skulls (B. 70).

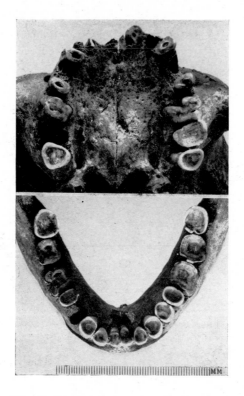

Fig. 6. The dentition of the same skull. There has been ante-mortem loss of some teeth; e.g. the right maxillary incisors, and the pulp cavities of several teeth are exposed by wear. Most of the enamel has been worn from the occlusal surfaces of M_3. The age of the subject was estimated to be 55 years.

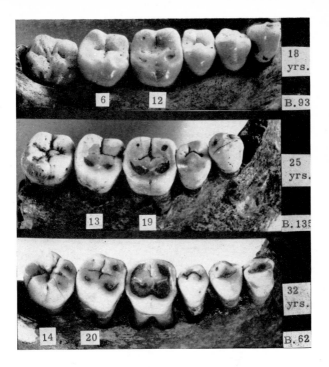

FIG. 7. *Above*. Mandible estimated—because M_3 is partially erupted—to be from a person aged about 18 years. Hence the functional age of M_1 is 12 years. *Middle*. Mandible of which M_2 shows a degree of wear similar to that of M_1 in the 18-year specimen above. The age is therefore estimated to be 25 years and it follows that the functional age of the M_1 is 19 years. *Below*. Mandible of which M_3 shows a degree of wear similar to that of M_2 of the 25-year specimen. The age is therefore estimated to be 32 years and it follows that the functional age of M_2 is 20 years and accords well with the close similarity between its state of wear and that of M_1 of the middle specimen. The serial numbers of the specimens and their estimated ages appear on the right. Figures overprinted on the specimens are the deduced functional ages of certain teeth.

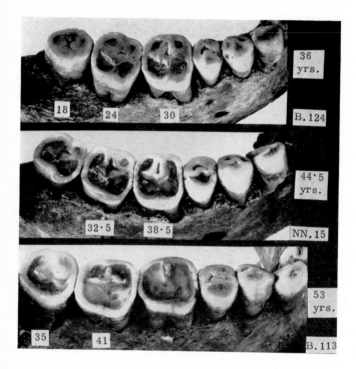

FIG. 8. Three mandibles of which, in order from above downwards, the states of M_1, M_2 and M_3 are judged to be similar. The serial numbers of the specimens, and their estimated ages, appear on the right. Figures overprinted on the specimens are the deduced functional ages of certain teeth.

as in the second and third molar regions. From our observations on wear of the first and second molars in the 32 skulls of known age, however, it seems likely that these factors tend to cancel one another out and attrition appears to proceed at a relatively constant rate. The impression was gained that the rate of wear of the first molar was not slowed by the appearance of the second molar as a working unit in the mouth but, as mentioned, second molars did seem to wear at a slightly slower pace than first molars.

As a next step in building up an age-determined series, skulls were selected which, from the small amount of wear of the third molars, could not be much older than those of the "known age" group. These were first put into serial age order on the basis of the amount of molar wear and then their ages were estimated by reference to the "known age" group by careful comparison of the amount of second and third molar wear with first and second molar wear in the skulls of "known age"; for example, a small facet of wear on the approximal surface of a third molar suggested that it had been erupted for not more than 2 years before death and led to a conclusion, providing other factors were consistent, that the skull was 20 years of age. If the second molars showed a degree of wear equal to 11 years of first molar wear it was taken to indicate that the second molars had also functioned for 11 years, or a little more, say one additional year, leading to an estimation for the age of the skull as 24 years. Finally, account was taken of the amount of wear shown by the third molars in comparison with the early degrees of wear of first and second molars in the series of "known age". In this way the data from the "known age" group was projected forward for another 6 years to extend the period of what could be regarded as reasonably confident estimation up to 24 years. This new group, added to the 32 skulls of "known age" gave us 38 skulls ranging from 6 years up to 24 years to provide a basis on which up to 18 years of M_1 wear could be compared with up to 12 years of M_2 wear and up to 6 years of M_3 wear. This group was regarded as the baseline on which the ages of the other specimens could be assessed.

During the course of the work each molar tooth was matched
in years of functional age with others in the group and the
impression gradually became stronger that the second and third
molars wear at a slower rate than the first molars. In fact, it is
evident that there is a gradient of rate in the molar region which
diminishes slightly from before backwards. This gradient has
been noted by other workers, particularly by Murphy (1959).
For my purpose it was necessary to give the gradient some form
of mathematical expression, however inaccurate. After careful
study of the attrition it was decided that the steepness of the
gradient could be reasonably expressed by the ratio of 6 : 6·5 : 7.
This means that it takes only 6 years for first molars to reach a
state of wear that it takes second and third molars respectively
6·5 and 7 years to reach. It also means that if a third molar
is found which matches a first molar which shows 18 years of
functional age, by a simple calculation it is possible to say that
the third molar is 21 years of functional age. It is necessary to
emphasize that the ratio that has been employed is merely an
expression of a subjective assessment and to guard against the
implication of mathematical precision that the use of figures
tends to convey.

Making the assumption that the rates of wear of the molars
remained constant throughout the life of the dentition, it was
now possible to project our data still further to assess the age of
older groups. Once more skulls were selected which were
functionally somewhat older than the preceding group and

Specimen B.70.

M_2 wear = 43 years of M_1 wear
$$43 + 4 + 12 = 59$$

M_3 wear = 33 years of M_1 wear
$$33 + 6 + 18 = 57 \longrightarrow 5$$

M_3 wear = 30 years of M_2 wear
$$30 + 2 + 18 = 50$$

FIG. 9. A typical example of the manner in which the age
was estimated by calculating functional age from comparisons of wear of the molar teeth.

again, by comparing the third molar wear with the second molar wear in the preceding groups and using the ratio 6 : 6·5 : 7 to calculate the functional age of the third molars, age assessments for the skulls were arrived at. The third and second molars were then compared with first molar wear of the basic group. Similar calculations gave two additional age assessments for the skull. The mean of the three estimates was taken to be the presumptive age of the skull (Figs. 7, 8 and 9).

The ages given by the three separate calculations were usually not widely divergent as they would have been had the principle of the method or the ratio used been completely wrong.

By taking successive groups of skulls and treating them in the same way the system was gradually extended by more and more periods which, because the initial intervals between eruption of the molars are 6 years, tended to amount each time to an advance of 6 years.

Figure 10 depicts the system diagrammatically. The various stages of wear of the occlusal surface of M_1 are depicted against time scales of both age of the individual and functional age of the tooth. The comparable stages of wear of M_2 and M_3 are similarly depicted. The diagonal lines indicate the system of making the comparison between the states of wear of the three generations of molars and also serve to emphasize that when the age of skulls up to a presumptive age of about 30 years was assessed comparison was being made directly with the baseline group, whereas over that age the comparison was made with groups progressively more distant from the baseline group. The system is, therefore, one of decreasing reliability with increasing age.

It was found possible, in this way, to include 73 of the skulls in an age-determined series. By the presumptive age of 45–50 years, however, the dentition was becoming so worn that teeth were being lost either by exposure of the pulp, by abscesses resulting from food wedging between the teeth or by accidents and disease processes of various kinds.

Finally, there was a residue of skulls of a large variety of ages in which the dentition was too incomplete by ante-mortem or post-mortem loss for the wear of the teeth to be used systematic-

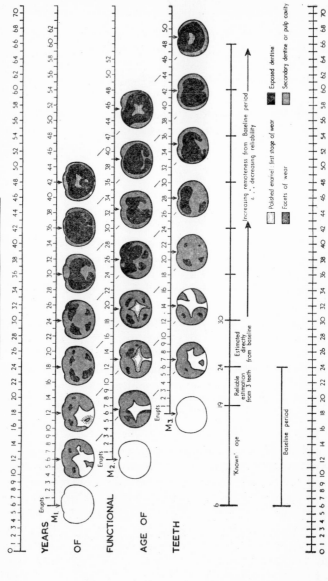

ally in the way described. The ages of these were estimated by simply matching the amount of wear of the dentitions against the range of ones already estimated systematically. Where there was ante-mortem loss of teeth or abscesses or other lesions likely to be painful were present, a subjective allowance was made for the fact that a bigger load of work would fall on other parts of the dentition and some teeth would become completely functionless.

The final result was a group of 157 skulls to which an age was assigned. Although, until some method can be found of checking

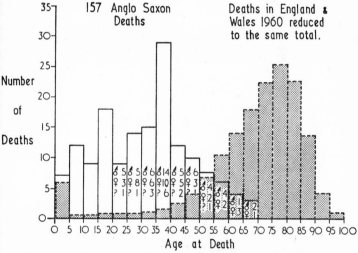

FIG. 11. Histogram (unshaded columns) of estimated ages of the 133 Anglo-Saxon skulls in 5-year groups. A histogram (shaded columns) representing the age distribution of 157 hypothetical deaths for a 1960 population is superimposed.

FIG. 10. Diagram showing the systematic use of molar wear for age assessment. The stages of wear of M_1 at 6-year intervals are depicted against time scales of age of subject and functional age of tooth. The comparable stages of wear of M_2 and M_3, linked by diagonal broken lines, are indicated, but at 6·5- and 7-year intervals in accord with the 6 : 6·5 : 7 gradient of molar wear.

the validity of the method employed to assess the ages, these findings must be regarded as tentative ones, they are given in Fig. 11 in the form of a histogram with the skulls grouped into 5-year periods. There are peaks at the 15–20 and 35–40 year periods. Using the conventional criteria of sex (Montagu, 1960) it was possible to form an opinion regarding the sex of 95 of the skulls. Fifty-two were regarded as male and 43 as female. Except in a few instances, it had not been possible to recover any of the post-cranial skeleton from the graves. Bearing in mind that about one-fifth of the sex estimates must be regarded as unreliable because the sex characteristics of the skulls were ill-defined, such differences as appear in the sex distributions within the various age groups cannot be regarded as significant.

I am greatly indebted to Mr. J. A. Heady of the M.R.C. Social Medicine Research Unit, The London Hospital, for the preparation of the superimposed histogram for 157 hypothetical contemporary deaths derived from the 1960 age-at-death figures for England and Wales. A comparison of the histograms can reasonably be made if it is assumed that the Breedon Anglo-Saxon population was a fairly stable one with a birth-rate about equal to the death-rate and with no marked immigration or emigration taking place. If this basic assumption is made the average age of all the 157 specimens, namely 31 years, gives a rough estimate of the expectation of life at birth for that population for comparison with an expectation of life at the present time for England and Wales, which is 71 years in recent times and in 1937 was 62 years. It is of particular interest to compare the estimate of 31 years for the expectation of life for this Anglo-Saxon population with estimates of 30 years for the expectation of life in Ancient Greece and 35 years in thirteenth-century England, quoted by Dublin, Lotka and Spiegelman (1949).

Reverting to the superimposed histogram, although there is a certain general similarity in the shapes of the curves, there are three notable differences. Firstly, the highest peak of the Anglo-Saxon curve is at 35–40 years whereas that of the hypothetical 1960 population is at 75–80 years. Secondly, there is in the Anglo-Saxon material no infant mortality peak. This could easily be accounted for by the failure of fragile infantile skeletal remains to survive centuries of burial. Thirdly, the peak of 15–20 year specimens in the Anglo-Saxon series is hard to account for unless it represents a "young warrior" class. This would be a more convincing suggestion if the peak was a little later, say at 20–25, but reconsideration of the age estimates of this particular group, which are based mainly upon the status of the third molars, has provided no reason to doubt their validity, unless the time of eruption of the third molars was, in fact, several years later than the estimated 18 years. The sex characteristics of this young group of skulls were too ill-defined for any worthwhile sex discrimination to be attempted.

There was a group of 24 skulls or skull fragments which were without jaws or had too few teeth for an age estimation to be made in the way described. It seemed possible that a high proportion of these might be of subjects of advanced age and that the exclusion of them from the series might have substantially modified the pattern of age distribution. This did not appear to be so, however, because when, on the basis of the general appearance of the skulls, they were separated into two categories, those thought to be under 40 years and those thought to be over that age, there were 13 in the first category and 11 in the other. The inclusion of these in the series on the basis that those in the first category were 30 years of age and those in the second 55 years of age gave a recalculated mean age of 32 years.

It must be very evident that the Breedon data could not be applied directly to any other collections of skulls, except, possibly, those where it is reasonable to assume a closely similar way of life, especially in respect of food habits; for instance, it might be justifiable to use it cautiously to assess the ages of Anglo-Saxon material of similar antiquity. Nevertheless, the basic principle of the method and even the ratio should be applicable to any group of skulls provided it includes sufficient dentally immature specimens to form a "baseline group". The application of the method would be very much aided if it could be shown that, although the actual rates of wear may differ in various populations according, principally, to the nature of the diet, the ratio between the rates of wear of first, second and third molars is more or less constant. Assuming that the ratio is constant, it would be necessary to establish the ratio more accurately than has been possible on the Breedon material. It might be possible to do this by studying the dentitions of living subjects if access could be obtained to people who not only experience a good deal of attrition but whose third molars, unlike those of most contemporary Europeans, do erupt and become fully functional.

REFERENCES

BRAUER, J. C. and BAHADOR, M. A. (1942) Variations in calcification and eruption of the deciduous and the permanent teeth, *J. Amer. Dent. Assoc.* **24**, 1373.

BROOKS, S. T. (1955) Skeletal age at death. The reliability of cranial and pubic age indicators, *Amer. J. Phys. Anthrop.* N.S. **13**, 567.

DEMISCH, A. and WARTMANN, P. (1956) Calcification of the mandibular third molar and its relation to skeletal and chronological age in children, *Child Development* **27**, 459.

DUBLIN, L. I., LOTKA, A. J. and SPIEGELMAN, M. (1949) *Length of Life. A Study of the Life Table.* 2nd ed. The Ronald Press Company, New York.

FANNING, E. A. (1961) A longitudinal study of tooth formation and root resorption, *N.Z. Dent. J.* **57**, 202.

GARN, S. M., LEWIS, A. B., KOSKI, K. and POLACHECK, D. L. (1958) The sex difference in tooth calcification, *J. Dent. Res.* **37**, 561.

GARN, S. M., LEWIS, A. B. and POLACHECK, D. L. (1959) Variability of tooth formation. *J. Dent. Res.* **38**, 135.

GLEISER, I. and HUNT, E. E. Jr. (1955) The permanent mandibular first molar: its calcification, eruption and decay, *Amer. J. Phys. Anthrop.* N.S. **13**, 253.

GRAY, S. W. and LAMONS, F. P. (1959) Skeletal development and tooth eruption in Atlanta children, *Amer. J. Orthodont.* **45**, 272.

GUSTAFSON, G. (1950) Age determination of teeth, *J. Amer. Dent. Assoc.* **41**, 45.

HUNT, E. E. Jr. and GLEISER, I. (1955) The estimation of age and sex of preadolescent children from bones and teeth, *Amer. J. Phys. Anthrop.* N.S. **13**, 479.

KRAUS, B. S. (1959) Calcification of the human deciduous teeth, *J. Amer. Dent. Assoc.* **59**, 1128.

KRONFELD, R. (1935) Development and calcification of the human deciduous and permanent dentition, *The Bur.* **35**, 18.

LOGAN, W. H. G. and KRONFELD, R. (1933) Development of the human jaws and surrounding structures from birth to age of fifteen years, *J. Amer. Dent. Assoc.* **20**, 379.

MASSLER, M. and SCHOUR, I. (1946) The appositional life span of the enamel and dentine-forming cells, *J. Dent. Res.* **25**, 145.

MILES, A. E. W. (1958) The assessment of age from the dentition, *Proc. Roy. Soc. Med.* **51**, 1057.

MONTAGU, M. F. ASHLEY (1960) *An Introduction to Physical Anthropology.* 3rd ed. Thomas, Illinois.

MURPHY, T. (1959) Gradients of dentine exposure in human molar tooth attrition, *Amer. J. Phys. Anthrop.* N.S. **17**, 179.

NOLLA, C. M. (1960) The development of the permanent teeth, *J. Dent. Child.* **27**, 254.

SCHOUR, I. and MASSLER, M. (1941) The development of the human dentition, *J. Amer. Dent. Assoc.* **28**, 1153.

STACK, M. V. (1960) Forensic estimation of age in infancy by gravimetric observations on the developing dentition, *J. Forens. Sci. Soc.* **1**, 49.

STEGGERDA, M. and HILL, T. J. (1942) Eruption time of teeth among Whites, Negroes and Indians, *Amer. J. Orthodont.* **28**, 361.

ZANDER, H. A. and HÜRZELER, B. (1958) Continuous cementum apposition, *J. Dent. Res.* **37**, 1035.

VARIATIONS IN THE FREQUENCY OF SHOVEL-SHAPED INCISORS IN DIFFERENT POPULATIONS

by **VIRGINIA M. CARBONELL***

Department of Dental Histology,
The London Hospital Medical College

A MAJOR aspect of the study of human dentition is the recognition and assessment of morphological variations. One such characteristic is the presence of structural formations referred to as "shovel-shape", manifested by the prominence of the mesial and distal ridges enclosing a central fossa in the lingual surface of incisor teeth, differentiating them from types without the shovel character. Shovel-shaped incisors are frequently found among the upper incisors and occasionally among the lower incisors. Generally they are bilateral, although in rare instances they are not (Hrdlicka, 1920).

The shovel character of incisor teeth has been described in early scientific literature (Carabelli, 1844; Muhlreiter, 1870; Tomes, 1876; Wortman, 1886; Black, 1894) and the presence of this morphological variation in the lingual surface of incisors is now common knowledge.

Anthropologists and odontologists have employed this feature as a criterion for assessment of population affinities and to help to trace population migration (Riesenfeld, 1956). Hrdlicka (1920) observed a high frequency of the shovel character in the lingual surface of the upper incisors of American Indians, and this study led to further such investigations in other populations. Other investigators (Montelius, 1933;

---

*Present address: Zoller Dental Clinic, University of Chicago, Chicago 37, Illinois.

211

Morse, 1937; Nelson, 1937–8; Stevenson, 1940; Lasker, 1945; Pedersen, 1949; Tratman, 1950; Dahlberg, 1951; Moorrees, 1957; Oschinsky 1960) working on the dentition of peoples with Mongoloid affinities, observed the high frequency of shovel-shaped incisors, and thus favourably confirmed Hrdlicka's earlier observations (Table III). Very little information has been reported on the incidence of shovel-shaped incisors in Caucasoid populations except in American "Whites" (Hrdlicka, 1920; Lasker, 1957), and Finns (Koski and Hautala, 1952).

The mode, origin, inheritance, and phylogenetic significance of shovel-shaped incisors is not yet understood, and there is still much data to be collected on the various racial groups. The purpose of this paper, therefore, is to:

1. Present additional information regarding the frequency of shovel-shaped incisors in ten relatively homogeneous groups of people: Romano-British, Anglo-Saxon (Early British), Danes, Swedes, Norwegian Lapps, Bantu, Arabs, Indians, East Greenland Eskimo, and a combined Japanese, Chinese and Tibetan series.

2. Analyse statistically the correlation of shovel morphology between the median and lateral incisors.

3. Trace the incidence of the shovel-trait in earlier forms of man.

The materials used in this study were available in the form of post-mortem remains (teeth) and dental casts (Table I). Each specimen was represented by an upper median and lateral incisor, in one side of the jaw. Employing Hrdlicka's (1920) subjective scale for degrees of shovelling (shovel, semi-shovel, trace shovel, and no shovel) and with the aid of standard models of the variations of the lingual surface of maxillary incisors[†] each tooth was examined separately. With the use of a measuring

†Prepared by A. A. DAHLBERG, *Models of Teeth* (Plaque PI. In his reference series: *Materials for the establishment of standards for the classification of tooth characters attributes and techniques in Morphological Studies of the dentition* (Zoller Laboratory of Dental Anthropology, University of Chicago).

‡Devised by A. A. Dahlberg and O. Mikkelson (1947).

TABLE I

LIST OF MATERIAL STUDIED AND THE INSTITUTIONS WHERE IT WAS MADE
AVAILABLE

Population	No.	Nature of specimens used	Source
Romano-British	100	Skulls with dentition	Natural History Museum London Duckworth Laboratory, Cambridge University
Anglo-Saxons	127	Skulls with dentition	Natural History Museum, London Royal College of Surgeons, London
Danes	89	Dental casts	Royal Dental School, Copenhagen, Denmark
Swedes	100	Dental casts	Royal Dental School, Copenhagen, Denmark
Lapps	98	Skulls with dentition	Anatomical Institute, University of Oslo, Norway
Bantu	122	Dental casts	Royal Dental School, Copenhagen, Denmark
Arabs	28	Skulls with dentition	Natural History Museum, London Duckworth Laboratory, Cambridge University
Indians	43	Skulls with dentition	Royal Dental School, Copenhagen, Denmark Natural History Museum, London Duckworth Laboratory, Cambridge University
East Greenland Eskimo	76	Dental casts	Royal Dental School, Copenhagen, Denmark
Japanese, Chinese and Tibetans	70	Dental casts and skulls with dentition	Royal Dental School, Copenhagen, Denmark Natural History Museum, London

device (modified bowley gauge)‡ the depth of the lingual fossa
was measured from a point midway between the incisal and
gingival margins, and midway from the mesial and distal
enamel margins. A measure of 1+mm was considered as
shovel, 1 mm as semi-shovel, and 1−mm as trace-shovel. At

the same time the correlation of the degree of shovel-shape observed in the median and in the lateral incisors was analysed statistically since in most cases shovel-shapes were frequently observed in the lateral incisors. Therefore, a score was designated for each degree of shovel, which was later entered in the statistical analysis: § 3 for shovel, 2 for semi-shovel, 1 for trace-shovel, and 0 for no shovel (Fig. 1).

RESULTS OF PRESENT STUDY AND ANALYSIS OF DATA

The histogram in Fig. 2 presents the data gathered from this investigation. Shovel-shaped incisors are present in varying frequencies among the groups studied. There is a definite range in the frequency of shovel-shaped incisors in Mongoloid and non-Mongoloid groups. A high frequency of shovel-shaped incisors is found in groups with Mongoloid affinities, compared to the low frequency of shovel-shaped incisors in Caucasoid groups (as exemplified by the Romano-British, Anglo-Saxons, Danes and Swedes). At the same time, the claim that the lateral incisor is more affected by shovelling is to some degree supported by my own work, although the difference is not very significant.

Variations in the frequency of different degrees of shovelling were also observed among the ten ethnic groups and also between the median and lateral incisors in each group. There is indeed a tendency for shovel-shaped incisors to be found more often in populations with Mongoloid affinities shown by the high frequency of shovel-shaped incisors in the East Greenland Eskimo, and the combined Japanese, Chinese and Tibetan

§Correlation coefficient test: R was calculated from the formula:

$$R = \frac{\frac{1}{n} \, \sigma \, u \, v - \bar{u} \, \bar{v}}{\sigma \, u \, \sigma \, v}$$

and its significance from:

$$t = \frac{r \, \sqrt{(n-2)}}{\sqrt{(1-r^2)}}$$

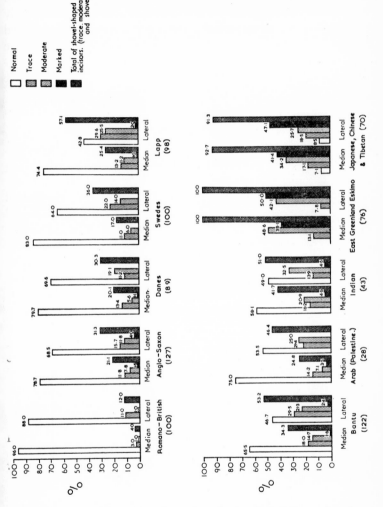

FIG. 2.   Histograms representing the results of the study of
shovel-shaped upper median and lateral incisors in ten
relatively homogeneous populations.

Table II

Results of Correlation Coefficient Test†

Population	Frequency	Degrees of freedom	R (to 2 dec. places)	T test	Probability
Romano-British	100	98	0·70	9·6	<0·001
Anglo-Saxons	127	125	0·81	15·4	<0·001
Danes	89	87	0·77	11·4	<0·001
Swedes	100	98	0·67	8·9	<0·001
Lapps	98	96	0·49	5·5	<0·001
Bantu	122	120	0·81	15·1	<0·001
Arabs	28	26	0·72	5·3	<0·001
Indians	43	41	0·95	18·7	<0·001
East Greenland Eskimo	76	74	0·62	6·8	<0·001
Japanese, Chinese and Tibetans	70	68	0·84	12·8	<0·001

†Correlation between median and lateral incisors for shovel morphology.

groups, while in the Caucasoid groups absence of shovel-shape is the characteristic feature of incisor teeth.

Table II presents a statistical analysis of the correlation of morphology observed in the median and lateral incisors. All the data collected on these two teeth presents highly significant correlations, which are mostly in the range of $r=0·6$ and above, except in the Lapp group where r is only $0·49$ (but still in the range of significance). When the shovel form is present in the median incisor, it is therefore usual to find it also in the lateral incisor, to the same degree. However, in a few instances this does not occur owing to the greater variability of the lateral incisor. The cases observed in the groups which I studied all conform to the normal pattern, although abnormal forms may sometimes occur in a population sample. These latter cases have been attributed to aberrant development (Hallet, 1953; Miles, 1954), and it is possible that some observers have included such incisors in their data.

In view of the noticeable correlation of such morphological

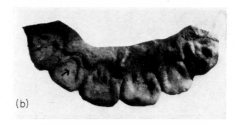

Fig. 1. The four types of shovel-shapes established by Hrdlicka (1920), illustrating the scales and scores employed in evaluation. Arrow indicates the point where the measurement was taken from. (Dental casts prepared by Dr. A. A. Dahlberg; Plaque 1 of his reference series.) (a) Shovel: the enamel rim and the enclosed fossa are well developed and pronounced. 1 +mm. in depth from the fossa to the rim of the enamel margin. Score: 3. (b) Semi or moderate shovel: the enamel rim is distinct but the fossa is shallow. 1 mm. in depth. Score: 2. (c) Trace shovel: trace of shovel character is distinct. 1 —mm. in depth. Score: 1. (d) Non-shovel: there is no perceptible trace of rim or fossa formation, or where faint or imperfect enamel margin is present. No measurement, Score: 0.

Fig. 3. Upper median and lateral incisors of a Romano-British skull showing a slightly shovel-shaped median incisor and a moderately shovel-shaped lateral incisor (E 11.8. 385 BNHM).

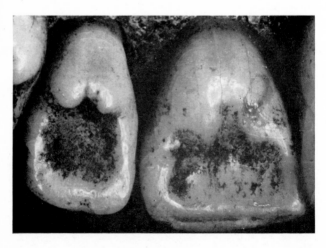

Fig. 4. Upper median and lateral incisors of an Anglo-Saxon skull showing a moderately shovel-shaped lingual surface (E 11.9. 496 BNHM).

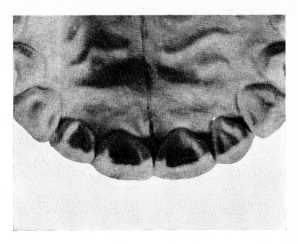

Fig. 5. Dental cast of an East Greenland Eskimo with shovel-shaped upper median and lateral incisors (No. 183, after P. O. Pedersen).

Fig. 6. Shovel-shaped upper incisors of a Chinese skull (As. 60. 750 BNHM).

Population and Investigator	MEDIAN					LATERAL				
	No.	No shovel	Trace	Moderate	Shovel	No.	No shovel	Trace	Moderate	Shovel
Chinese (Hrdlicka 1920)	♀ 208	3·8	1·0	12·5	82·7	♀ 208	3·4	1·0	13·5	68·8
	♂1094	7·8	1·8	23·5	66·2	♂1094	9·5	1·5	24·0	56·9
Mongolian (Hrdlicka 1920)	24	—	8·5	29·0	62·5	24	—	—	25·0	75·0
Eskimo (Hrdlicka 1920)	40	—	15·0	47·5	37·5	37	—	—	43·0	57·0
Pima Indian (Dahlberg 1951)	♀ 125	—	1·0	—	99·0	♀ 119	—	7·0	—	81·0
	♂ 101	—	4·0	—	96·0	♂ 93	1·0	13·0	—	81·0
Japanese (Hrdlicka 1920)	♂ 344	4·0	—	18·0	77·9	♂ 344	4·0	—	20·3	72·7
Aleut* (Moorrees 1957)	75	—	2·7	34·7	62·6	70	—	2·9	31·4	65·7
N. Chinese (Stevenson 1940)	904	18·2	19·7	53·9	8·3	904	4·1	85·9†		0

Median and Lateral Incisors Combined

Population and Investigator	No.	No shovel	Trace	Moderate	Shovel
East Greenland Eskimo (Pedersen 1949)	116	—	1·7	14·7	83·6
American Born Chinese (Lasker 1945)	269	2·2	13·0	66·2	18·6

*Shovel and marked types combined.   †Trace and moderate combined.

characters of the median and lateral incisors, it seems possibl
that a common genetic factor is involved.

PREVIOUS STUDIES ON SHOVEL-SHAPED INCISORS

Previous dental investigations on different early and presen
populations report the incidence of shovel-shaped incisors ir
varying degrees of frequency. Table III presents some of the
data collected by previous investigators from populations witl
Mongoloid elements.

Hrdlicka (1920) reports a high frequency of shovel-shapec
median and lateral incisors in the Chinese, Mongolians
Eskimo, and Japanese, with a very low frequency of non-shovel
shaped incisors in the Chinese and Japanese, and absence o:
non-shovel-shaped incisors in the Mongolians and Eskimo
Dahlberg (1951) and Moorrees (1957) found a similar high
frequency of shovel-shaped incisors in Pima Indians and Aleut:
respectively.

In 30 Knoll Indian individuals (Dahlberg, 1951) moderate
and shovel-shaped incisors were found in 98·5 per cent, which
is as high as observed in the Pima Indians; and Sarnas (personal
communication) reports 66 per cent shovel-shaped median and
65 per cent shovel-shaped lateral incisors in 110 Knoll Indian
skulls, while an absence of shovelling was found in 14 per cent
median and 16 per cent lateral incisors. Shovel-shaped incisors
were also observed in very high frequency among the Northwestern Coast Indian populations of North America (Nootka,
Chinook, Kwakiutl, Tlingit and Tsimshian); where the shovel
morphology is very marked and similar to the double shovel-
shape† type frequently found among other American Indians
and Eskimos (Carbonell, unpublished). Campbell (1925)
reports that shovel-shaped incisors are also found among the
Australian Aboriginals but with a very low frequency. Prominent lateral borders and lingual fossa, reflecting the character of
shovel-shape, were observed in some Tasmanians (Abrahams,
1950). Shovel-shaped incisors were recognized in 5 Aeta skulls

†The labial as well as the lingual surface has a central depression
as related to the mesial and distal margins (Dahlberg, Plaque 1, d).

out of 7 individuals (Genet-Varcin, 1951). In 47 Hawaiian skulls Chappel (1927) observed 27·6 per cent shovel-shaped incisors although some are only slightly shovel-shaped. Hrdlicka (1920) investigated shovel-shaped incisor teeth in 59 Hawaiian individuals observing a 93·2 per cent occurrence among the cases examined. The latter observation on the same ethnic group thus presents a much higher frequency than in the investigation by Chappel, the difference in the results being perhaps largely due to discrepancies in subjective methods of evaluation by the different investigators, and also to differences in the geographical location of the population samples.

Differences in the frequencies of shovel-shaped incisors have been analysed in the inhabitants of Indonesia (93 per cent), Micronesia (78 per cent), Polynesia (79 per cent), Fiji (48 per cent), New Guinea (49 per cent), Ralum (19 per cent), Solomons (41 per cent), Melanesia (50 per cent), and Australia (64 per cent) to trace the Mongoloid cline along the route from Indonesia, through Micronesia, and to Polynesia (Riesenfield, 1956).

Moderate shovel-shaped incisors show a high frequency (66·2 per cent) in the American born Chinese (Lasker, 1945), and Stevenson (1940) notes the same trend in the Northern Chinese. The differences in the frequency of shovel morphology between the median and lateral incisors are not greatly significant. The non-shovel-shaped incisor values are all very low except in the Northern Chinese where they are 18·1, which is still relatively low compared with "White" populations. Montelius (1933) reports a figure of probably more than 79 per cent of shovel-shaped incisors in 3520 Chinese individuals. Morse (1937) observed sexual dimorphism in the occurrence of shovel-shaped incisors while studying the dentition of the Chinese; he found that pronounced shovel-shaped incisors were more frequent in females than in males, a fact which supports the earlier evidence by Hrdlicka (1920). Morse (1937) also observed differences in the geographical distribution of shovel-shaped incisors in the Chinese; higher frequencies being found in East, North and Central China, while the Western and Southern inhabitants showed the lowest figures. H.R.H. Prince

Peter of Greece and Denmark (1957) in his anthropological investigation of a Tibetan population in West Bengal, India, found that shovel-shaped incisors were prevalent in the upper incisors of this population. In two ancient Chinese burial sites (later period of Shang Dynasty, 1766–1122 B.C.) 80–90 per cent of shovel-shaped incisors were observed in the human remains (Mao and Yen, 1959).

The data collected from the East Greenland Eskimo, and Japanese, Chinese and Tibetan groups in the present study favourably conform with the observations made by previous investigators in Mongoloid populations.

Information regarding the frequency of shovel-shaped incisors in other racial groups is indeed very scanty. Table IV presents the data gathered by other investigators on racial groups other than Mongoloids. In some of the populations listed in this table, shovel-shaping displays a higher frequency in the lateral incisors than in the median. The differences, however, are not very significant in all the groups. Marked shovel-shaped incisors are very rare in these groups and non-shovel-shaped incisors show a higher frequency than shovel-shaped incisors, except in the Finns (Koski and Hautala, 1952) where non-shovel is very low. Shaw (1931) reports a low frequency of shovel-shaped incisors in his Bantu material. The American Negro group (Hrdlicka, 1920) shows a frequency closer to the data collected on American "Whites" (Hrdlicka, 1920).

The medieval population of Westerhus, Sweden, was found to have a frequency of 24·1 per cent of all degrees of shovelling in the females and 38·5 per cent among the males (Gejvall, 1960). Moderate shovel-shaped incisors are characteristic of the Middle Minoans (1750–1550 B.C.) with a frequency of 46 per cent; and marked shovel incisors have noticeably high incidence (27 per cent) in early Crete (Carr, 1960) compared with the frequencies listed in Table IV. Brabant (1961) notes shovel-shaped incisors in the Bronze Age human remains from Matelles, France (2500–1500 B.C.), which have a frequency of 29·3 per cent; and shovelling has also been noted in the incisors of the early inhabitants of Switzerland, 1750–1550 B.C. (Schwerz,

TABLE IV

DISTRIBUTION OF SHOVEL-SHAPED INCISORS IN WHITE POPULATIONS AND OTHER NON-MONGOLOID GROUPS (IN PERCENTAGES)

Population and Investigator	MEDIAN					LATERAL				
	No.	No shovel	Trace	Moderate	Shovel	No.	No shovel	Trace	Moderate	Shovel
American Whites (Hrdlicka 1920)	♂1000 ♀1000	66·5 70·4	24·5 21·8	7·6 5·2	1·4 2·6	♂1000 ♀1000	50·0 59·6	36·4 29·9	8·8 7·4	1·4 1·0
Finns (Koski and Hautala 1952)	423	9·0	76·4	10·9	3·8	408	7·1	73·3	16·7	2·9
American Whites (Lasker 1957)	642	55·0	45·0†		0	642	50·0	50·0†		0
Human Remains from Matelles* (Brabant et al. 1961)	58	56·8	13·7	29·3‡		66	50·0	12·1	37·8‡	
American Negro (Hrdlicka 1920)	♂618 ♀1000	54·5 56·0	33·0 32·6	7·6 8·0	4·9 3·6	♂618 ♀1000	42·1 47·5	38·0 35·1	12·8 11·1	4·5 3·8
Median and Lateral Incisors Combined										
Bantu (Shaw 1931)	264	83·4	1·5	8·3	6·8					
Middle Minoans (Carr 1960)	26	8·0	19·0§	46·0	27·0					
Westerhus Skulls* (Gejvall 1960)	♂ 62 ♀ 57	75·9 61·4	24·1§ 38·5§							

*Figures reported by investigators converted in percentages for this report. †Trace and moderate combined.

‡Moderate and shovel combined. §All degrees of shovel combined.

mentioned by Hrdlicka, 1920). Senyürek (1952) and Krogman (1937) have noted slightly shovel-shaped incisors in individuals from Chalcolithic, Copper and Early Bronze Age sites in Anatolia. A high proportion of the skulls from Troy and Western Anatolia from Troy I to late Roman times are slightly or moderately shovel-shaped (Angel, 1951). It therefore seems likely that slight and moderate degrees of shovel-shaped incisors were not infrequent among the ancient inhabitants of Anatolia.

In the series of dentitions from Kish, Mesopotamia (3000 B.C.) only one slightly shovel-shaped median incisor was observed among 23 median incisors, and there was an absence of the trait in 26 lateral incisors (Carbonell, 1958). However, although shovel-shaped upper incisors were apparently not characteristic of this particular population, dental tubercles with a well-defined cuspule on the lingual surface were frequent.

The Nakuru skull (IX) (Kenya Neolithic c. 850 B.C.) from East Africa (Leakey, 1935) displays moderate shovel-shaped lateral incisors. The morphology of the lingual surface of the median incisors was not perceptible because of the heavy incisal and lingual attrition on these surfaces.

SHOVEL-SHAPED INCISORS IN FOSSIL MAN

Earlier hominid forms share with modern man the character of shovel-shape in their upper incisors. A number of these have been reported in the literature, especially in the Neanderthal and Australopithecine groups. Hrdlicka (1920) states, "we should also expect to find a large proportion of shovel-shaped teeth in early and prehistoric ancestors, with a gradually increasing proportion as we proceed backwards". He continues, "shovel morphology is a necessity for strengthening of the incisor teeth which seems quite relevant with the gradual diminishing of shovel-shape character in the upper incisors of modern cultured man and also in Egyptians".

Unfortunately fossil hominid upper incisor teeth are very rare, and the number with characteristic shovelling is extremely small covering a time period of about 1,000,000 years and representing many world populations (Fig. 7).

The Neanderthals are relatively well represented as regards

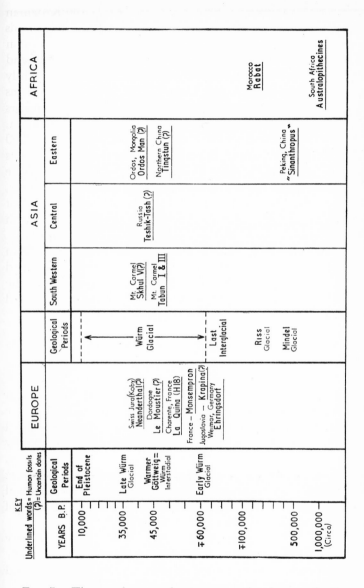

FIG. 7.   Time and space chart representing human fossils with upper shovel-shaped incisors.

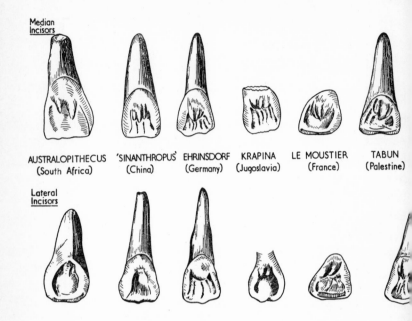

FIG. 8.   Morphological structures of the lingual surface of upper incisors in early forms of man.

the shovel-shaped incisor which is surprisingly consistent in form (Fig. 8). In the Krapina fossils described by Garjanovic-Kramberger (1906), one maxillary fragment consists of median and lateral incisors which are shovel-shaped, accompanied by the presence of a lingual tuberosity. An examination of the maxillary cast was undertaken to determine the shovel character of the incisors in this fossil, which in my opinion resembles the shovel form found occasionally in modern populations. Disagreement has been expressed among investigators regarding the difference between the Krapina incisors and other Neanderthals (Adloff, 1938).

Koby (1956) reports on Neanderthal remains found in a cave in the Swiss Jura; he says, "The tooth shows the classical Neanderthalian characteristic, enormous development of the

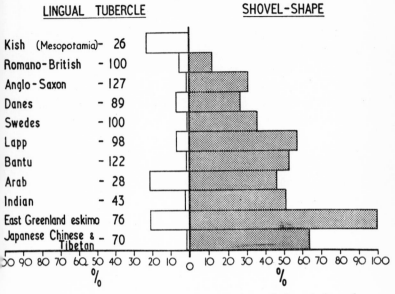

FREQUENCY OF LINGUAL TUBERCLE AND
SHOVEL—SHAPE FORM ON LATERAL INCISORS

LINGUAL TUBERCLE   SHOVEL—SHAPE

Kish (Mesopotamia)— 26
Romano—British   — 100
Anglo—Saxon   — 127
Danes   — 89
Swedes   — 100
Lapp   — 98
Bantu   — 122
Arab   — 28
Indian   — 43
East Greenland eskimo 76
Japanese Chinese & — 70
       Tibetan

Fig. 9.   Frequency of lingual tubercle and shovel-shaped
form on lateral incisors.

tubercula dentalia and marked marginal ridges". Another
approximately contemporaneous fossil was uncovered in
Dordogne, France. The upper incisor teeth were described by
Gregory (1920–1) as follows: "The lingual surface shows a
slight folding around the sides in continuation with the cutting
edge, so that if the tooth were much worn it would approximate
to the shovel-shaped section in the Krapina and various modern
races, but there is little if any fossa or concavity in the lingual
surface . . .". Illustrations (Weidenreich, 1937) and a cast of the
Le Moustier incisors show the marginal ridges accompanied
by the presence of a dental or lingual tubercle. The lingual
surface is moderately shovel-shaped. The reason why Gregory
(1920–1) described the lingual fossa as "very little", was

probably because it does not simulate the heavy strong character of the typical shovel type.

The fossil record from Southwestern Asia includes two series of human remains from Mt. Carmel, the Skhül fossils and the earlier Tabun series (McCown and Keith, 1939); representing two different stages of human evolution. The Skhül incisors are not very well described in the literature and there is only one skull which has a complete dentition in the upper jaw. Personal inspection of the cast is not very satisfactory, although a slight ridge along the margin of the left lateral incisor is evident. The Tabun teeth include a number of incisors, but only a median and two lateral incisors were complete enough to examine for shovelling. These teeth exhibit a considerable degree of shovel-shaping, with pronounced mesial and distal ridges accompanied by a multicusped tubercle in the median incisor and a cuspule in the lateral incisor.

The Neanderthal child from Teshik-Tash Cave in Southern Uzbekistan has "an extreme shovel-shaped form of the lateral incisors which resembles the characters of the Mt. Carmel incisors", according to Weidenreich (1945), "thus exhibiting Mongolian racial characteristics". In Eastern Asia, the discovery of the Ordos Man, in Inner Mongolia, represents the second stage of human evolution in North Eastern Asia (Licent and Chardin, 1922). The lateral incisor was described as shovel-shaped in the lingual surface besides bearing a prominent basal tubercle. Tingstun Man (Woo, 1956), from China, who was probably contemporaneous with Ordos Man, provides three more incisors for study; both the median and lateral incisors were both markedly shovel-shaped resembling characteristics found in modern Mongoloids.

The earliest evidence of the Neanderthal group is to be found in France and Germany. The La Quina youth's dentition was studied by Martin (1926) who described the concavity of the lingual surface formed by the marginal ridges, and a pronounced eminence representing the lingual tubercle. Both the median and lateral incisors are shovel-shaped. The incisors from Monsempron (Vallois, 1950–3) were described as shovel-shaped in the lingual surface of the median and lateral incisors, exhibiting a lingual tubercle. Illustrations (Weidenreich, 1937) of the Ehringsdorf Child incisors clearly present their shovel-shaped character, which resembles the morphology of the lingual surface of the incisors of some other Neanderthals; marginal ridges accompanied by a dental tubercle both in the median and lateral incisors.

In Northern Africa shovel-shaped incisors are present in the Moroccan Rabat Man which Vallois (1960) describes as "spatulate" and not as markedly shovel-shaped as in the Mongoloids and *Sinanthropus*. An examination of the cast of the Rabat fossil revealed a moderately shovel-shaped lingual surface which agrees favourably with Vallois' evaluation.

One of the earliest representatives of man, from Choukoutien, Peking, displays incisor teeth which are markedly shovel-shaped, resembling the shovel character of the incisors of modern Mongoloid populations. The typical shovel character is accompanied by the presence of a strongly developed basal tubercle. Because of the resemblance of the morphology of the *Sinanthropus* incisors to the modern Mongols, and in view of the geographical proximity, Weidenreich (1937) concluded that *Sinanthropus* is directly related to modern Mongolian populations.

"Moderate shovel-shaped incisors is characteristic of the Australopithecines." Robinson in his monumental paper on the dentition of the Australopithecines (1956) described in detail the teeth including the incisors. In *Australopithecus* a more moderate shovel-shape is found in the lateral incisor than in the median incisor. Robinson observed that moderate shovel-shaped incisors are usual but in the lateral incisors variation in the degrees of the shovel character exists.

The fossil specimens cited in this paper are the only ones recorded with shovel incisors. However, with the scarcity of fossil material, especially the incisor teeth, it is therefore difficult to evaluate the true frequency of this dental trait in prehistoric men. It is, however, obvious that shovel-shaped incisors do exist in the dentitions of man's early ancestors, displaying the same morphological features found in modern races. Variations in the degree of shovel-shape were also observed in the fossil hominids and these degrees of variations are also found duplicated in modern races (Robinson, 1956).

DISCUSSION AND CONCLUSIONS

On the basis of this study, it is evident that shovel-shaped incisors vary considerably in different recent populations, the feature also being present in the incisors of palaeoanthropic man. In modern populations, marked shovel morphology usually suggests Mongoloid affinities. Trace and absence of shovel types occurs infrequently in Mongoloids (Hrdlicka, 1920; Dahlberg, 1951; Moorrees, 1957; and others), and this has been observed in the present study in the East Greenland Eskimo, and combined Japanese, Chinese and Tibetan groups. In Caucasoid races, moderate and shovel forms are very rare, while trace shovel form represents the highest frequency among shovel types, but with a higher frequency of non-shovel-shaped incisors (Hrdlicka, 1920). This pattern of frequency was also observed in the present study among the Romano-British, Anglo-Saxons, Swedes, and Danes. However, trace shovel incisors were predominant in the Finns (Koski and Hautala, 1952) associated with a low frequency of non-shovel-shaped incisors which does not at all conform with the trend of pattern found in other "White" races. Lasker (1957) found that 40–50 per cent of the upper incisors in American "Whites" are shovel-shaped, a fact incompatible with Hrdlicka's (1920) data on the same ethnic group. However, more recently, Lasker (1960) modifies his previous figures and notes that the shovel-shape is found in 14 per cent of the American population, and that half the population shows the tendency to manifest mesial and distal ridges. Hrdlicka's (1920) data agree with the other data on "White" populations given in the present study, which confirms the rarity of shovel-shape in "White" populations.

Differences in frequency and variations in degree of shovel-shaped incisors within racial groups are evident from a study of the differences in frequency of shovel-shaping among the different tribes of American Indians (Hrdlicka, 1920), in the Chinese from different geographical areas (Stevenson, 1940; Lasker, 1945), and perhaps also among the ancient Hawaiians

(Chappel, 1927; Hrdlicka, 1920). There is also a difference in the observations made by Shaw (1931) on shovel-shaped incisors in his Bantu series compared to the Bantu group presented in this study; and although both of them belong to the same broad ethnic group, they may well have come from different areas of South Africa and may therefore represent two isolates.

Moderate shovel and shovel forms are more frequent in earlier populations represented by the Middle Minoans (Carr, 1960), and the human remains from Matelles, France (Brabant, Sahly and Bouyssou, 1961). The medieval Westerhus skulls (Gejvall, 1960) from Sweden exhibit a frequency conforming to the observations gathered from other Caucasoid groups (Hrdlicka, 1920, and observations in the present study).

Shovel-shaped incisors in early man were observed to be associated with the presence of a lingual tubercle. This feature is quite consistent, especially in the upper lateral incisors observed in the Neanderthals, *Sinanthropus*, and Australopithecines (Vallois, 1950–3; Weidenreich, 1937; Robinson, 1956). The association of shovel-shape with a lingual tubercle in modern man is infrequent. The Japanese, Chinese and Tibetan group in the present study, exhibit the lowest frequency of lingual tubercle, 1·4 per cent, while in the Arabs it attains the high figure of 21 per cent. Adloff (1938) distinguishes two types of incisor, the cusp form and the shovel form; and he interprets the shovel form as being secondarily derived from the cusp form by a reduction of the lingual tubercle. According to Robinson (1956) the facts are against the view that the lingual tubercle is a primitive hominid structure, although Adloff (1908) and Weidenreich (1937) regard it as a primitive character.

The results of this study suggest the continued modification of the structural pattern in the lingual surface of upper incisor teeth from early to modern man. Shovel character associated with a lingual tubercle was almost consistently found in palaeoanthropic man. In modern man, considerable diversity was observed, the shovel character being with or without the presence of a lingual tubercle and vice versa; confirming previous observations by Dahlberg (1951) and Moorrees (1957).

The origin of the shovel trait is obscure (Krogman, 1960). The phylogenetic significance of these characters, shovel-shape, lingual tubercle, and marginal ridges remains to be investigated further, in order to understand the morphological differentiation of these features. Family studies would greatly enhance the knowledge of shovel morphology and the different degrees c variation; so far few have considered the genetics of the trait. Abrahams (1949) observed the apparently recessive characte of the shovel trait in the Cape Malay peoples in South Africa where it is more infrequent than in the ancestral indigenou Malays. Lasker (1950) has noted the concordance of the degree and expression of shovel-shape in monozygous twin pairs.

An evaluation of the degree of shovel character is to some extent largely subjective, and discrepancies in results gathered from the same ethnic groups by different workers certainly occur; for example, in the data collected on the East Greenland Eskimo groups (Pedersen, 1949, and the present study). The discrepancy is probably due to the fact that the number o subjects in both studies is different. In any case a more accurate method of evaluating shovel-shape would seem to be urgentl needed at present. Dahlberg and Mikkelson's method (1947) of measuring the depth of the fossa on the highest parts of the rim and the deepest point of the fossa is indeed the first attempt to use a metrical system for the evaluation of the shovel character. However, in the present study, some modification of their technique was necessary in order to eliminate anatomica structures on the lingual surface, such as lingual tubercles, which would obscure the correct evaluation. A standard method of estimating the degree of shovel-shape would certainly help to eliminate the subjective errors of different workers.

ACKNOWLEDGEMENTS

The author wishes to express her sincere gratitude to Professc A. E. W. Miles and to Dr. K. P. Oakley, F.B.A., for thei untiring guidance; also to Professor P. O. Pedersen and Professor A. Bjork and to Professor J. Torgersen for permission to examine material in their departments. I am also indebted to the National Institute of Health (Dental Research), U.S.A., whose research grant enabled this work to be undertaken.

Thanks are also due to Dr. Francis Steel for statistical assistance and Miss Rosemary Powers for much general help.

REFERENCES

Abrahams, L. C. (1949) Shovel-shaped incisors in the Cape Malays, *J. Dental Assoc., South Africa* **4**, (1), 7.

Abrahams, L. C. (1950) Dental Conditions among the Tasmanian Aborigines, *The Official Journal of D.A.S.A.* **5**, 326.

Adloff, P. (1908) *Das Gebiss des Menschen und der Anthropomorphen.* Springer, Berlin.

Adloff, P. (1938) Das Gebiss von Sinanthropus Pekinensis. *Z. Morphol. Anthropol.* **3**, 490.

Angel, J. L. (1951) *Troy. The Human Remains.* Supplementary Monograph. Princeton University Press. (Cited by Senyürek, 1952.)

Black, G. V. (1894) *Descriptive Anatomy of the Human Teeth,* 3rd ed. White, Philadelphia.

Brabant, H., Sahly, A. and Bouyssou, M. (1961) Etude des dents prehistoriques de la Station archéologique des Matelles. *Bull. du G.I.R.S.* **4**, 382.

Campbell, T. D. (1925) *The Dentition and Palate of the Australian Aboriginal.* Sheridan Foundation, University of Adelaide.

Carabelli, G. (1844) *Systematisches Handbuch der Zahnheilkunde.* 2 vols. Wien. (Cited by Hrdlicka, 1920.)

Carbonell, V. M. (1958) *The Dentition of the Kish Population,* 3000 B.C. Dissertation for the Masters Degree, University of Chicago.

Carr, H. G. (1960) Some dental characteristics of the Middle Minoans, *Man* **9**, 119.

Chappel, H. G. (1927) Jaws and teeth of ancient Hawaiians, *Mem. Bishop Mus.* **9**, 249.

Dahlberg, A. A. (1951) The dentition of the American Indian. In W. S. Laughlin (ed.) *The Physical Anthropology of the American Indian,* p. 138. Viking Fund, New York.

Dahlberg, A. A. and Mikkelson, O. (1947) The Shovel-shaped Character in the teeth of the Pima Indians, *Amer. J. Phys. Anthrop.* N.S. **5**, 234.

Garjanovic-Kramberger, K. (1906) *Der Diluviale Mensch von Krapina in Kroatien.* Kreidel, Wiesbaden.

Gejvall, Nils-Gustaf (1960) *Westerhus. Medieval Population and*

Church in Light of Skeletal Remains. University of Lund Publication.

GENET-VARCIN, E. (1951) *Les Negritos de l'Ile de Lucon (Philippines)* Paris.

GREGORY, W. K. (1920) *The Origin and Evolution of the Human Dentition.* Baltimore, Williams and Wilkins.

HALLETT, G. E. M. (1953) The Incidence, Nature, and Clinical Significance of Palatal Invaginations in the Maxillary Incisor Teeth. *Proc. R. Soc. Med.* **46**, 491.

HRDLICKA, ALES (1920) Shovel-shaped teeth, *Amer. J. Phys. Anthrop.* **3**, 429.

H.R.H. PRINCE PETER OF GREECE and DENMARK (1957) Attrition of the teeth among Tibetans, *Man* **57**, 177.

KOBY, E. F. (1956) Une Incisive Neanderthalienne Trouvée en Suisse. *Verh. Naturf. Geo. Basel.* **67**, 1.

KOSKI, K. and HAUTALA, E. (1952) On the frequency of Shovel-shaped incisors in the Finns, *Amer. J. Phys. Anthrop.* **10**, 127.

KROGMAN, W. M. (1937) Cranial types from Alisar Hoyük and their relations to other racial types, ancient and modern, of Europe and Western Asia. In Von der Ostens, *Alisar Hoyük Seasons of 1930–1932*, Part III, OIP., Vol. XXX. *Researches in Anatolia* pp. 213–93, Vol. IX. Chicago. (Cited by Senyürek, 1952.)

KROGMAN, W. M. (1960) Oral Structures genetically and anthropologically Considered, *Ann. New York Acad. Sciences.* **85**, 17.

LASKER, G. (1945) Observations on the teeth of Chinese born and reared in China and America, *Amer. J. Phys. Anthrop.* N.S. **3**, 129.

LASKER, G. (1950) Genetic analysis of racial traits of the teeth, *Cold Spring Harbor Symposia on Quantitative Biology*, **15**, 191.

LASKER, G. and MARJORIE LEE (1957) Racial traits in the human teeth. Presented before the sect. Anthrop. and Med. of the Am. Asso. for the Advancement of Science. Dec. 1956. N.Y City.

LEAKEY, L. S. B. (1935) *The Stone Age Races of Kenya.* Oxford University Press, London.

LICENT, E., DE CHARDIN, TEILHARD, and BLACK, DAVIDSON (1926) On a presumably Pleistocene human tooth from the Sjara osso-gol (South Eastern Ordos) deposits, *Bull. Geol. Soc. China* **5**, 285.

MAO HSIEH-CHÜIN and YEN YIN (1959) Dental condition of th Shang Dynasty skulls excavated from Anyang and Huu-Xian *Vertebrata Palasiatica* **3**, 185.

MARTIN, H. (1926) *L'Enfant Fossile de la Quina.* Vol. IV: *Recherche sur l'evolution du Moustérien dans le gisement de La Quina (Charente)* Angoulême.

McCown, T. and Keith (1939) *The Stone Age of Mt. Carmel*, II: *The Fossil Human Remains from the Levalloiso-Mousterian*. Oxford.

Miles, A. E. W. (1954) Malformations of the teeth, *Proc. Roy. Soc. Med.* **47**, 817.

Montelius, G. A. (1933) Observations on the teeth of Chinese, *J. Dent. Res.* **13**, 501.

Moorrees, C. F. A. (1957) *The Aleut Dentition. A Correlative Study of Dental Characteristics in an Eskimoid People*. Harvard University Press. Cambridge.

Morse, W. R. (1937) Schedule of physical anthropological measurements and observations on ten ethnic groups of Szechwan Province, West China, *J.W. China Border Res. Soc.* **8**, supplement. (Cited by Lasker, 1945.)

Muhlreiter, E. (1870) *Anatomie des Menschlichen Gebisses*. 1st ed. Leipzig. (Cited by Hrdlicka, 1920.)

Nelson, C. T. (1937) The teeth of the Indians of Pecos Pueblo, *Amer. J. Phys. Anthrop.* **23**, 261.

Oschinsky, L. and Smithurst, Roy (1960) On Certain dental Characters of the Eskimo of the Eastern Canadian Arctic, *Anthropologica* N.S. **2**, 105.

Pedersen, P. O. (1949) The East Greenland Eskimo Dentition, *Meddelelser om Gronland* **142**. Copenhagen.

Riesenfield, A. (1956) Shovel-shaped incisors and a few other dental features among the native peoples of the Pacific, *Amer. J. Phys. Anthrop.* N.S. **14**, 505.

Robinson, John T. (1956) *The Dentition of Australopithecinae*. Transvaal Museum Memoir No. 9. Pretoria, South Africa.

Sarnas, K. V. Personal communication.

Senyürek, M. S. (1952) Study of the dentition of the ancient inhabitants of Alaca Höyük, *Belleten, Ankara* **16**, 154.

Shaw, J. C. Middleton (1931) *The Teeth, the Bony Palate, and the Mandible in Bantu Races of South Africa*. Bale and Danielsson, London.

Schwerz, F. (1914) Über Zähne frühhistorischer Völker der Schweiz, *Vierteljahrschr. f. Zahnheilk.* **24**, 142. (Cited by Hrdlicka, 1920.)

Stevenson, P. H. (1940) Detailed anthropometric Measurements of the Chinese of the North China Plain, *Anthrop. Sinica*, No. 2.

Tomes, C. S. (1876) *A Manual of Dental Anatomy, Human and Comparative*.

Tratman, E. K. (1950) A Comparison of the teeth of people, Indo-European racial Stock with the Mongoloid racial Stock, *Dental Record* **70**, 31, 63.

Vallois, H. (1945) L'Homme fossile de Rabat, *C.R. Acad. Sc.* **221**, 669.

VALLOIS, H. (1950–1953) Le gisement prehistorique de Monsempron
  Annals de Palontologie, 36, 20.
VALLOIS, H. V. (1960) L'Homme de Rabat, Bulletin d'Archeologi*
  Morocaine 3, 88.
WEIDENREICH, F. (1937) The Dentition of Sinanthropus Pekinensis
  Palaentologia Sinica. N.S. No. 1. Peiping.
WEIDENREICH, F. (1945) The Palaeolithic Child from Teshik-Tash
  Cave in Southern Uzbekistan (Central Asia), Amer. J. Phys
  Anthrop. N.S. 3, 151.
WOO, JU KANG (1956) Human fossil found in China and their
  significance in human evolution, Scientia Sinica 5, 389.
WORTMAN, J. (1886) Comparative anatomy of the teeth of verte-
  brata. In The American System of Dentistry, pp. 351–515.

DOUBLE-ROOTED HUMAN LOWER CANINE TEETH

by V. ALEXANDERSEN

The Royal Dental College, Copenhagen

In the order primates, canine teeth are as a rule single-rooted. Double-rooted lower canines may occur in the permanent dentition of man as a variation in the form of the root. They have been considered a rare phenomenon conceived either as a *lusus naturae* or as an atavism reproducing conditions seen in some Mesozoic mammals.

THE FREQUENCY OF DOUBLE-ROOTED LOWER CANINES IN HUMAN POPULATIONS

An investigation of the frequency of double-rooted lower canines has been undertaken; the material consisting of teeth from Danish populations mainly from the Middle and Late Neolithic periods (2000–1500 B.C.) and from the Middle Ages (1200–1500 A.D.). The results of these investigations are presented in Table I.

The number of root-tips irrespective of the size of the roots determined whether a tooth should be considered double-rooted or not. Alveoli belonging to double-rooted canines reproduce the double-rooted conditions by means of mesiodistal septa alveoli. Alveoli of canines, lost post-mortem, were inspected and the number of roots determined.

The frequency of double-rooted canines in the Neolithic material is 5·6 per cent and in the medieval populations from two localities on the island of Zealand 8·0 per cent and 5·1 per cent respectively. The results obtained in this study show that double-rooted lower canines are not very rare in some human populations. Earlier data on the same subject are presented in

TABLE I

THE FREQUENCY OF DOUBLE-ROOTED LOWER CANINES IN DANISH POPULA-
TIONS

Period	Root form				No. of double rooted lower canines (%)
	Single-rooted		Double-rooted		
	teeth	alveoli	teeth	alveoli	
Neolithic					
Early	4	2			0
Middle and Late	96	56	7	2	5·6
Middle Ages					
Æbelholt	289	20	23	4	8·0
Naestved	291	79	19	1	5·1

Table II, and it will be seen that previous investigations have
mainly been concerned with European populations. In order
to test the hypothesis that the European groups examined are
homogenous in regard to the frequency of double-rooted lower
canines, a comparison has been made by means of the χ^2-test
between observed and expected frequencies of double-rooted
canines in these populations. Differences were found to be
insignificant (5 per cent $<P<$ 10 per cent) and the European
populations in question may thus be considered homogenous
with regard to this characteristic.

In order to evaluate the low frequencies found in the small
populations of non-European peoples the probability was
calculated of getting one, one and nought double-rooted lower
canine in samples of 62, 72 and 94 lower canine from a larger
population with double-rooted lower canines occurring with a
frequency of 5·7 per cent (the European populations in Table II
combined). The probability of getting such low frequencies of
double-rooted lower canines as found in Bantu Negroes and
East Greenlandic Eskimos is sufficiently high to indicate that
these ethnic groups do not necessarily have a lower frequency
of double-rooted lower canines than the European populations.
This does, however, seem to be the case with the Pecos Pueblo

TABLE II

FORMER INVESTIGATIONS ON THE FREQUENCY OF THE DOUBLE-ROOTED LOWER CANINE

Author	Ethnic Group	No. of teeth	No. of lower canines	
			1 root	2 roots
HILLEBRAND (1909)	Hungarians	1707	1604	103 (6%)
SCHWERZ (1916)	Alemanns	507	476	31 (6·1%)
Fabian (1928)	Germans	315	295	20 (6·4%)
HJELMMAN (1929)	Finns	98	93	5 (4·9%)
VISSER (1948)	Dutchmen	2488	2365	123 (4·9%)
HUCHE (1954)	Frenchmen	282	254	28 (10%)
SHAW (1931)	Bantu	62	61	1 (1·6%)
NELSON (1938)	Pecos Indians	94	94	0
PEDERSEN (1949)	East Greenlandic Eskimo	72	71	1 (1·3%)

Indians, where the probability of getting no double-rooted canines in a sample of 94 is less than 1 per cent, the frequency of double-rooted lower canines in the population being 5·7 per cent. Further investigations are obviously desirable to determine whether the differences found between frequencies of double-rooted canines in White and coloured populations really are statistically significant. Special note should also be taken of the correlation existing between the two sides of the mandible. It has not been stated by the authors mentioned in Table II, whether both canines from each mandible were inspected. In the Danish material a small number of teeth (33 lower canines) were not examined, because the teeth could not be removed from their alveoli. An X-ray analysis of the roots of these teeth did not give conclusive information on the form of the root.

The ratio between mandibles with one double-rooted lower canine and mandibles with two double-rooted canines was approximately 3 : 1 in the Danish population. Double-rooted teeth were found as often on the right as on the left side of the mandible.

MORPHOLOGICAL VARIATIONS IN HUMAN LOWER CANINES

An analysis of the morphological variation of the lower canine teeth in the Danish populations mentioned in Table I has been carried out to demonstrate the development of two roots in the lower canines.

Single-rooted lower canines

The root is always somewhat compressed. Cross-sections of the root are oval with the longer axis oriented facio-lingually (Fig. 1b). The proximal contours of root cross-sections from the cervical part of the root converge lingually, while the proximal contours in cross-sections from the middle and apical parts of the root are parallel. Grooves on the proximal surfaces of the root are seen as notches in the circumference of root cross-sections, sometimes giving mid-root cross-sections the appearance of an hour-glass.

The enamel line is of the same general form as that on the incisors. The cervical curvature reaches its most apical level on the facial surface of the tooth and its most occlusal level on the mesial surface. The enamel line on the mesial surface of the tooth is symmetrical, and in shape is rather like a Gaussian curve (Fig. 2). The same curve can be indicated on the distal surface, but most often the distal enamel line is asymmetrical. The labial half of the line is steep, whereas the lingual half of the enamel line is almost horizontal, continuing without marked change in level to the lingual surface of the tooth. The passage from the lingual to the mesial surface is more abrupt, often showing a marked angle (Fig. 3b).

The proximal surfaces of the root taper evenly into a more or less pointed tip. The facial and lingual surfaces of the root vary with regard to convexity. From a proximal view the facial root-surface is convex in the facial direction, either all the way from the cervical to the apical part of the root, or in the cervical part of the root only, whereas the apical half of the contour is concave. The distribution between the two possibilities was found to be approximately 75–25 per cent. The lingual root-surface varies just like the facial surface (convex contour approximately 75 per cent; concave approximately 25 per cent) although the convexity rarely is so pronounced on this surface

(a)　　　　　(b)

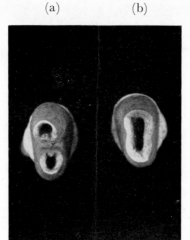

Fig. 1.　Lower canines, right and left, from one mandible
(Æbelholt No. 664). Cross-sections of the not completely
developed roots of a double-rooted (a) and a single-rooted
(b) lower canine. The junction line of the inter-radicular
dentine processes is visible as a groove on the lingual
surface of the facial root of the double-rooted canine. ($2\frac{1}{2}$ ×.)

(a)　　　　　(b)

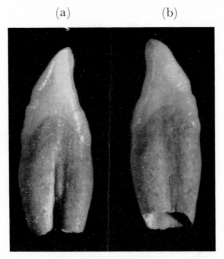

Fig. 2. Lower canines, right and left, from one mandible
(Æbelholt No. 664). Mesial aspect of the teeth shown in
Fig. 1. ($2\frac{1}{2}$ ×.)

Fig. 3. Lower canines, right and left, from one mandible (Æbelholt No. 139). Mesial surfaces showing grooves between the facial and lingual root-column as well as on the lingual root-column. Note how the enamel line on the single-rooted canine turns at a sharp mesio-lingual angle. (2×.)

Fig. 4. Lower canines from Æbelholt showing the range of variation found among double-rooted lower canines. Mesial surfaces. (1½×.)

as on the facial surface (Figs. 3b, 4a and 4b). In a few cases the lingual contour was totally concave.

The form of the root-tip depends on the contours of the facial and the lingual root-surfaces and varies between a very pointed tip (Fig. 4b) and a bluntly rounded apex (Fig. 3b).

The root-axis may be a straight continuation of the axis through the labial surface of the tooth-crown, but a rather common variation is for the tooth, in a labial or lingual view, to form a mesial or distal convex curve. The apical part of the root is very often slightly curved pointing in a mesial, distal or lingual direction.

As a rule the proximal root surface of lower canines has grooves situated either between the labial and the lingual root-column or upon one of the root-columns. Among 548 lower canines examined only 34 had no mesial grooves and only 4 had no distal grooves.

The most frequently found grooves on the proximal surfaces of the lower canine indicate a subdivision of the root into two root-columns. Provided the root-columns are of equal size, the grooves are situated as more or less wide vertical depressions along the middle third of the proximal surfaces (Figs. 2b and 3b). The root-columns may be of a different size, however, and in this case the grooves are displaced on the proximal surfaces in the direction of the minor root-column. Even on the same tooth a difference can be found between the position of the grooves on the two proximal surfaces. A groove in the middle third of the proximal surface is combined with a groove which is usually displaced in a lingual direction on the other proximal surface. Grooves on the distal surface of the root tend to be more pronounced than grooves on the mesial surface. There might be a connection between this condition and the fact that a lack of the distal groove is rarer than a lack of the mesial groove.

Grooves situated on the root-columns are more infrequent than grooves between the root columns. A groove on a root-column can be observed from the cervical part to the apical part of the root (Fig. 3b). Sometimes a groove starts on a root-column but unites, in the middle part of the root, with the groove separating the root-columns, forming an accentuation in the bottom of the broader groove. Grooves on root-columns were found in 3 per cent of the teeth inspected. The grooves were most often found on the mesial side of the lingual root-column but were at times seen distolingually as well as mesiolabially and distolabially on the labial root-column.

On the individual tooth only one groove on a root-column was found and in my material only one of the two lower canines in one mandible had a groove on a root-column.

Very short, shallow grooves placed irregularly on the root-columns are not considered as being related to the grooves mentioned above.

Double-rooted lower canines

Double-rooted lower canines are distinguished from single-rooted canines by the number of root-tips. Apart from this essential distinction a comparison made between a single-rooted and a double-rooted lower canine from one mandible shows pronounced similarities with regard to the form of the root and to grooves on the root-surfaces.

Division of the root is related to grooves on the proximal surfaces of the root. Special attention will be drawn to the double-rooted lower canine as shown in Figs. 1 and 2, the root of which is not completely developed. In this tooth is clearly shown how the subdivision of the root by a deepening of the grooves separating the root-columns is effectuated by pre-domanent horizontal growth of inter-radicular dentine processes (Jørgensen, 1950). The inter-radicular dentine tongues are fused at a junction line during the development of a sub-pulpal wall.

The subdivision of the root may be the result of a more gradual deepening of the grooves than seen in Fig. 1. In that case the sub-pulpal wall tapers in an apical direction and the subdivision is completed in the apical third of the root. Slender inter-radicular processes result in the formation of two roots placed close to each other (Figs. 2a, 4a and 4d).

Most double-rooted lower canines are formed by a deepening of the grooves separating the root-columns. According to the varying distribution of these grooves the apices of the two roots formed by subdivision of the root vary in size in conformity with the size of the root-columns. Subdivision of a root by a deepening of two grooves on one root-column or by a deepening of a groove situated on the root-column on one of the proximal surfaces and a groove on the opposite surface separating the root-columns, results in the formation of one small root and one much larger root (Figs. 3a, 4c). The smaller root is usually placed lingually in relation to the major root. It is rather short and curves towards the larger root. Six of 56 double-rooted lower canines had a pronounced difference in size, but a gradual variation was found between these double-rooted teeth and canines with two roots of equal size (Fig. 4).

It is impossible to distinguish between distinct types of double-rooted lower canines by reference to variation in size and form of the two roots or to the varying distribution of grooves in which deepening and subdivision has taken place. This is because a continuous variation is observed in a large collection of double-rooted canines with regard to size of the roots and to the placing of grooves between, upon, or partly on and partly between the root-columns.

Similarities even in regard to minute details between double-rooted canines and molars in corresponding ontogenetical stages (Jørgensen, 1950) lead to the assumption that development of more than one root on a tooth by subdivision of the primary apical foramen may in some instances occur in the canine region of the mandible as well as in the molar (and premolar) regions. This can be considered as the result of an extension forward in the dentition of the morphogenetic field determining the formation of roots in cheek teeth.

THE OCCURRENCE OF DOUBLE-ROOTED CANINES IN THE ORDER OF PRIMATES

The occurrence of double-rooted lower canines in man has been considered as an atavism. The theory of atavism is based on the supposition that double-rooted canines represent the original mammalian condition and the occurrence of double-rooted upper canines in some recent Prosimii (Leche, 1897) caused supporters of the theory of atavism to believe that fossil primates also had double-rooted canines.

Double-rooted canines have been found in the upper jaw as well as in the lower jaw of several Mesozoic mammals (Simpson, 1928, 1929). In the earliest Insectivora double-rooted upper canines are not rare, but double-rooted lower canines are, to the best of my belief, not known (see Saban, 1958, for compilation of literature). It is impossible, in view of our present knowledge of Mesozoic Pantotheria and of early Eutheria, to decide upon the exact phylogenetic relationship between the few known fossils.

In searching the literature concerned with dentitions of fossil primates, I have only been able to find double-rooted upper canines in the Paleocene genera *Navajovius* and *Phenacolemur* (Simpson, 1935, 1955) and in these genera the teeth in question are not even proved canines. No mention of double-rooted lower canines (neither in fossil Prosimii nor fossil Simii including Pongids and Hominids) has been found, although it must be stressed that the fossil material available is scanty.

In recent primates double-rooted upper canines have occasionally been found in some tupaioids (Clark, 1926), lorisoids (Leche, 1897) and in one specimen of *Galago* (*senegalensis?*) with double-rooted upper milk canine (Alexandersen, unpublished) and perhaps, though very seldom, in some Lemurs (Leche, 1897). The lower canines in recent Prosimii are single-rooted in the milk dentition as well as in the permanent dentition.

Among recent Simii the Cercopithecoids with grooved canines may show double-rooted conditions. Terra (1905) has recorded double-rooted upper canines in two of 30 *Cynocephalus* (*Papio*) monkeys, while the author in a collection of 24 specimens of *Papio* (in the Zoological Museum of the University of Copenhagen) found faint indications of root subdivision of a lower canine and an upper deciduous canine in two specimens.

Some tendency towards double-rooted conditions can be seen in recent Pongids, particularly in the milk dentition of Hylobatidae (Remane, 1960). In the milk dentitions of ten specimens of *Hylobates lar* and *H. moloch*, examined by the author, seven specimens had double-rooted upper milk canines and one had a double-rooted lower milk canine. In recent Hylobatidae as well as in other Pongids the permanent canines are usually single-rooted, although a photograph of a female Chimpanzee with a double-rooted lower canine is shown by Schwarz (1931).

CONCLUSION

Before discussing the evidence available in favour of the theory of atavism it is necessary to state what is meant here by atavism. In my conception of this theory I follow Remane (1956). He recognizes a group of atavistic tendencies which are brought about by mutations that, in some individuals of a recent species, cause structural features similar to those in phylogenetically determined ancestors.

In no specimens of fossil Hominoidea have double-rooted canines been found, but the regrettable lack of adequate fossil material prevents any final decision as yet on this theory of atavism. The sporadic existence of double-rooted canines in several groups of recent primates seems to be rather incidental. This view might need modification, however, when more material has been examined. The knowledge of regional displacement during evolution of traits occurring in metameric organs, such as teeth (Remane, 1956), lead to the conclusion that the varying extent of the region of multi-rooted teeth in the jaws of primates may sometimes incorporate the region of the canine, which might likewise have happened to some extent in the evolutionary stages leading to *Homo sapiens*.

REFERENCES

ALEXANDERSEN, V. (1962) Rodforholdene hos menneskets under-kæbehjørnetænder med særligt henblik på torodede hjørne-tænder. I. Den morfologiske variation. With an English summary, *Tandlægebladet* **66**, 53.

ALEXANDERSEN, V. (1962) Rodforholdene hos menneskets under-kæbehjørnetænder med særligt henblik på torodede hjørne-tænder. II. Forekomst af torodede hjørnetænder i underkoeben hos *Homo sapiens* og hos andre primater. With an English summary. In press.

CLARK, W. E. LE GROS (1926) On the anatomy of the pen-tailed tree-shrew (*Ptilocercus lowii*), *Proc. Zool. Soc. Lond.*, 1179.

FABIAN, H. (1928) *Spezielle Anatomie des Gebisses*, No. 12. Klinkhardt, Leipzig.

HILLEBRAND, E. (1909) Beiträge zur Morphologie der menschlichen Zähne. *Pester Medicinisch-Chirurgische Presse* **45**, 1.

HUCHE, R. LE (1954) Quelle est la fréquence de la bifidité de la racine de la canine inférieure? *Rev. de Stom.* **55**, 656.

HJELMMAN, G. (1929) Morphologische Beobachtungen an den Zähnen der Finnen, *Acta Soc. Med. Fenn.* **11**, 1.

JØRGENSEN, K. DREYER (1950) Macroscopic observations on the formation of the subpulpal wall, *Odont. Tidskr.* **58**, 83.

KOENIGSWALD, G. H. R. v. (1959) *Die Geschichte des Menschen.* Verständliche Wissenschaft Bd. 74. Springer Verlag, Berlin.

LECHE, W. (1897) Untersuchungen über das Zahnsystem. *Festschrift z.70. Geburtstag v. C. Gegenbauer.* **3**.

NELSON, C. T. (1938) The teeth of the Indians of Pecos Pueblo, *Amer. J. Phys. Anthrop.* **23**, 261.

PEDERSEN, P. O. (1949) The East Greenland Eskimo Dentition. Numerical variations and anatomy, *Meddelelser om Gronland* **142**. Copenhagen.

REMANE, A. (1956) *Die Grundlagen des natürlichen Systems, der vergleichenden Anatomie und der Phylogenetik.* Akademische Verlagsgesellschaft. Leipzig.

REMANE, A. (1960) Zähne und Gebiss. In *Primatologia, Handbuch der Primatenkunde.* 111/2: 637.

SABAN, R. (1958) Insectivora. In *Traité de paléontologie*, **6**, 822.

SCHWARZ, R. (1931) Das Abstammungsproblem des Menschen. In Misch, *Die Fortschritte der Zahnheilkunde* **7**, 753.

SCHWERZ, F. (1916) Morphologische Untersuchungen an Zähnen von Alamannen aus dem V. bis X. Jahrhundert, *Arch. f. Anthrop.* **15**, 1.

SHAW, J. C. MIDDLETON (1931) *The Teeth, the Bony Palate and the Mandible in Bantu Races of South Africa.* Bale and Danielsson, London.

SIMPSON, G. G. (1928) *A Catalogue of the Mesozoic Mammalia in the Geological Department of the British Museum.* British Museum (Natural History), London.

SIMPSON, G. G. (1929) American Mesozoic Mammalia. *Mem. Peabody Mus. Yale Univ.* **3**, 1.

SIMPSON, G. G. (1935) The Tiffany fauna, upper Paleocene. 3. Primates, Carnivora, Condylarthra and Amblypoda, *Amer. Mus. Novitates*, No. 817, 1.

SIMPSON, G. G. (1955) The Phenacolemuridae, new family of early Primates. *Bull. Amer. Mus. Nat. Hist.* **105**, 415.

TERRA, M. DE (1905) *Beiträge zu einer Odontographie der Menschenrassen.* Berlinische Verlagsanstalt, Berlin.

VISSER, J. B. (1948) *Beitrag zur Kenntnis der menschlichen Zahnwurzelformen.* Diss. Rotting, Hilversum.

VARIATIONS IN THE MICROSTRUCTURE AND BIOCHEMISTRY OF HUMAN TEETH

by A. J. CLEMENT

University of the Witwatersrand,
Dental School and Oral Hospital

THE teeth provide the most imperishable record of mankind now available, and from an anthropological point of view it is obviously of paramount importance that every piece of information locked away in this practically indestructible material is utilized to the full.

Recent technical advances have now made the microscopic study of fossil, as well as recent, teeth a practical undertaking. In the following review attention is primarily directed towards such considerations as previous studies of ancient teeth and technical considerations; microscopic post-mortem changes; signs of developmental disturbance; the effect of *in vitro* acid action and of fluorine on the microstructure of teeth; distinguishing microscopic features of caries; the comparative microstructure of primitive and civilized teeth (with particular reference to caries immunity); and finally the comparative chemical composition of primitive and civilized dentitions.

PREVIOUS STUDIES OF ANCIENT TEETH AND TECHNICAL CONSIDERATIONS

C. S. Tomes (1892) must have been one of the earliest dental microscopists to attempt the sectioning and microscopic examination of ancient human teeth. Another examination was carried out a few years later by Duckworth (1901), and Hopewell Smith (1903) subsequently re-examined the material used by Duckworth. Later German studies by Werner (1937) and Schwartz and Bay (1943) were carried out to check the presence of dental caries in fossil teeth. Within the last decade Hammarlund-Essler (1952) has examined a collection of teeth from the Danish Middle Ages, and Sognnaes (1955, 1956) has sectioned ancient human teeth for evidence of post-mortem microscopic defects and developmental dental pathology and Falin (1961) has investigated the microscopic variability of Russian Stone Age teeth.

Ancient teeth are always hard and brittle, and it is obvious that any section which can be prepared for microscopic examination will be correspondingly fragile. In fact it was only when plastic material was used as an embedding matrix that the inherent difficulties were eventually overcome. Sognnaes (1955) describes a so-called petrification technique which is specially designed for hard and brittle dental specimens. Methyl methacrylate is used for infiltration, hardening and protection of the brittle dental tissues during the technical processes of sectioning and grinding. After sectioning the plastic material is removed by soaking in a monomer and is then routinely stained and mounted. In extremely dehydrated brittle teeth the sections are so fragile that they disintegrate if the embedding material is removed; in such cases the embedding material is permanently retained, and only the suitably mounted ground section is utilized for examination. The application of the so-called replica method to teeth by Scott and Wyckoff (1946), whereby a thin film of 2 per cent colloidon is floated off teeth, shadowed by oblique metal evaporation under a high vacuum and then viewed under the electron microscope, has enabled the examination of tooth surfaces to be carried out at a higher magnification than is theoretically possible with standard optical microscopy techniques. Such features of the tooth surface as perikymata patterns, enamel rod-ends, laminations and micro-pits can now be studied at a magnification which was not visualized as possible a few years ago.

MICROSCOPIC POST-MORTEM CHANGES IN ANCIENT TEETH

Approximately a century ago Wedl (1864) sectioned teeth which had been left in a polluted glass of water for 10 days;

he found canals running into the dentine and cementum from the external surface. Similar canals were later described by Tomes (1892), Duckworth (1901) and Hopewell Smith (1903); the latter authority actually examined the same specimen as Duckworth. Wedl (1864) attributed the canals to fungoid invasion, whereas Hopewell Smith linked their presence in the cementum of Duckworth's specimen with *Sacc. mycoderma*; the abnormal channellings of the enamel were believed to be the result of developmental abnormality. At a much later date Euler and Werner (1936) attributed the post-mortem reaction of tooth disintegration to the influence of soil acids and microscopic worms; however, in a subsequent paper Werner (1937) proposed both algae and worms as the causative organisms.

Only recently has the nature and distribution of these microscopic post-mortem canals been thoroughly investigated by Sognnaes (1955). He sectioned representative teeth from 11 periods (Palaeolithic to Recent), the teeth originating from 6 different geographical areas. He observed that the enamel showed surprisingly few post-mortem histological changes, whereas striking alterations were noticeable in the dentine and cementum. These post-mortem changes were readily distinguishable from all normal pathological processes such as dental caries, and were classified as canals, diffuse disintegrations and surface erosions.

The most common post-mortem changes in the dentine were the appearance of irregular canals (the so-called Wedl's canals) of several different patterns; the canals either effected entry from the inside of the tooth via the predentine, or alternatively penetrated from the exterior via the cementum-covered roots. Some canals (2–10 μ in diameter) were long, narrow and occasionally corkscrew in shape; more commonly they were 15–25 μ in diameter and with a marked tendency to branching. Giant canals (50–100 μ in diameter) with ampulla-shaped expansions were also observed. The major characteristic of these canals was their large width in comparison with the normal diameter of dentinal tubules and their unorthodox course: they penetrated dentine in all directions and tended to run across the intertubular matrix rather than along the course of the tubules. Radiographically they showed increased radiolucency. There was no evidence of any vital response (i.e. secondary or transparent dentine) which is so characteristic of caries. Similar canals have been described in exhumed bone by Roux (1887).

So-called diffuse disintegrations and petrification of the dentine (possibly due to the deposition of calcium carbonate) were also observed, and provided evidence of a high content of relatively homogenous inorganic matter which Sognnaes attributed to secondary petrification.

Least common of the post-mortem changes noticed in ancient teeth was the presence of surface erosions; this was the only type of change observed in dental enamel. At the histological level such teeth showed an irregular etching of the enamel, but one which was not like the diffuse etching produced by exposure of the tooth surface to acid.

Sognnaes points out that the degree of post-mortem change in teeth is no reliable criterion of the age of the particular specimen. He stresses the importance of differential diagnosis of the above post-mortem changes from developmental disturbances and post-formative *intra vitam* lesions of the teeth, and particularly so with regard to developmental disturbances of the enamel which, as will subsequently be mentioned, are reflected in deviations of the normal arrangement of the Striae of Retzius. Post-formative *intra vitam* enamel lesions cause a break in the incremental contour lines and give rise to what Sognnaes describes as "a secondary discontinuity of the formative pattern of the enamel": if the tooth is functional at the time, there may be an additional reaction in the underlying dentine (i.e. a demarcation barrier or secondary dentine formation). Post-mortem changes in teeth characteristically produce no evidence of any biological reaction on the part of the teeth.

No real attempt was made to evaluate the causative agent or agents of these changes, but Sognnaes found somewhat slender evidence of thread forms in certain specimens. He remains somewhat dubious about the influence of the acid–soil environment. He points out that, although enamel is the most exposed and acid-soluble of the dental tissues, it was usually found to be less affected than the cementum by surface erosion.

DEVELOPMENTAL DENTAL PALAEOPATHOLOGY

The development of the dental enamel takes place in two well-defined stages, that is matrix formation and maturation or calcification of the matrix. If the matrix is adversely influenced during its development then hypoplasia or defective enamel structure ensues; if maturation is deficient there is hypocalcification or mineral deficiency. In either case the microstructure of teeth is affected.

Hypoplasia commonly affects the teeth of the deciduous dentition or the six anterior teeth or first molars of the permanent dentition: thus the hypoplastic agent appears to be most active between the fifth month *in utero* and the end of the first year of post-natal life. This characteristic tends to nullify the conception that the exanthematous fevers are a common cause of hypoplasia. In view of the fact that it is the matrix stage and not the phase of maturation which is affected by hypoplasia, it is not—as is commonly supposed—possible to assess accurately the location of the lesion against the chronological background, an assessment usually attempted on the basis of the cervico-incisal or cervico-occlusal placement of the area of hypoplasia.

Either hypoplasia or hypocalcification are attributable to systematic, local or hereditary influences. Hypoplasia may be of a chronic or acute variety and either confined to a single zone or multiple: its extent and nature are obviously related to the duration and degree of activity of the hypoplastic agent. The commonly accepted systemic causes of hypoplasia in human teeth are metabolic factors (such as calcium, phosphorus and vitamin D deficiency; certain abnormal Ca-P dietary ratios; rickets; hypoparathyroidism; vitamin A deficiency) and certain infections (either the so-called exanthematous diseases of childhood, or congenital syphilis). Acute diseases are probably not as influential as chronic ones in producing hypoplastic lesions; it may be that an acute disease is only effective when its influence is superimposed on an additional

R

nutritional deficiency. Local hypoplasia is probably brought about in the main by the infection of the pulp of a deciduous tooth and the subsequent spread of the infection to the periapical tissues, in which area the infection very evidently interferes with the development of the underlying permanent tooth. On this basis it follows that this type of hypoplasia is mainly to be found in permanent teeth. Injury is another cause of localized hypoplasia. The hereditary type of this anomaly is believed to be due to a Mendelian character of a dominant nature, and as such the entire enamel of all deciduous and permanent teeth is affected; the enamel being either excessively thin or alternatively completely absent.

According to Schour (1938) the response of the enamel to hypoplastic agents is limited to a greater or lesser retention of the organic material in the Striae of Retzius in direct proportion to the degree of disturbance. The neonatal line (produced by an accentuation of the Striae and, also found as a linear accentuation of the corresponding incremental lines of the dentine) is the result of a disturbance in enamel formation due to the drastic environmental changes brought about by birth. A fainter line often marks the advent of weaning. Prenatal enamel appears structurally better than the postnatal tissue.

Disturbances in body metabolism (of a similar nature to those causing enamel hypoplasia), also cause changes in the dentine, but the response of the dentine is far more variable. As seen microscopically the dentine reaction varies from an accentuation of the normal incremental pattern in minor disturbances, to marbled or dappled dentine in the more severe sub-clinical range, and thence to incomplete globular fusion, interglobular dentine formation (and occasionally abnormally wide areas of predentine, sometimes with vascular inclusions) and scattered calcospherites in the most severe types of disturbance.

When the systemic disturbance is of the acute variety there is a narrow zone of abnormal structure (the so-called "calcio-traumatic ring"); in chronic disturbances the calcio-traumatic ring is wide. This ring or zone "is therefore pathognomic of the cause of the disturbance, reflecting its intensity, time and duration" (Schour, 1938).

It might be supposed that monkeys and primates—generally accredited with being fairly caries-immune in the wild state—possess teeth which are structurally superior to those of man. Czerwinski (1926) and Mellanby (1930) for example, found that the enamel of rhesus monkeys was homogeneous in structure and without pronounced Striae of Retzius; a similar observation has been made on the teeth of marmosets (Shaw and Anskaps, 1954). However, both Walkhoff (1895) and Munch (1926) found that both the Striae of Retzius and inter-globular dentine spaces were present in the teeth of the orang-utan, and Colyer (1936) states that slight transverse and longi-tudinal grooves—as well as shallow depressions—are by no means uncommon on the anterior teeth (especially the canines) of wild apes, and are also to be found on the teeth of monkeys. Hypoplasia was noted in several species of monkeys, but was often limited to certain specific anterior teeth. Widdowson (1936) has also noted the presence of horizontal grooves in the incisors of the chimpanzee. A very thorough examination by microscopy and the replica technique of the teeth of rhesus monkeys, gibbons, gorillas, orang-utans and chimpanzees by Schuman and Sognnaes (1956), showed that the teeth of wild rhesus monkeys which had been reared in their natural native environment were remarkably free of developmental defects: the Striae of Retzius were practically invisible. On the other hand the teeth of the anthropoids were much more prone to developmental irregularities: granular, areolar and interglobular dentine were observed in many instances, and the presence of externally visible hypoplasia (transverse grooves in the anterior teeth) and accentuated incremental lines confirmed for the enamel. Irregular perikymata, micro-pits, prominent enamel rod-ends and laminations also occurred on the surface of primate teeth. In fact in the chimpanzee perikymata irregu-larities in the molar teeth were more frequently observed than in American whites by Pedersen and Scott (1951), although their frequency of occurrence was fairly comparable with the findings for Alaskan and Greenland Eskimo teeth. Coming closer to *Homo sapiens*, it is of interest to recall that Robinson (1952) has noted the presence of hypoplasia in a considerable number of teeth of the so-called South African ape-men (Australopithecinae). Perhaps, as Colyer (1936) suggests certain animals in the wild state experience nutritional deficiencies from time to time.

In fairly recent times Sognnaes (1956) has undertaken an exploratory histological survey of the developmental quality of ancient human teeth originating from Palaeolithic man in Palestine, prehistoric Greeks, Predynastic Egyptians, the ancient Irish, medieval Norsemen and early American Indians. Compared with the near perfect teeth of the rhesus monkey these ancient human teeth exhibited considerable developmental microscopic defects, and to a far greater extent even than the wild sub-human primates. A comparative diagnosis was carried out on the basis of an accentuation of the incremental lines, pigmentation of the enamel, diffuse prism structure, a concentration of the enamel tufts, signs of fusion of the interprismatic substance with the prisms (a characteristic feature of mottling), marked scalloping of the amelo-dentinal junction, the frequency of occurrence of the interglobular spaces, granularity of the dentine and the presence of secondary dentine.

Mellanby (1930, 1934) has strongly advocated the association of certain types of hypoplasia with caries susceptibility, and her views—which have been widely disseminated in the literature —have tended to encourage the opinion that the caries-susceptible teeth of modern civilized man are structurally inferior (i.e. as demonstrated by the presence of varying degrees and types of hypoplasia) to the caries-immune teeth of primitive peoples. Nevertheless, it has been recently shown (Clement 1961) that hypoplastic teeth are present in very many contemporary racial groups, some relatively caries-immune whereas others are caries-susceptible.

THE EFFECTS OF *IN VITRO* ACID ACTION AND FLUORINE ON THE MICROSTRUCTURE OF TEETH

The effects of acid action (either *in vivo* or *in vitro*) produce certain well-defined changes in the structural appearance of teeth, and it is of obvious importance that the effects of acid action should be distinguished from caries in fossil material.

Acid action alone gives a chalky appearance to surface enamel; according to Gottlieb (1947) the production of chalky enamel or of sub-surface patches of cloudy enamel is probably the result of mild acid action (such, for example, as is likely to be produced by acidogenic micro-organisms acting on vital teeth). Opaque sub-surface patches of enamel, however, appear to be produced by more strong concentrations of acid. Gottlieb attributes the occurrence of areas of transparent enamel to the hypercalcification which is the result of acid action producing a shift of calcium salts from neighbouring decalcified areas; in vitro decalcification experiments with teeth apparently produce opaque patches surrounded by transparent zones. One other prominent effect, apparently associated with acid action, is the accentuation of the cross-striation of the enamel prisms. In the dentine acid action, proceeding via the external layer, is said to produce an opaque strip resembling secondary dentine.

The whole subject of the effects of acid action on the microstructure of teeth—both in vivo and post-mortem—is undoubtedly in need of considerable further investigation. Grenz ray studies are likely to be particularly helpful.

Human teeth are particularly sensitive to fluorine, and fluorosis is possible—at an intake level which varies according to individual susceptibility—when the drinking water (the normal agent) contains more than 1 ppm of fluorine. Unlike the agents of hypoplasia which affect the matrix formation of enamel, the effects of fluorine are operative at the later stage of enamel maturation. Fluorine thus produces the microscopic signs of hypocalcification, and certain characteristic features of fluorosed teeth are of assistance in microscopic diagnosis. Fluorosed teeth can be distinguished from systemic hypoplasia by a consideration of the time basis, for fluorine is able to affect the crowns of teeth calcifying at different times, that is provided a constant and prolonged exposure to fluorine-containing drinking water can safely be assumed. Fluorine appears to affect the anterior teeth more than the posterior ones and, apart from the third molar, crown defects are limited to the first 8 years of life; in view of the correlation of the stage of enamel maturation with the age of the individual it is possible to estimate the approximate date and duration of exposure. A characteristic feature of the influence of fluorine is that it normally appears to affect only the outer third or last formed layer of enamel, that is except in the area where the enamel is particularly thin (for example, near the tooth cervix). The deciduous dentition is rarely affected due to the relative impermeability of the placenta to fluorine.

Teeth affected by fluorine show a very similar histological appearance to the effects produced by acid action. According to Gottlieb (1947) an external opaque layer of hypocalcification (not always present) frequently overlies an area of hypercalcified transparent enamel, the latter produced by a shift of calcium salts. Microscopically the typical mottled tooth shows irregular enamel surface areas in which areas of hypocalcification are interspersed with areas of hypercalcification or normal enamel. Mottled teeth show a fusion of the interprismatic substance with the prisms, and there is a tendency for surface enamel to fracture at right angles to the Striae of Retzius, thereby producing a series of angular outcrops on the floor of the surface pits. Where the enamel is entirely affected—as at the cervix—the underlying dentine may show an opaque area overlying transparent dentine, and there may be accentuation of the incremental stratification: interglobular spaces may be present in the severest cases.

Mottled teeth erupt in an unstained condition and only acquire pigmentation thereafter; the stain apparently affects the less calcified incremental strips. The effect of soils with a high fluorine content on the microstructure of buried teeth— structurally normal prior to burial—has not yet been investigated to my knowledge, but it seems reasonable to suppose that the surface enamel takes on different characteristics due to the chemical affinity of fluorine and calcium salts.

THE DISTINGUISHING MICROSCOPIC FEATURES OF CARIES IN FOSSIL TEETH

Caries appears to be the result of local acid action combined with proteolysis which is due to the activity of pigment-producing micro-organisms. The pigmentation is a marked characteristic of caries, although it must be borne in mind that yellow pigmentation is often a feature of failure of enamel maturation; for example mottled teeth. The acid or decalcification phase of caries leads to characteristic features such as the accentuation of the cross-striation of the prisms, chalky surface enamel and patches of cloudy enamel; the cloudy enamel—often pigmented—may be surrounded by the zone of hypo-calcified or transparent enamel described by Gottlieb (1947). Probably the acid action in vital caries is not sufficiently strong under normal circumstances to produce opaque patches. The yellow pigmentation frequently forms the spearhead of caries (although this is by no means universal), and proceeds along the enamel lamellae, whereas the acid tends to attack along the prism sheaths. According to Gottlieb a typical picture of dentinal caries consists of a peripheral ring of light decalcified dentine overlying an area of hypercalcified, opaque dentine: this in turn surrounds a second zone of hypercalcified, light dentine. Other authorities, however, do not agree with this assessment.

THE COMPARATIVE MICROSTRUCTURE OF PRIMITIVE AND CIVILIZED TEETH

Pickerill (1914) was one of the first investigators, if not the earliest, to search for a difference between primitive and European teeth at the microscopic level. He felt that the small cup-like depressions observed at the surface ends of the enamel rods of malacotic (i.e. caries-susceptible) teeth, were indicative of eruption prior to completion of calcification or alternatively of premature atrophy of the ameloblasts. He also mentions (1914, 1923) that the horizontal or imbrication lines of the primitive surface enamel (ridges and furrows, each furrow apparently a termination of one of the Striae of Retzius) were finely drawn and less marked than in modern man.

Bodecker (1930), who studied pre-Columbian American Indian teeth, found that enamel fissures or defects were as common in these ancient teeth as they are in the teeth of modern man, but they do not appear to have led to a predisposition to caries.

Staz (1938) investigated the microscopic structure of the teeth of primitive Bantu. The basic structure of enamel (that is, calcified prisms and a highly calcified interprismatic substance) was found to be similar to that normally encountered in European enamel. There were no traces of tubular enamel. Decalcification techniques showed all the familiar characteristics of the civilized enamel pattern such as needle-like splitting, fibrillation and cross-striation of the prisms and interprismatic bridges. The cross-sectional appearance of the enamel prisms was basically a hexagonal shape, modified slightly in a circular or round direction, and with a slight concavity of some of the surfaces; the appearance is said to be identical with the normal appearance of European enamel. There was similar conformity in the organic structure of the enamel; prism sheaths were observed, and enamel lamellae were always evident. According to Staz it does not appear that the presence of the lamellae is associated with dental caries. The presence of the Striae of Retzius, enamel tufts, spindles and Bands of Schreger was confirmed. These latter features were very numerous and were taken to be indicative of a strong enamel structure; variations in staining gave a hint that, in primitive enamel, the bands are due to a difference in calcification of the associated areas as well as to a directional change in the prisms. The amelo-dentinal junction had the normal scalloped appearance. Mottled enamel was noted in the teeth of those Bantu exposed to a high fluorine intake in endemic areas.

Bantu dentine was also found to resemble closely the structure of dentine in the civilized tooth. Special attention was paid to the occurrence of interglobular spaces beneath the amelo-dentinal layer for, according to certain schools of thought, these spaces are believed to be indicative of poor calcification. In primitive dentine however, they were found to be of the same appearance and of the same order of frequency as the inter-globular spaces in European dentine. The presence of the granular layer of Tomes in primitive dentine was confirmed, and dentinal tubules were found to exhibit similar primary and secondary curvatures, branches and divisions to the dentine of the modern tooth. Dentinal sheaths were recognizable at the periphery of the tubules, and the lumen of the tubules was occupied by a typical dentinal fibril.

The appearance of caries was apparently very similar in both groups, even to the occurrence of secondary dentine (translucent zones and dead tracts) in advance of the carious lesion.

In collaboration with Sognnaes, Moorrees (1957) has recently studied the histological characteristics of Aleutian Eskimo teeth; five good permanent first molars—representative of young, middle-aged and elderly Aleuts—were examined for the general appearance of the incremental pattern of enamel and dentine, the presence, size and number of interglobular spaces and the nature and presence of secondary dentine formation.

A failure in the fusion of calcified globules, resulting in interglobular spaces, was noted in teeth from young individuals: in one specimen 25–30 interglobular spaces were noted in a single field of vision. A specimen from the middle-age group showed accentuated incremental lines in the enamel and dentine, representing a disturbance of metabolism in early life; 15–20 interglobular spaces were observed in the occlusal area. A tooth from the oldest age group showed no inter-globular spaces in the dentine, but the presence of slight granularity was indicative of areolar dentine; secondary dentine was also observed in the pulp chamber. There was no accentuation of the incremental lines, and interglobular spaces were absent from the enamel. To Moorrees it appears that the older Aleuts had structurally superior teeth: their dental enamel was of a yellow hue in contrast to the bluish-white colour of the teeth of the younger Aleuts.

According to Cran (1955) the perikymata are more pro-nounced in Australian aboriginal teeth than in European specimens; this feature is regarded as evidence of disturbed enamel formation. Later, Cran (1959) commented on the relationship of Australian aboriginal diets to the caries incidence, and gives preliminary reports of a histological study of 24 aboriginal teeth. The interprismatic substance was said to be well in evidence, fissures were variable (some shallow, some deep), the Striae of Retzius prominent, pigmentation of the enamel common and enamel tufts and spindles present in a high percentage of cases: the spindles were said to be particularly prominent underneath cusps. A more detailed paper by the same author (1960) confirmed the previous picture, and led to the conclusion that the low incidence of caries in the primitive aboriginal was not due to any intrinsic difference in tooth structure. An interesting observation was the absence of non-tubular secondary dentine from aboriginal teeth: secondary dentine was always of the tubular variety.

The development of the metal-shadowed colloidon replica technique has led to a considerable extension of our knowledge relating to the surface structure of the teeth. However, it is only fair to state that some of the findings obtained with the ultra-microscope are so different from those to which one is accustomed with the older technique of optical microscopy, that their interpretation is by no means always easy.

Pedersen and Scott (1951), as already mentioned, have carried out replica studies of the tooth surfaces of the teeth of Alaskan Eskimo, West Greenland Eskimo and American whites. The facial, lingual and proximal surfaces of large numbers of assorted teeth from all three groups were examined in relation to perikymata, enamel rod-ends, cracks, scratches and micro-pits. Two additional features were described for the first time, namely laminated and reticulated areas.

Summarizing their results, these authors note the same microscopic features on the tooth surfaces of all three ethnic groups. Their main conclusions are as follows:

(a) Alaskan and Greenland Eskimo teeth show a higher incidence of macroscopic surface irregularities (that is, pits and grooves) than those of American whites.

(b) The course of the perikymata is markedly more irregular

on the surfaces of the Alaskan and Greenland teeth than in the American group.

(c) The prevalence of laminated and reticulated areas is much greater in the Alaskan and Greenland samples.

(d) The disappearance of surface structure (enamel rod-ends and perikymata) with advancing age progresses at much the same rate in all three groups. Grouping of the samples by age and degree of occlusal attrition showed that factors causing occlusal wear do not appear to contribute appreciably to smooth surface structure loss.

(e) The high proportion of microscopic and macroscopic surface irregularities in the Arctic groups probably results from influences of a non-genetic nature occurring during tooth formation.

The most recent studies on the microscopic appearance of primitive teeth are those which Tollens (1958) carried out on various Papuan teeth. Initially a unique lamination and reticulation was observed on the surface of these teeth. At the × 30 microscopic level, Tollens noted a geographical variation in the incidence of enamel surface irregularities: more irregularities were noted in mountainous than coastal areas. The principal defects observed were severe corrosion, deep fissures, irregular perikymata and characteristic boundary lines between enamel, dentine and cementum; lamination was also noted. Enamel disfiguration (the so-called "reticulation" of Pedersen and Scott (1951) was not found in the Papuan teeth, but macroscopic and microscopic pits were occasionally seen. The disappearance of enamel surface features was associated with advancing age, and not significantly linked with the factors which cause attrition. Micro-tubules (said to be identical with the "micro-pits" of Pedersen and Scott) were also observed. The high proportion of various macroscopic and microscopic surface irregularities present in Papuan teeth is said to have arisen as the result of influences of a non-genetic nature which had been present during or immediately after tooth formation; this would seem to confirm Pedersen and Scott's opinion that the microscopic structure of enamel cannot be influenced by genetic factors.

THE BIOCHEMISTRY OF HUMAN TEETH

Apart from possible structural differences, it is quite conceivable that the superiority of the primitive tooth in regard to caries resistance might be associated with a chemically different type of calcification. According to Rabkin (1941, 1942, 1943), many of the teeth in olden times were larger, thicker and denser. Holmer and Maunsbach (1957, 1958) express a similar viewpoint when they state that the teeth and jaws of Neolithic Swedes were of better quality and contained more favourable proportions of the essential chemical elements than modern teeth.

The present status of our knowledge relating to the calcification of the enamel and the dentine has been well covered in a fairly recent publication by Irving (1957). The earlier literature on the subject has been equally well reviewed by Leicester (1949). From these and other works it is apparent that the range of composition of individual teeth is fairly wide, being most marked for the moisture content but also quite appreciable in the case of calcium, and to a lesser extent variable even with respect to the phosphorus component.

Animal experiments by Sobel and Hanok (1948) indicate that the Ca/P ratio of the diet may be influential—not only in altering the Ca/P ratio of the blood—but also in varying the ratio of the minerals deposited in the developing teeth and bones. Even post-developmental influences are suggested by the results of McClure and Folk (1953), who are of the opinion that an excessive intake of sugar and other refined carbohydrates may interfere with the normal maturation of the enamel and its subsequent mineral exchange. In view of the known influence of mineral metabolism, vitamin intake and hormonal balance on tooth composition, it is questionable whether the term "normal tooth" is anything but a statistical abstraction. This lack of a standard chemical composition for teeth is a point which makes for great difficulty in determining whether the primitive tooth differs chemically in any way from its civilized counterpart.

The chemical composition of the tooth is also known to show contrasting values in different anatomical zones, and is even apt to vary with age due to changes brought about by re-mineralization.

Armstrong (1951) has summarized the existing theories of the chemical composition of bone and tooth salt as follows:

(i) Bone salt is believed by some authorities to be a carbonate hydroxyapatite with the carbonate present as a surface component or as a separate phase.

(ii) According to Dallemagne (1945) and his school, bone salt is a tri-calcium phosphate hydrate with the carbonate present as $CaCO_3$ in a separate phase. These workers suggest that bone, dentine and cementum consist essentially of a tricalcium phosphate—$3Ca_3 (PO_4)_2 2H_2O$—whilst enamel is said to be of slightly different composition, consisting of about 60 per cent carbonate-apatite located in the enamel prisms, 30 per cent a-tricalcium phosphate located in the interprismatic substance, and a residuum of calcium carbonate, minor materials and organic matter. A certain amount of doubt has however, been cast upon the accuracy of the methods which have been employed in an attempt to justify this hypothesis.

(iii) Others claim that bone salt is a hydroxyapatite, a viewpoint which is certainly in close agreement with the basic lattice structure of bone, provided due consideration is given to the influence of the surface phenomena.

Years ago Gassmann (1909) attempted to analyse a primitive human tooth; however as the tooth was dated to 200–50 B.C. there is some doubt as to whether the owner was free from the influences of civilization. Nevertheless, with due regard to the inaccurate analytical methods utilized (there was no separation of enamel and dentine) in the earlier days of these investigations, the figures are as follows:

$Ca = 39.90$, $P = 16.95$, $CO_2 = 4.02$, Ca/P ratio $= 2.35$, $H_2O = 8.20$, organic matter $= 25.20$, inorganic matter $= 66.60$.

These figures can be compared with those of Leicester (1949) who summarizes the average chemical composition of enamel and dentine as follows:

Enamel: $Ca = 36$, $P = 17$, $Mg = 0.4$, $CO_2 = 2.5$

Dentine: $Ca = 27$, $P = 13$, $Mg = 0.8$, $CO_2 = 3.0$

Gassmann's analysis does not indicate that there was any

separation of the enamel and dentine, and the figures do not include any allowance for the chemical processes which accompany fossilization.

French, Tefft, Rathbun, Eckhardt, Welch and Hodge (1939) analysed 32 pre-Columbian American Indian teeth and compared the results with figures which they obtained from modern teeth (and also from the interpretation of various published analyses of fossil animal teeth), using identical analytical methods. These results are summarized in Table I.

TABLE I
(AFTER FRENCH AND CO-WORKERS (1939))

	Enamel		Dentine	
	Modern	Pre-Columbian	Modern	Pre-Columbian
Ca	36·10	37·7	26·1	28·4
P	17·3	17·9	12·6	13·2
CO_2	3·05	2·02	2·94	2·63
Ca/P	2·09	2·12	2·07	2·15

French *et al.* conclude that the enamel values for pre-Columbian and modern teeth are strikingly similar for every component with the exception of CO_2, of which latter component the former group of teeth appear to contain about 30 per cent less than is the case for modern teeth. The enamel values for the P content are approximately the same in both groups, but the Ca values and the Ca/P ratios are a little higher for the pre-Columbian teeth; this slight discrepancy could be the result of exposure to calcium-rich water. The investigators draw attention to the fact that the Ca/P ratio approaches the figure 2·15, which is the theoretical value for hydroxyapatite.

In the case of dentine the calcium and phosphorus values were higher, and the CO_2 values 10 per cent lower, than in modern teeth. The increased values were ascribed to a remineralization process in which the organic structures were replaced by calcium phosphates.

No satisfactory explanation on the basis of the removal of carbonates by the weak acids of soil water could be offered for the puzzling lower Ca values in enamel, for the enamel of very ancient animal fossil teeth had higher CO_2 values than either pre-Columbian or modern teeth. Furthermore the CO_2 values of pre-Columbian or fossil dentine were lower than in modern teeth.

French et al. (1939) comment on the constancy of composition of modern, pre-Columbian and fossil teeth, as well as the stability of tooth calcium phosphate subjected to various conditions of soil water over a long period of time.

The only other investigator who appears to have tackled the problem of the chemical composition of primitive teeth is Staz (1938). He analysed the organic content of the enamel and the calcium content of the dentine of two hundred primitive Bantu of different tribes in an attempt to determine whether differences in the primitive and civilized diets could lead to variations in the composition and calcification of the teeth. The results of his two analyses are shown in Table II.

Enamel solubility tests of European, urban Bantu and rural or primitive Bantu teeth were inconclusive. The loss in weight of carefully prepared enamel samples which had been immersed for varying periods of time in 0·3 per cent hydrochloric acid and 5, 10 and 15 per cent solutions of lactic acid showed great discrepancy between the findings in various series: thus in one series of experiments it appeared that urban Bantu enamel was less resistant than European enamel to decalcifying procedures, a feature which was not borne out in other series of readings. Staz was of the opinion that some of these discrepancies were explicable on the grounds that a constant area of enamel had not been exposed to acid action in the wax window technique which he employed.

Staz reached the conclusion that there was no evidence of any fundamental difference between primitive and civilized enamel and dentine, either in their basic structure or in their degree of resistance to decalcifying acids.

Steadman, Brudevold, Smith, Gardner and Little (1959) undertook the study of the trace element composition of ancient

TABLE II
THE PERCENTAGE ORGANIC CONTENT OF ENAMEL AND THE CALCIUM OXIDE
AND TOTAL LIME SALT CONTENT OF DENTINE IN THE TEETH OF PRIMITIVE
BANTU
(Partly after Staz (1938))

	1st analysis	2nd analysis	Average
A. ENAMEL (ORGANIC CONTENT)			
i. Total insoluble organic matter	4·19%	1·46%	
ii. Range of total insoluble organic matter in European enamel (various authorities)	0·0–5·0%		—
iii. Carbon or C content	2·60%	0·88%	—
iv. Nitrogen or N_2 content	0·527%	0·206%	—
v. Nitrogen expressed as protein: $N \times 6·25$	3·3%	1·29%	
B. DENTINE (CaO CONTENT)			
i. Total lime or CaO content	38·27%	38·72%	38·495%
ii. Total lime salts	—	—	70
iii. Total lime or CaO content in European dentine (various authorities)	38·5–38·89%		—
iv. Total lime salts in European dentine (various authorities)	—	—	70

Note: The first analysis of the organic content of enamel is said to be rather high due to contamination with dentine.

North American Indian teeth—some teeth were estimated to be 5000 years old—in order to test the validity of the belief that teeth buried in the soil for hundreds of years would acquire many trace elements. Contrary to expectation there was little penetration of trace elements into the bulk of the tooth substance, and the concentrations of trace elements were only conspicuously high in the outer portions of the enamel and the tooth roots. Steadman and his colleagues feel that the dehydration which occurs under post-mortem conditions may provide an explanation: that is the loss of the hydration shell which promotes the rapid exchange reactions on the surface of the apatite crystals. All trace elements found in the fossil teeth have been detected in modern teeth, and apparently only small amounts of fluorine had been taken up during several hundred years of burial.

Oakley (1955) provides figures for the fluorine, nitrogen and uranium contents of certain fossil animal teeth of considerable antiquity: the analyses are with reference to the dating of these teeth.

Perhaps mention should be made at this point of the fact that Ockerse (1949) has analysed the calcium, phosphorus and magnesium content of carious and sound enamel and dentine in teeth from various parts of South Africa. Although the quantity of these elements in the soil and water of different geographical areas appears to vary considerably, these variations apparently do not affect the teeth. The fluoride content appears to vary considerably however; for example, the enamel and dentine of teeth associated with the fluorosis area of Calvinia, Cape Province, was found to contain nearly three times as much fluorine as teeth from Knysna—in the Cape coastal belt—where the water is very deficient in minerals.

As the hardness, permeability and acid solubility properties of teeth depend to a very large extent on their chemical properties, it seems appropriate that they should not altogether escape attention.

Pickerill (1923) formed the opinion that the enamel of the caries-immune Maori teeth which he investigated was denser, harder, more compact and of a higher specific gravity (specific gravity=2·85 as opposed to 2·723 in malacotic teeth), less permeable to stains such as 10 per cent silver nitrate, but more resistant to acid action (for example, lactic, citric, hydrochloric acids) than was the case in corresponding caries-susceptible European teeth. He also found that whereas erupted Maori teeth took up less silver nitrate stain than European teeth, the unerupted teeth of the primitive Maori show a similar degree of

s

permeability; it appears from Pickerill's experimental investigations that both erupted sclerotic and malacotic teeth become more impermeable with the passage of time, but the primitive or "native" tooth decreases in permeability much more quickly (Pickerill classified teeth as native, sclerotic and malacotic). Rabkin (1941, 1942, 1943), as already mentioned, is also of the opinion that the teeth in olden times were larger, thicker and denser than their modern counterparts.

Nevertheless, there is a certain amount of available evidence in the literature which casts an element of suspicion on these conclusions. Karlstrom (1941), for example, could find no difference between the hardness of modern teeth and the 2000 year-old caries-immune teeth of the Northmen (Vikings), and furthermore points out that the hardness and specific gravity of the caries-immune dental enamel of the dog, ox, pig, elephant and hippopotamus are of considerably lower value than is the case in man. Davidow (1942) states that Bantu teeth are harder than European teeth, but Shaw (1941) and Staz (1938) were unable to find any consistent relationship between tooth hardness and caries either in Bantu or European teeth. As already mentioned, comparative solubility tests of enamel had likewise proved inconclusive in an investigation carried out by the latter author.

REFERENCES

ARMSTRONG, W. D. (1951) No title. *Trans. 2nd Conf. Metab. Interr.*, 144. Josiah Macey Jnr. Found, New York.

BODECKER, C. F. (1930) Concerning defects in the enamel of teeth of ancient American Indians, *J. Dent. Res.* **10**, 313.

CLEMENT, A. J. (1961) *Caries Immunity in Primitive Peoples.* Thesis for M.D.S. degree, University of the Witwatersrand.

CRAN, J. A. (1955) Notes on teeth and gingivae of Central Australian aborigines, *Austral. J. Dent.* **59**, 356.

CRAN, J. A. (1959) The relationship of diet to dental caries, *Austral. Dent. J.* **4**, 182.

CRAN, J. A. (1960) The histological structure of the teeth of Central Australian aborigines and the relationship to dental caries incidence, *Austral. Dent. J.* **5**, 100.

COLYER, F. (1936) *Variations and Diseases of the Teeth of Animals.* J. Bale and Danielsson, London.

Czerwinski, R. (1926) *Vergleichend anatomisch-histologische Untersuchungen über den Bau der harten Zahnsubstanzen beim Macacus rhesus.* Inaugural Diss. (Med.). Becker, Wurzburg.

Dallemagne, M. J. (1945) Données récentes sur la nature et le metabolisme de l'os, *Actualitees biochemique,* No. 2. Masson, Paris.

Davidow, S. (1942) A discussion on an examination of the jaws and teeth of 3,000 natives, *S. Afr. Dent. J.* **16**, 160.

Duckworth, W. L. H. (1901) Some dental rudiments in human crania, *Trans. Odont. Soc.* **33**, 89.

Euler, H. and Werner, H. (1936) Die Entwicklung der Karies im heutigen Schlesien im Verlauf von vier Jahrtausenden, *Deut. Zahnarztl. Wschr.* **39**, 657, 931, 1107, 1201.

Falin, L. I. (1961) Histological and histochemical studies of human teeth of the Bronze and Stone Ages, *Arch. Oral. Biol.* **5**, 5.

French, E. L., Tefft, H., Rathbun, M., Eckhardt, J., Welch, E. and Hodge, H. C. (1939) Composition of Precolumbian teeth. Calcium, phosphorus and carbon dioxide determinations on all the dentine and all the enamel, *J. Dent. Res.* **18**, 547.

Gassmann, T. (1909) Chemische Untersuchungen der Zähne, *Z. Physiol. Chem.* **63**, 396.

Gottlieb, B. (1947) *Dental Caries.* Lea and Febinger, Philadelphia.

Hammarlund-Essler, E. (1952) Histologisk undersokning av tander och käkben från medeltidsskelett, *Svensk tandläk-Tidskr.* **45**, 275.

Holmer, W. and Maunsbach, A. B. (1957) Odontologische Untersuchung von Zähnen und Kiefern der Menschen aus der Steinzeit in Schweden, *Odont. Tskr.* **64**, 437.

Holmer, W. and Maunsbach, A. B. (1958) Examination of teeth and jaws of Stone Age man found in Sweden, *Dent. Abs.* **3**, 46.

Hopewell Smith, A. (1903) *The Histology and Patho-histology of the Teeth and Associated Parts.* Dent. Manufacturing Co., London.

Irving, J. T. (1957) *Calcium Metabolism.* Methuen, London.

Karlstrom, S. (1941) In *Dental Caries,* 2nd ed., p. 143. Am. Dent. Ass. p. 143 N. York.

Leicester, H. M. (1949) *Biochemistry of the Teeth.* Mosby, St. Louis.

McClure, F. J. and Folk, J. E. (1953) Skim milk powders and experimental rat caries, *Proc. Soc. Exp. Bio. Med.* **83**, 21.

Mellanby, M. (1930) *Diet and the Teeth,* Pt. IIB. Diet and dental structure in mammals other than the dog. *Med. Res. Coun. Spec. Rep.* Series 153. H.M.S.O., London.

Mellanby, M. (1934) *Diet and the Teeth,* Part III. The effect of diet on dental structure and disease in man. *Med. Res. Coun. Spec. Rep.* Series 191. H.M.S.O., London.

Moorrees, C. F. A. (1957) *The Aleut Dentition.* Harvard U. Press, Cambridge, (Mass.)

MUNCH, A. (1926) Beitrag zur Struktur der Zähne des Orangutan unter besonderer Berücksichtigung der Linien des Retzius, *Deut. Monat. f. Zahnheil* **44**, 137.

OAKLEY, K. P. (1955) Analytical methods of dating bone, *Advancement of Science* **11**, 3.

OCKERSE, T. (1949) *Dental Caries*. Dept. Health, Union of S. Africa, Pretoria.

PEDERSEN, P. O. and SCOTT, D. B. (1951) Replica studies of the surfaces of teeth from Alaskan Eskimo, West Greenland Natives and American Whites, *Acta. Odont. Scand.* **9**, 262.

PICKERILL, H. P. (1914) The aetiology of dental caries, *Trans. 6th Int. Dent. Cong.* **120**.

PICKERILL, H. P. (1923) *The Prevention of Dental Caries and Oral Sepsis*. 3rd ed. Baillière, Tindall and Cox, London.

RABKIN, S. (1941) In *Dental Caries* 2nd ed. p. 194 *Am. Dent. Ass.*, N. York.

RABKIN, S. (1942) Dental conditions among prehistoric Indians of Northern Alabama, *J. Dent. Res.* **21**, 211.

RABKIN, S. (1943) Dental conditions among prehistoric Indians of Kentucky. The Indian Knoll collection, *J. Dent. Res.* **22**, 355.

ROBINSON, J. T. (1952) Some hominid features of the ape-man dentition, *J. Dent. Ass. S. Africa* **7**, 102.

ROUX, W. (1887) Über eine im Knochen lebende Gruppe von Fadenpilzen, *Zoologie* **45**, 227.

SCHOUR, I. (1938) *Tooth Development*. Chap. I. In *Dental Science and Dental Art*, ed. Gordon, S. M. Lea and Febiger, Philadelphia.

SCHUMAN, E. L. and SOGNNAES, R. F. (1956) Developmental microscopic defects in the teeth of subhuman primates, *Amer. J. Phys. Anthrop.* **14**, 193.

SCHWARTZ, R. and BAY, R. (1943) Scheinbare und echte Zahnkaries, *Schweiz. Montat. f. Zahn.* **7**, 705.

SCOTT, D. B. and WYCKOFF, R. W. G. (1946) Shadowed replicas of tooth surfaces, *Pub. H. Rep.* **61**, 697.

SHAW, J. C. M. (1941) In *Dental Caries*. 2nd ed., p. 175. Am. Dent. Ass., N. York.

SHAW, J. H. and ANSKAPS, A. M. (1954) Studies on the dentition of the marmoset, *Oral. Surg., Med. and Path.* **7**, 671.

SOBEL, A. E. and HANOK, A. (1948) Calcification of teeth: composition in relationship to blood and diet, *J. Bio. Chem.* **176**, 1103.

SOGNNAES, R. F. (1955) Post-mortem microscopic defects in the teeth of ancient man, *Arch. Path.* **59**, 559.

SOGNNAES, R. F. (1956) Histologic evidence of developmental lesions in teeth originating from Palaeolithic, Prehistoric and Ancient Man, *Amer. J. Path.* **32**, 547.

STAZ, J. (1938) Dental caries in South Africa, *S.A.J. Med. Sc.* ? (Supp.), 1.

STEADMAN, L. T., BRUDEVOLD, F., SMITH, F. A., GARDNER, D. E. and LITTLE, M. F. (1959) Trace elements in ancient Indian teeth, *J. Dent. Res.* **38**, 285.

TOLLENS, H. L. (1958a) Schmelzoberflächenuntersuchungen an Papua-Zähnen. *Schweiz. Monat. f. Zahn.* **68**, 113.

TOLLENS, H. L. (1958b) Examination of enamel surfaces of teeth of Papuan natives, *Dent. Abs.* **3**, 600.

TOMES, C. S. (1892) Casual communication. *Trans. Odont. Soc.* **24**, 90.

WALKHOFF, O. (1895) Über das Wesen und die Entstehung von Entwicklungsfehlern in der Struktur menschlicher Zähne und ihre Bedeutung für das spätere Leben *Deut. Monat. f. Zahnheil.* **13**, 305.

WEDL, C. (1864) Über einem im Zahnbein und im Knochen keimenden Pilz, *Sitzung. d.k. Akad. d. Wissensch., Vienna* **50**, 1.

WERNER, H. (1937) Scheinbare und wirkliche Karies an prähistorischen Zähnen, *Zeitschr. f. Rassenkunde.* **5**, 70.

WIDDOWSON, T. W. (1936) *Special Dental Anatomy and Physiology and Dental Histology.* Staples, London.

THE MACROSCOPIC DENTAL PATHOLOGY
OF SOME EARLIER HUMAN POPULATIONS

by DON. R. BROTHWELL
Sub-Department of Anthropology,
British Museum (Natural History)

A GENERAL survey of dental variability in human groups would be incomplete without some consideration of pathological differences. These may reflect variations in the genetic, dietary, bacteriological and physiological aspects of man, and thus touch upon a wide field of oral biology. The purpose of this paper is to consider various macroscopic changes, whereas microscopic and biochemical differences are considered elsewhere in this symposium by Dr. John Clement.

It need hardly be said that the complexity and rapidly changing pattern of dental pathology in most living populations —principally the result of unnaturally soft civilized foodstuffs and the spread of refined sugars and flours—is beyond the bounds of anthropological study. For this reason I have limited this survey to earlier peoples, especially those preceding 1000 B.C. The majority of the groups to be considered were unlikely to have been influenced by refined foods or to have experienced much "cultural intervention" in the form of dental treatment.

Admittedly there is evidence that extractions and the treatment of dental abscesses were undertaken in the eastern Mediterranean area as early as 3000 B.C. (Weinberger, 1940; Sigerist, 1951), and that the removal of calculus and prosthetic treatment was well established by about the middle of the first millenium B.C. (Densham, 1909; Weinberger, 1940); however, such primitive dentistry is unlikely to have affected more than a very small segment of the population. We may therefore assume that the pathological lesions present in these

271

early groups represent the unrestricted results of "natural" processes. A vast literature has developed on the relationship between civilization and dental diseases, but surprisingly little detailed work has been published on pre- or proto-civilized groups although the presence of dental lesions in these peoples should certainly be noted in any consideration of aetiology.

Indeed, in the case of caries, for example, insufficient recognition of it in prehistoric human groups—as well as in natural populations of primates (Colyer, 1936; Schultz, 1956) —has given rise to the misguided conception of it as a "disease of civilization".

It must be emphasized at the outset of this paper that the data collected so far is by no means satisfactory, and it is to be hoped that in future studies, more detailed but concise methods will be used to record information than those previously employed. At present, definitions of degrees of involvement may be far from comparable as regards, for instance, the degree of enamel hypoplasia and the amount of alveolar recession resulting from periodontal disease. Some statements have clearly been made on far too few specimens; Baudouin (1923), for example, states that in Neolithic teeth occlusal caries is never present, but in a study of 11,717 French Neolithic teeth Hartweg (1945) found 30 cases of occlusal caries and 40 other cavities on the crowns of the teeth.

A major problem encountered in studying material excavated without sufficient archaeological care is that some teeth, especially the anterior ones, have been lost by careless handling either during removal from the soil or in the museum. As Brinch and Møller-Christensen (1949) have pointed out, there appears to be a tendency for a proportion of infected teeth to be less firmly held in their sockets and thus more likely to fall out than healthy ones. They demonstrated in a study of complete and incomplete dentitions, from the same period and site, that a small difference in the caries frequency for both series does occur. This error would probably be less if the eight types of teeth could be considered separately, there being less likelihood of the posterior teeth being lost in this manner; unfortunately, the sample number is usually so small for earlier populations that to undertake any division of this sort makes comparative work even more perilous.

Obviously, it is not possible to discount the considerable number of prehistoric dentitions which have suffered some post-mortem loss, but it is clear that in such cases large samples are very necessary. Unlike modern skeletal material, there is little good evidence that the excavated specimens forming large collections were in any way specially selected.

Although the oral pathology of prehistoric man includes more than a consideration of the teeth themselves, in the present survey I shall discuss only those aspects which directly affect the teeth.

It is evident from various modern data that some age division should be made when considering dental disease. In archeological material such divisions are very restricted, at least at present, owing to the fact that the majority of skulls available for study are not associated with post-cranial remains (or only with very fragmentary ones). In view of the doubtful nature of cranial sutures in ageing it is therefore only possible to separate immature from adults with any certainty if the skull alone remains. Only frequencies for adult dentitions are given here, owing to the lack of any large series of immature specimens. Fortunately, the available evidence indicates that only a very small percentage of the adults in these ancient populations survived 40 years of age (see the recent review by Howells, 1960), so that the adult frequency may approximately represent the 20–40-year age group for each series.

DENTAL CARIES

Owing to the staining and erosion which may affect a tooth during the post-mortem period, only well defined caries cavities are usually recorded in studying earlier dentitions. Frequencies determined in this way will therefore tend to underestimate the true figure.

The earliest examples of caries in the hominidae are to be found in the Australopithecine apes of South Africa. Robinson (1952) noted well-defined caries cavities in *Australopithecus* (*Paranthropus*) *crassidens* in a maxillary first and second molar.

Later, Clement (1956) found two further carious cavities in *Telanthropus* (? *Homo*) *capensis*. Although a consideration of the dental pathology of *Pithecanthropus* does not appear to have been so thorough, signs of caries have been affirmed by Brodrick (1948) and Rabkin (1960).

Surprisingly enough, the Neanderthal group—with many more teeth available for study—has not so far yielded clear evidence of caries, although in the "Proto Cro-Magnon" group from the Skhul Cave, Mr. Carmel (Brothwell, 1961) one cavity is definitely present (Sognnaes, 1956).

By far the most remarkable Upper Pleistocene fossil, from the point of view of its dental pathology, is of course the Rhodesian I Skull (Fig. 1). In the 13 teeth available for examination (and excluding those where the crown is broken off) 11 are carious. Upper Palaeolithic teeth from Europe again show some evidence of caries, though probably not more than 1 per cent of the teeth were involved.

Teeth from a number of Mesolithic sites have been studied and the high figure of 7·7 per cent of caries thus seems likely to represent European and North African Mesolithic groups generally. This frequency is much higher than most of those for populations living about 3000–1000 B.C. (Table I), and clearly demonstrates that cariogenic factors were well in evidence before the Neolithic Revolution (and all that this implied in terms of cereal cultivation and dietary refinement). This is not to say that there was not a link between more cultural development and caries increase; the early British frequencies, for example, show clearly how the present high rate of decay was established after the introduction of sugar and refined white flour (Brothwell, 1959; Hardwick, 1960). There is, however, clearly a case for suggesting that some cariogenic factors—"swamped" in civilized man by his great intake of refined carbohydrates—were operating to produce caries in at least some pre-Neolithic populations. Whether such ancient caries was again primarily dictated by diet (honey and pulpy plant carbohydrates, for example, would be available at times), must remain open to question until more detailed information

TABLE I

FREQUENCIES OF DENTAL CARIES IN SOME EARLIER HUMAN POPULATIONS
(Adults only)

Approx. time span	Series	Author	No. of teeth examined	No. with caries	% caries
70000–35000 B.C.	European Neanderthal‡	Brothwell†	259	0	0
35000–10000 B.C.	M. Carmel (Skhul) and European Upper Palaeolithic groups§	Brothwell†	523	5	1·0
	Rhodesian Man	Carter (1928) Brothwell (1959)	13	11	
10000–3000 B.C.	European and North African Mesolithic	Pequart, Boule, and Vallois (1937); Brothwell†	1148	88	7·7
3000–1000 B.C.	French Neolithic	Hartweg (1945)	11,717	379	3·2
	German Neolithic	Brinch and Moller-Christensen (1949)	1589	27	1·8
	Swedish Neolithic	Holmer and Maunsbach (1956)	6402	91	1·4
	Danish Neolithic	Christophersen and Pedersen (1939)	3612	56	1·6
	British Neolithic	Brothwell (1962)	1151	36	3·1
	Predynastic Egyptian	Brothwell, Wood Robinson and Carr†	1742	40	2·3
	Greece (3000–1000 B.C.)	Angel (1944)	1404	116	12·1
	Crete (1750–1550 B.C.)	Carr (1960)	1498	135	9·0
	China (1766–1122 B.C.)	Mao and Yen (1959)	884	38	4·3
	Total (3000–1000 B.C.)		29,999	918	3·1

†Unpublished data.

‡Only specimens are included which were examined by the author, or have published information on dental pathology.

§In view of the fact that carious teeth have been recorded in more than one skull from Vallee du Roc (Vallois, 1936) a minimum number of two caries cavities has been counted in the present estimates.

is obtained on caries development in modern primitive communities not as yet influenced by "civilized" diets.

Other factors known to be involved in the promotion or prevention of caries in modern man might well have been as important in the past. Saliva was no doubt as important then as now in the lavage of the teeth, as a buffering agent, and for the antibodies to oral bacteria it may contain.

As there is clear evidence of bacteriological variability related to dental health in modern man (Hoffman, 1957; Clement, 1957; Weisenstein and Green, 1957, and others) it seems likely that differences were also present in earlier populations. Minor faults in enamel structure were certainly present in prehistoric groups and the stagnation of food debris around the teeth probably occurred even though vigorous chewing action would keep most of the tooth surfaces clean.

TABLE II

INCIDENCE OF DENTAL CARIES IN THREE POPULATIONS WITH REFERENCE TO DIFFERENCES BETWEEN TEETH

Tooth	Middle Minoans[†]		French Neolithic[‡]		26th–30th Dynasty Egyptians[*]	
	TN	%C	TN	%C	TN	%C
I	112	1·8 (1)	992	0·3 (1)	120	0 (1)
I_2	113	8·0 (5)	1067	1·0 (3)	130	0 (2)
C	203	5·4 (2)	1395	0·4 (2)	153	0·7 (4)
PM1	189	8·5 (6)	1630	1·8 (4)	226	1·8 (5)
PM2	194	6·7 (3)	1479	3·2 (5)	229	0·4 (3)
M1	268	7·5 (4)	1961	5·5 (7)	327	3·4 (7)
M2	280	12·9 (7)	1914	6·0 (8)	339	5·3 (8)
M3	146	18·5 (8)	279	4·7 (6)	218	2·3 (6)

TN, number of teeth examined.
C, number of carious teeth.
[†]From data in Carr (1960).
[‡]From data in Hartweg (1945).
[*]Unpublished data of D. R. Brothwell, C. Wood Robinson and H. G. Carr.
Numbers in parentheses refer to the order of increasing liability.

Regional Variation within the Dentition

It is difficult to consider the relative liability to caries of various parts of the dentition in prehistoric groups owing to the usually insufficient numbers of teeth. Table II gives data for three groups where caries has been considered for each tooth form. Comparative data in modern Europeans are far from satisfactory, although it seems certain that the first molars are the most liable to caries—followed by the second molars (Colyer and Sprawson, 1946). It is interesting to note that in the three earlier groups considered the second molar invariably shows a greater frequency than the first molar. It could be that such earlier figures, especially if large samples are available as for the French Neolithic, may provide a true picture of caries liability in man.

ANTE-MORTEM TOOTH LOSS

It is normal in modern dental practice to consider much of the tooth loss in a group as primarily resulting from caries. With this in mind, estimates of the true caries picture have been attempted for some earlier populations by including a percentage of the teeth lost *antemortem*. In the case of early British series, Hardwick (1960) has attempted a correction of this sort by assuming that 25 per cent of the teeth extracted or lost through disease were lost due to caries when the proportion of carious teeth was under 5 per cent; 33 per cent when the proportion of carious teeth was 5 to 20 per cent; and half when the proportion of carious teeth was above 20 per cent. There is, however, an important objection to any such weighting of early caries frequencies, for it seems very likely that the aetiological factors determining tooth loss have changed in importance through time and from area to area. This point I shall discuss further when considering pulp exposure.

Thus unless the dentitions to be compared are precisely known in terms of caries and pulp exposure frequencies and as regards the degree of periodontal infection (which is well in evidence even by Neanderthal times), tooth loss would seem to be best considered as a separate (aetiologically multifactorial) category.

TABLE III

ANTE-MORTEM TOOTH LOSS IN TEN PREHISTORIC POPULATIONS
(Adults only)

Group	Author	Number of teeth possible	No. lost *ante-mortem*	% lost
European Neanderthal	Brothwell†	444	21	4·7
Upper Palaeolithic	Brothwell†	592	29	4·9
Mesolithic‡	Brothwell†	1118	102	9·1
Predynastic Egyptian	Brothwell, Wood Robinson and Carr†	3326	287	8·6
French Neolithic	Hartweg (1945)	12,061	344	2·9
Danish Neolithic	Christophersen and Pedersen (1939)	5739	112	2·0
British Neolithic	Brothwell (1962)	2058	221	10·7
Middle Minoan (1750–1550 B.C.)	Carr (1960)	1352	185	13·7
Ancient Greek (3000–1000 B.C.)	Angel (1944)	2605	320	8·1
Prehistoric Gran Canaria	Fuste (1961)	4536	903	19·9

†Unpublished data.   ‡Excluding loss by tooth evulsion.

In Table III, tooth loss values are given for a number of prehistoric populations. Compared with the relevant caries frequency for each group, the much higher percentage of loss in the Neanderthal, Predynastic Egyptian, and British Neolithic populations strongly suggests that caries is a minor factor in at least these cases.

PULP EXPOSURE THROUGH ATTRITION

As yet there is no satisfactory analysis of pulp exposure in prehistoric populations, although it is obviously a very important aspect to consider. Thoma (1917) was one of the first to call attention to pulp exposure—and the often associated chronic abscess—in Egyptian material as early as Predynastic times. Leigh (1934) also remarks on the susceptibility of early Egyptian teeth to this condition, especially the first molars.

TABLE IV

PULP EXPOSURE IN FOUR EARLY POPULATIONS†

Group	Individuals			Teeth		
	With expos-ure	No. exam-ined	% expos-ure	With expos-ure	No. exam-ined	% expos-ure
European Neanderthals	4	24	16·7	16	318	5·0
Upper Palaeolithic Man	3	28	10·7	6	432	1·4
Combined North African and European Mesolithic	19	47	40·4	39	910	4·3
Egyptian (2nd–6th century A.D.)	1	48	2·1	7	782	0·9

†In the case of fossil man, the figures do not represent the total number of individuals so far discovered, but only those which the author examined, or could be fairly certain of from details in the literature.

From the meagre evidence available it would seem that pulp exposure was not uncommon during the more recent part of the Stone Age (Table IV). Whether the increase during the Mesolithic times represents a general increase seems debatable, as the majority of these dentitions represent North African groups where there might well have been more likelihood of sand and siliceous dust getting chewed with foodstuffs. This point is rather borne out by later comparative material from Egypt and Europe of about 2000–1000 B.C.: where the latter group in particular displays relatively little exposure. Recent work by Brothwell, Wood Robinson and Carr (unpublished) on fairly large series of Egyptian dentitions (Predynastic to Early Christian) does, however, show that even in dry sandy environments there is a decline with increasing cultural development. Considering the frequency of chronic apical abscesses in relation to pulp exposure it is interesting to see that abscess figures do not continue to decrease through time in the Egyptian populations. This, I think, may well demonstrate a change in the major aetiological factor in abscess formation during this period of about four thousand years. In view of the definite presence of pulp exposure prior to 3000 B.C., but the relative lack of caries, chronic abscesses and tooth loss may well have been dictated to a considerable extent during this period by

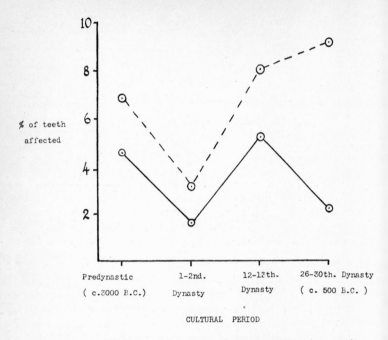

% of teeth affected

Predynastic (c. 3000 B.C.)   1-2nd. Dynasty   12-13th. Dynasty   26-30th. Dynasty (c. 500 B.C.)

CULTURAL PERIOD

FIG. 2. The changing frequency of pulp exposure (————) and chronic abscesses (— — —) in early Egyptian populations, showing the marked deviation between the two in the 26th–30th Dynasty group. The low frequencies of the 1st–2nd Dynasty (Abydos Royal Tombs) series is probably explained by the sample representing to some extent a different social stratum to the others.

exposure. With increasing cultural complexity there appears to have been reversal in this relationship (suggested by the data in Fig. 2).

ENAMEL HYPOPLASIA

Although various authors have reported microscopic hypoplasia in ancient teeth (Sognnaes, 1956; Held and Baud, 1958; Falin, 1961; Clement, 1962) few have considered macroscopic enamel defects, although in terms of analysis this latter anomaly allows much larger samples to be considered and involves less

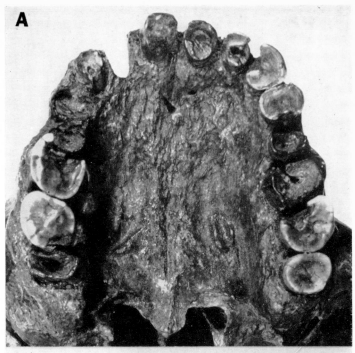

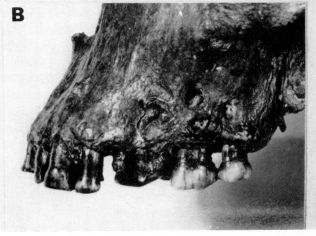

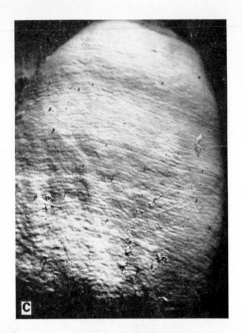

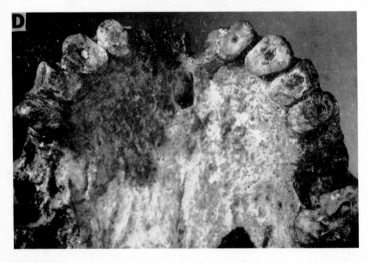

Fig. 1. A and B, Palatal aspect and left lateral view of the Rhodesian I upper jaw. Caries cavities (A), associated in some instances with chronic abscesses (B), are clearly seen. C, Labial aspect of the unerupted crown of the upper right medial incisor in the Neanderthal child Gibraltar II. D, Palatal aspect of Gibraltar I with evidence of pulp exposure on some anterior teeth.

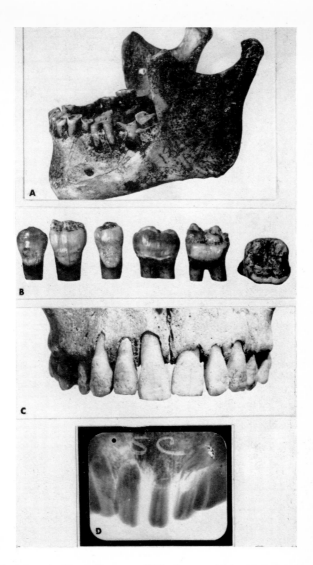

FIG. 3. A, Egyptian mandible from a 12th–13th Dynasty
series displaying pulp exposure associated with chronic
abscesses on the left first and second molars. B and C,
Varying degrees of enamel hypoplasia—mainly shown as
pits—in Iron Age teeth from Ireland (B) and an English
Bronze Age Specimen (C). D, The upper anterior teeth of
Shanidar I, as seen by X-ray. Pulp exposure is present in the
central incisors, spaces around the root tips of these teeth
probably indicating chronic infection. (*By courtesy of
Dr. T. D. Stewart.*)

time and labour. Of the primates this defect is not limited to man, and in a recent study Schuman and Sognnaes (1956) found marked differences in the incidence of hypoplastic defects between wild rhesus monkeys and a series of anthropoids.

Macroscopic enamel hypoplasia is easily discernible, even without recourse to a hand lens, and appears either as pits or shallow transverse grooves, especially in the canines and molars (Fig. 3). In the majority of modern cases the tooth surface is only slightly affected, while less than 1 per cent display severe changes (as shown in the Iron Age specimen in Fig. 3). A recent study of this feature in American Whites, Alaskan Eskimo and West Greenland Eskimo (Pedersen and Scott, 1951) has shown clearly that noticeable variation occurs in human groups. Not only did they note a difference in the number of individuals affected, but also found an average difference in the number of hypoplastic grooves on a tooth surface. These minor defects are generally thought to result from disturbances during tooth formation and in view of their common occurrence, and frequent presence over much of a tooth surface, it may be concluded that the factors involved are recurrent during the childhood phase. Clinical and experimental evidence suggests that these defects can be related to a wide range of systemic disturbances (Kreshover, 1960). Faulty nutrition was probably an important factor in determining this defect in earlier groups, but as Hardwick (1960) has pointed out, difficult living conditions in primitive and earlier populations—at times making survival hazardous—might also account for such trophic disturbances.

The apparent universal occurrence of this feature in the hominidae is clearly demonstrated by its presence even in the Australopithecine apes. Robinson (1952) noted that 29 per cent of 47 isolated teeth of *Australopithecus* (*Paranthropus*) *crassidens* displayed hypoplastic deformity, usually to a slight degree. In other *Australopithecus* specimens also he found occasional mild instances of this defect. More recently Clement (1956) noted hypoplasia in the teeth of *Telanthropus* (? *Homo*) *capensis*. Although Weidenreich (1937) in his monumental study of the dentition of *Pithecanthropus pekinensis* does not discuss

T

these surface defects, in view of the detailed and high quality illustrations, slight hypoplastic irregularity on at least one or two of the 147 teeth appears to be present. In the case of Neanderthal man, it is definitely present in Spy II, and to a lesser degree in two other specimens. It may be as well to note here that there appears to be no work as yet on exactly what range of smoothness (and roughness) may be regarded as "normal" in man. Thus, in the case of the unerupted medial incisor of the Gibraltar II child (Fig. 1) it seems debatable whether the enamel should be termed hypoplastic or whether the regular, shallow grooves extending over the anterior surface of the tooth represent the limits of normal variation.

In order to abbreviate further discussion, evidence of enamel hypoplasia in pre-Neolithic man is given in Table V. It will be seen that there is a higher percentage of Mesolithic man affected than in previous groups, and even taking account of the small sample sizes, this might well indicate a greater likelihood of the anomaly in more recent peoples. French Neolithic series show very little evidence of this defect (Hartweg, 1945) and Brabant, Sahly, and Bonyssou (1961) found only 0·03 per cent in 2850 teeth. More evidence of it is found in British material, and in a general survey of early teeth, mainly of post-Bronze Age date, 58 per cent of the individuals were found to show this defect in more than one tooth (Brothwell, 1959).

HYPERCEMENTOSIS

The deposition of excessive amounts of cementum may result from a number of aetiological factors, and may affect the root to a varying degree. In view of the difficulty of studying this pathology, and the lack of published data on it, only a brief review is possible. The presence of hypercementosis in fossil man is, however, fully established and the aetiology may to some extent be discerned. At least three Neanderthal specimens show some root swelling, namely, Gibraltar I, La Ferrassie I, and a mandibular fragment from Monsempron. Only in Gibraltar I is the hypercementosis marked. In view of the fact that the condition in modern man may be associated

TABLE V

MACROSCOPIC SURFACE DEFECTS IN STONE AGE MAN

Population	Maximum degree of hypoplastic involvement (as a % of N)				No. of individuals N †
	None	Slight	Medium	Marked	
Combined Neanderthal and Upper Palaeolithic Series	69·0	27·6	3·4	0	29
Combined European and North African Mesolithic	11·9	69·1	19·1	0	42

†Only specimens well described in the literature or examined by the author are included. The figures, therefore, do not represent the total world sample available for study.

with attrition, "compensating for the continuous eruption of the tooth" (Thoma and Goldman, 1960), and because other evidence of pathology is absent, it seems likely that these fossil cases of cementum increase are also the result of tooth wear.

In the case of Rhodesian Man and the Upper Palaeolithic male skull from Kilgreany Cave, Ireland, the aetiology is different. The beginnings of apical hypercementosis—resulting from a low-grade infection of the tooth (Stones, 1954)—is present in at least two molars of Rhodesian Man, while in the Kilgreany skull, three teeth display root swelling associated with pulp exposure and chronic abscesses.

ANTE-MORTEM EROSION

The aetiology of this lesion is by no means fully understood in the modern cases available for study. In this condition the tooth surface shows a clear-cut smooth surfaced hollow, either restricted to the enamel or involving also dentine and even cementum. Other than in "civilized" people it has received little attention, although Campbell (1925) notes instances of it in his large survey of Australian aboriginal teeth. Unlike the teeth of civilized man, he noted that among the Australians it occurred nearly always on molars, always on the mesial or distal surfaces, and generally near the cervical margin of the tooth.

The anomaly is basically due to chemical activity quite divorced from bacterial action. Zipkin and McClure (1949) have suggested, though rather inconclusively, that this disintegration of the tooth surface may be a localized non-acid demineralization due to a calcium solubilizing ion such as a citrate. Considerable nervous strain is thought to be a predisposing factor, at least in some instances (Bunting and Hill, 1940). Because of its non-carious appearance dental erosion seems to have suffered considerable mistaken diagnosis; a number of authors having attributed these erosive patches to the continued use of a tooth-pick (Martin, 1923; Patte, 1941; Hartweg, 1945).

As early as 1911, Siffre brought attention to "tooth-pick" grooves in Mousterian teeth. Martin (1923) described in some detail these lesions in the La Quina skull. They are present in the cervical region of the lower left first and second molars, reaching almost a millimetre in depth; also to a lesser extent on the same teeth on the right side of the mandible. Patte (1941) notes similar instances in Neolithic Melanesian teeth and also in *Pithecanthropus pekinensis*. In the latter, contrary to the opinion of Weidenreich, he concluded that tooth-picking is the only factor which could produce such grooves. Finally, in a survey of French Neolithic teeth, Hartweg (1945) found examples of this non-carious groove on the mesial and distal surfaces at cervical level, especially in the molar region. Surprisingly, none of these authors would appear to have considered ante-mortem erosion as a factor, although it is by far the most likely explanation, considering the form and restricted position of the lesion. Recently, in a study of Mesolithic and Neolithic teeth from Gua Cha, Malaya, I was able to examine such grooves on the upper first molars of a mesolithic male. The clear-cut nature of the erosion, quite unlike the post-mortem changes described by Sognnaes (1955), leaves no doubt as to its true nature. In all these probable examples of erosion, it is interesting to note that the molars are especially affected, as in the modern primitive dental series from Australia.

ACKNOWLEDGEMENTS

I should like to take this opportunity to thank all the museums and other institutions who have permitted me to examine human fossil and sub-fossil dentitions. In particular I extend my thanks to Professor H. V. Vallois, Institut de Paléontologie Humaine; Dr. Robert Gessain, Musée de l'Homme (Paris); and Professors A. Capart and F. Twiesselmann, Institut Royal des Sciences Naturelles de Belgique (Brussels). My work on the French and Belgian material was aided by a grant from the University of Cambridge.

Last, but not least, I am indebted to Dr. Virginia Carbonell for reading through this communication, and to Dr. T. D. Stewart for supplying unpublished information on the Shanidar I dentition.

REFERENCES

ANGEL, J. L. (1944) Greek teeth: ancient and modern, *Hum. Biol.* **16**, 283.

BRINCH, O. and MØLLER-CHRISTENSEN, V. (1949) On comparative investigations into the occurrence of dental caries in archaeological skulls, *Odont. Tidskr.* **4**, 357.

BRODRICK, A. H. (1948) *Early Man.* Hutchinson, London.

BROTHWELL, D. R. (1959) Teeth in earlier human populations, *Proc. Nutr. Soc.* **18**, 59.

BROTHWELL, D. R. (1961) The people of Mount Carmel. A reconsideration of their position in human evolution, *Proc. Prehist. Soc.* **27**, 155.

BROTHWELL, D. R. (1962) A note on the dental pathology of the West Kennet people, Appendix III. In PIGGOTT, S. *The West Kennet Long Barrow—Excavations* 1955–56. H.M.S.O., London.

BAUDOUIN, M. (1923) La carie dentaire il y a dix mille ans. I. Etudes des caries de la ciste des cous a Bazoges-en-Pareds (Vandée), *La Semaine Dentaire.* **5**, 444.

BRABANT, H., SAHLY, A. and BOUYSSOU, M. (1961) Etude des dents préhistoriques de la station archéologique des Matelles (Département de l'Hérault, France), *Bull. du G.I.R.S.* **4**, 382.

BUNTING, R. W. and HILL, T. J. (1940) *Oral Pathology.* 2nd ed. Lea and Febiger, Philadelphia.

CAMPBELL, T. D. (1925) *Dentition and Palate of the Australian Aboriginal.* Sheridan Foundation Publications, No. 1. University of Adelaide.

CARR, H. G. (1960) Some dental characteristics of the Middle Minoans, *Man* **60**, 157.

CARTER, J. T. (1928) The teeth of Rhodesian Man. In *Rhodesian Man and Associated Remains*, **64**. Brit Mus. (Nat. Hist.) London.

CHRISTOPHERSEN, K. M. and PEDERSEN, P. O. (1939) Investigations into dental conditions in the Neolithic Period and in the Bronze Age in Denmark, *Dental Record* **59**, 575.

CLEMENT, A. J. (1956) Caries in the South African ape-man: some examples of undoubted pathological authenticity believed to be 800,000 years old, *Brit. Dent. J.* **102**, 4.

CLEMENT, A. J. (1957) The bacteriology of the primitive mouth, *J. Dent. Ass. S. Afr.* **12**, 281.

CLEMENT, A. J. (1962) Variations in the microstructure and biochemistry of human teeth. Paper in the symposium.

COLYER, F. (1936) *Variations and Diseases of the Teeth of Animals.* Bale and Danielsson, London.

COLYER, J. F. and SPRAWSON, E. (1946) *Dental Surgery and Pathology.* 8th ed. Longmans and Green, London.

DENSHAM, A. (1909) A review of the progress of dental science and literature from the earliest ages, *Proc. R. Soc. Med. Odont. Sect.* **2**, 71.

FALIN, L. I. (1961) Histological and histochemical studies of human teeth of the Bronze and Stone Ages, *Arch. Oral. Biol.* **5**, 5.

FUSTE, M. (1961) Lesiones maxilo-dentarias en craneos prehistoricos de Gran Canaria, *Z. Morph. Anthrop.* **51**, 322.

HARDWICK, J. L. (1960) The incidence and distribution of caries throughout the ages in relation to the Englishman's diet, *Brit. Dent. J.* **108**, 9.

HARTWEG, R. (1945) Remarques sur la denture et statistiques sur la carie en France aux epoques prehistorique et proto-historique, *Bull. Mém. Soc. Anthrop.* **6**, 71.

HELD, A. J. and BAUD, C. (1958) Structure des tissus dentaires et pathogenèse de la carie dentaire, *Beiheft Nr. 7 der Internat. Z. Vitaminforschung: Vitamin D und Kariesprophylaxe.* Huber, Bern.

HOFFMAN, H. (1957) Oral microbiology, *Ann. Rev. Microbiol.* **11**, 183.

HOLMER, U. and MAUNSBACK, A. B. (1956) Odontologische untersuchung von Zähnen und Kiefern des Menschen aus der Steinzeit in Schweden, *Odont. Tidskr.* **64**, 437.

HOWELLS, W. W. (1960) Estimating population numbers through archaeological and skeletal remains. In HEIZER, R. F. and COOK, S. F. (eds.) *The Application of Quantitative Methods in Archaeology.* Viking Fund Publication, New York.

KRESHOVER, S. J. (1960) Metabolic disturbances in tooth formation, *Ann. New York Acad. Sciences* **85**, 161.

LEIGH, R. W. (1934) Notes on the somatology and pathology of ancient Egypt, *University of California Publications in American Archaeology and Ethnology* **34**. 1.

Mao, H. C. and Yen, Y. (1959) Dental condition of the Shang Dynasty skulls excavated from Anyang and Huü-Xian. I. Dental caries and periodontoclasia, *Vertebrata Palasiatica*. **3**, 79.

Martin, H. (1923) *L'Homme Fossile de La Quina*. Doin, Paris.

Patte, M. E. (1941) Paléontologie humaine—usures artificielles des dents chez le Sinanthrope, *Comptes-Rendus* **212**, 1054.

Pequart, M., Pequart, S.-J., Boule, M. and Vallois, H. (1937) *Teviec. Station-Necropole Mésolithique du Morbihan*. Arch. Instit. Pal. Hum. Mem. 18. Paris.

Pedersen, P. O. and Scott, D. B. (1951) Replica studies of the surfaces of teeth from Alaskan Eskimo, West Greenland natives and American Whites, *Acta Odontol. Scand.* **9**, 262.

Rabkin, S. (1960) Personal communication.

Robinson, J. T. (1952) Some hominid features of the ape-man dentition, *J. Dent. Ass. S. Afr.* **7**, 102.

Schultz, A. H. (1956) The occurrence and frequency of pathological and teratological conditions and of twinning among non-human primates, *Primatologia* **1**, 965.

Sigerist, H. E. (1951) *A History of Medicine: I. Primitive and Archaic Medicine*. Oxford University Press, New York.

Sognnaes, R. F. (1955) Post-mortem microscopic defects in the teeth of ancient man, *Arch. Path.* **59**, 559.

Sognnaes, R. F. (1956) Histologic evidence of developmental lesions in teeth originating from Paleolithic, prehistoric and ancient man, *Amer. J. Path.* **32**, 547.

Stones, H. H. (1954) *Oral and Dental Diseases*. Livingstone, Edinburgh.

Schuman, E. L. and Sognnaes, R. F. (1956) Developmental microscopic defects in the teeth of sub-human primates, *Amer. J. Phys. Anthrop.* **14**, 193.

Thoma, K. H. (1917) Oral diseases of ancient nations and tribes, *J. Allied Dent. Soc.* **12**, 327.

Thoma, K. H. and Goldman, H. M. (1960) *Oral Pathology*. Mosby, St. Louis.

Vallois, H. V. (1936) La carie dentaire et la chronologie des hommes prehistoriques, *L. Anthropologie* **46**, 201.

Weidenreich, F. (1937) The dentition of *Sinanthropus pekinensis*: a comparative odontography of the hominids, *Palaeontol. Sinica, Peking*, No. 101.

Weisenstein, P. R. and Green, G. E. (1957) Clinical and bacteriologic studies of caries-immune human beings, *J. Dent. Res.* **36**, 690.

WEINBERGER, B. W. (1940) Did dentistry evolve from the barbers, blacksmiths or from medicine? *Bull. Hist. Med.* **8**, 965.

ZIPKIN, I. and McCLURE, F. J. (1949) Salivary citrate and dental erosion: procedure for determining citric acid in saliva dental erosion and citric acid in saliva, *J. Dent. Res.* **28**, 613.